Mathematics
for Liberal Arts Students

Under the Editorship of

CARL B. ALLENDOERFER

Mathematics
for Liberal Arts Students

Gloria Olive

Senior Lecturer in Pure Mathematics at the
University of Otago in New Zealand
Formerly at the University of Wisconsin–Superior

The Macmillan Company NEW YORK

Collier-Macmillan Publishers LONDON

To my friends

THE MACMILLAN COMPANY
866 Third Avenue, New York, New York 10022

COLLIER-MACMILLAN CANADA, LTD., Toronto, Ontario

Library of Congress catalog card number: 73-190671

Printing: 1 2 3 4 5 6 7 8   Year: 3 4 5 6 7 8 9 0

Preface

This book is designed for a wide variety of college and university students, including those who have never had a course in high school mathematics. It is written in the hope that these students and others will want to become involved in mathematics so that they can learn to appreciate, understand, use, and enjoy it. A major objective is to present an interesting approach to mathematics that does not involve complicated algebraic manipulations. The topics were chosen on the basis of affirmative answers to each of the following questions: (1) Is it mathematically significant? (2) Is it easy to understand? (3) Is it interesting?

The chapter titles are as follows: (1) "Mathematical Recreations," (2) "What Is Mathematics?" (3) "Logic," (4) "Sets and Paradoxes," (5) "Geometry," (6) "Counting and Probability," (7) "Statistics," (8) "Linear Algebra," (9) "Game Theory," (10) "Calculus," (11) "Computers," and there is an appendix on the real number system. The first four chapters do not require any algebra; Chapter 5 introduces some basic rules of algebra via geometry; and the appendix presents some basic properties of the real numbers in an intuitive way. There is no attempt to present a formal development of the real number system.

The book can be used as a text in a variety of ways. For example, Chapters 1 through 4 can be used for a one-quarter course; Chapters 1 through 6 can be used for a one-semester course; and the entire book can be used for a full-year course. The instructor may also want to have students present reports on the lives of mathematicians or on mathematical topics related to the course. The Suggestions for Further Reading may help students select topics of real interest.

Students in the social, natural, and mathematical sciences may find some of the chapters to be of special interest. In particular, Chapters 6, 7, 8, 9, and 11 may be of special interest to those in the social sciences; Chapters 6, 7, 8, 10, and 11 may be of special interest to those in the natural sciences;

and Chapters 2, 3, 4, 10, and 11 may be of special interest to those in the mathematical sciences.

Although the book has been written for the novice, some of the problems may challenge students with a good background in high school mathematics. Those problems that have been rated "more challenging" or "optional" are preceded by the symbol °.

It is hoped that the student will enjoy reading this book—and will want to solve all the problems.

Acknowledgments

Many people have contributed to the preparation of this book and I am indeed grateful. First, I want to thank my students at the University of Wisconsin–Superior (UWS), who actively participated in the experimental course for which this book was written. I am also grateful to each of the following at UWS: to Ms. Barbara Grant for her accurate and speedy typing of the final copy; to my student Don Little for artistically drawing most of the figures in the final copy; to Mr. Edward Greve, Reference and Research Librarian, for excellent service and valuable suggestions; to Dr. Michael Behr (Economics), Dr. Francis Florey (Mathematics), Mr. Charles Johnson (Computer Science), Mr. Gerald Larson (Sociology), and Mr. Frank Meyer (Physics) for reviewing parts of the original manuscript and for making helpful suggestions. A special word of thanks goes to the many students at both UWS and the University of Otago who helped to prepare the preliminary and final copies—especially to Linda Brehmer, Lim Hoi Chan, David Cheung, Mark Fisher, Maria Mengel, and Kathy Stockley at UWS, and to Rose Lau, Angela Wei, and Catherine Ling at the University of Otago.

In addition, I want to thank each of the following for a variety of special reasons: Dr. Gordon Besch (Physics), Dr. Lydia Binger (Physical Education), Ms. Catherine Bowser (Library), Dr. Philip Brieske (CASE and Physics), Dean Cleo Casady (Business), Mr. Robert Comstock (Student Affairs), Vice-Chancellor John Danielson, Vice-Chancellor John Haugland, Mr. Richard Heim (Library), Mr. Carl Johnson (Library), Mr. Eugene Lundholm (Library), Ms. Bernice Paulhe (English), Mr. Gary Pothast (Computer Science), Dr. Michael Seltzer (Anthropology), and Mr. Charles Spain (Library)—all at UWS.

A special note of appreciation is for three of my favorite mathematicians: Professor Saunders Mac Lane (University of Chicago), Professor Cletus Oakley (Haverford College), and Professor Merrill Shanks (Purdue University).

G. O.

Contents

List of Symbols

SYMBOL	TRANSLATION	
$=$	equals	
$\neq$	does not equal	
$\doteq$	is approximately equal to	108
$\equiv$	is defined to be	
$\cdots$	and so on	
x^n	x to the nth	244
AMS	Abstract Mathematical Structure	10
iff	if and only if	25
$>$	is greater than	250
$\geq$	is greater than or equal to	250
$<$	is less than	250
$\leq$	is less than or equal to	250
$\sim p$	the negation of p or not p	24, 25
$\wedge$	and	25
$\vee$	or	25
$\rightarrow$	implies	25
$\leftrightarrow$	is equivalent to	25
$\{a, b, \cdots\}$	set containing a, b, and so on	42
$\{x \mid \cdots\}$	set of all x such that $\cdots$	42

SYMBOL	TRANSLATION	
$\in$	is an element of	43
$\notin$	is not an element of	43
U	universal set	43
$\emptyset$	null set *or* empty set	43
$\subseteq$	is a subset of	44
$\subset$	is a proper subset of	44
$A \sim B$	set A is equivalent to set B	46
$n(A)$	cardinal number of set A	47
$\aleph_0$	aleph-nought	48
c	cardinal number of the continuum	48
$\cup$	union	49
$\cap$	intersection	50
$\forall_x$	for all x	59
π	pi	73
Δx	delta x or change in x	88
${}_nP_r$	number of permutations of n distinct things taken r at a time	99
$n!$	n factorial or $1 \times 2 \times 3 \times \cdots n$	99
${}_nC_r$	number of combinations of n distinct things taken r at a time	101
$P(E)$	probability of E	106
$\overline{x}$	x-bar or arithmetic mean	118
SD	Standard Deviation	122
σ	sigma	124
μ	mu	124
$[a_{ij}]$	matrix with a_{ij} in the ith row, j^{th} column	137
$|A|$	determinant of matrix A	140
$A + B$	matrix A plus matrix B	142
$-A$	negative of matrix A	142

SYMBOL	TRANSLATION	
kA	k times matrix A	143
BA	matrix B times matrix A	145
I	identity matrix	146
A^{-1}	inverse of matrix A or matrix A inverse	147
roc	rate of change	184
wrt	with respect to	184
$f(x)$	f of x or function of x	197
$\lim\limits_{\Delta t \to 0}$	limit as Δt approaches 0	194
$\dfrac{dy}{dx}$	$dy\,dx$ or derivative of y with respect to x	199
y'	y prime or $\dfrac{dy}{dx}$	199
$f'(x)$	f prime of x or $\dfrac{df(x)}{dx}$	199
$\displaystyle\int_a^b f(x)\,dx$	integral of $f(x)\,dx$ from a to b	222, 224
$\ln x$	logarithm of x	225, 227
e^x	e to the x	227

CHAPTER 1

Mathematical Recreations

1.1 Introduction

The reader may ask, "Why should there be a special mathematics course for liberal arts students?" A partial answer is included in the major objectives of the course for which this book was written. These objectives are to encourage the student to (1) develop an *understanding* of and an *appreciation* for the meaning of mathematics; (2) want to become *involved* in mathematics by asking questions and trying to work all problems by himself; (3) reach a level at which he can *enjoy* at least some mathematics; and (4) develop ability to *apply* principles of mathematics to other subjects and his day-to-day experiences—especially logic.

With these objectives in mind, we believe the students who should take this course are those who want to learn what mathematics *really* is; and have, or could develop, an appreciation for the finer things in life.

After ascertaining the objectives and clientele for the course, we are ready to begin. Since many people think of mathematics as a collection of puzzles, and since puzzles (or mathematical recreations) are considered to be "fun" by a variety of people, we shall start by investigating some mathematical recreations.

EXAMPLE 1
Do the following in order: (a) think of a number, (b) add 3, (c) multiply by 2, (d) subtract 4, (e) divide by 2, (f) subtract the number you started with. What is your answer?

EXAMPLE 2
If in Example 1 you start with a different number in step (a), do you obtain the same final result? Why?

[1

EXAMPLE 3
Two civil service jobs have the same starting salary of $6,000 per year.
Mr. A gets an annual raise of $200 and Mr. B gets a semiannual raise
of $50. Which is better? Most people would answer that Mr. A will be
making more money. But on closer examination one should become aware
that it is Mr. B who is really better off. Can you explain why?

EXAMPLE 4
Can you explain what is wrong with the following argument?
(a) Assume $a = b$.
(b) Multiply each side by a so that we have

$$a^2 = ab.$$

(c) Subtract b^2 from each side to obtain

$$a^2 - b^2 = ab - b^2.$$

(d) Write each side in factored form:

$$(a + b)(a - b) = b(a - b).$$

(e) Divide each side by $a - b$:

$$a + b = b.$$

(f) Replace a by b [which is legal by virtue of step (a)]:

$$2b = b.$$

(g) Divide each side by b:

$$2 = 1.$$

Since the conclusion $2 = 1$ will be rejected by all people who are familiar
with the meaning of these symbols, it should be clear that at least one
of the steps is illegal. Can you find an illegal step? (**HINT**: Let $a = b = 7$
and see what happens as you go through all the steps.)

Problem Set 1.1

1. All of the following puzzles have logical answers, but they are not
   strictly mathematical. See how many you can answer.

   (a) How many 6-cent stamps are in a dozen?
   (b) How many telephone poles are needed in order to reach the
       moon?
   (c) How far can you walk into a forest?

(d) How much dirt is there in a hole that is 3 feet wide, 4 feet long, and 2 feet deep?

(e) There was a blind beggar who had a brother, but this brother had no brothers. What was the relationship between the two?

2. Optical illusions are vivid reminders of the fact that we cannot always trust our eyes. Can you trust yours? Test yourself and see. In each of the following pairings, first guess which of the line segments *a* or *b* is longer. Then use a ruler to check your estimate.

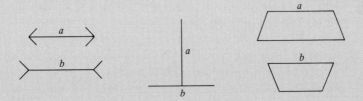

*3. A farmer wants to get a fox, a goose, and a bag of corn across a river in a boat that is only large enough for him and one of these three items. Now if he leaves the fox alone with the goose, the fox will eat the goose. If he leaves the goose alone with the corn, the goose will eat the corn. How does he get all items across the river?

4. A bottle and cork cost $1.50 together. The bottle costs one more dollar than the cork. How much does each cost?

5. A cat is at the bottom of a 30-foot well. Each day she climbs up 3 feet; each night she slides back 2 feet. How long will it take the cat to get out of the well?

*6. Use six match sticks, all the same size, to form the sides of four equilateral triangles. (All three sides of an equilateral triangle have the same length.)

*7. A sailor lands on an island inhabited by two types of people. The *A*'s always lie, and the *B*'s always tell the truth. The sailor meets three inhabitants on the beach and asks the first of these, "Are you an *A* or a *B*?" The man answers but the sailor does not understand him and asks the second person what he said. The man replies, "He said that he was a *B*. He is and so am I." The third inhabitant then says, "That's not true. The first man is an *A* and I'm a *B*." Can you tell who was lying and who was telling the truth? Explain.

8. A man goes to a well with three cans whose capacities are 3 gallons, 5 gallons, and 8 gallons. Explain how he can obtain exactly 4 gallons of water from the well.

9. Three men enter a hotel and rent a suite of rooms for $30. After they are taken to their rooms, the manager discovers he overcharged them; the suite rents for only $25. He thereupon sends a bellhop upstairs with the $5 change. The bellhop is dishonest and decides to keep $2 and return only $3. Now the rooms originally cost $30, but the men had $3 returned to them; this means that they paid $27. The bellhop kept $2. Since $27 + $2 = $29, what happened to the other dollar?

10. Estimate how long it would take to count to 1 billion at the rate of one number per second. Then compute this to the nearest day.

11. You are offered a job that pays 1 cent the first day, 2 cents the second day, 4 cents the third day, and so forth; that is, your wages are to be doubled each day. First estimate, then compute, your salary for the thirtieth day on the job.

*12. In Problem 11 compute the total salary that you will earn in 30 days. Try to find this sum without adding each of the daily salaries. To help you discover a way of doing this, consider these sums first:
   (a) $1 + 2 + 4$.   (c) $1 + 2 + 4 + 8 + 16$.
   (b) $1 + 2 + 4 + 8$.   (d) $1 + 2 + 4 + 8 + 16 + 32$.

13. Note each of the following relationships:
$$25^2 = 2 \times 300 + 25 = 625.$$
$$35^2 = 3 \times 400 + 25 = 1{,}225.$$
$$45^2 = 4 \times 500 + 25 = 2{,}025.$$

   (a) State a shortcut for squaring a two-digit number whose units digit is 5.
   *(b) Find an algebraic explanation for this shortcut.

1.2 Mathematical Patterns

When one studies mathematics, one soon becomes involved in making discoveries—especially the discovery of patterns.

EXAMPLE 1
Study the pattern at the top of the next page and use it to express the squares of 5, 6, and 7, in a similar manner.

$$1^2 = 1.$$
$$2^2 = 1 + 2 + 1.$$
$$3^2 = 1 + 2 + 3 + 2 + 1.$$
$$4^2 = 1 + 2 + 3 + 4 + 3 + 2 + 1.$$

EXAMPLE 2

If we try to determine whether there is a reason behind the pattern of Example 1, we are naturally led to investigate the square since the area of a square of side s is s^2. If $s = 2$, we have

and it is clear that counting the unit squares along the diagonals yields $2^2 = 1 + 2 + 1$. If $s = 3$, we have

and the counting of the unit squares along the diagonals now yields

$$3^2 = 1 + 2 + 3 + 2 + 1.$$

The reason for the pattern exhibited in Example 1 should now be clear.

Problem Set 1.2

1. Study the entries that follow and use the pattern that is exhibited to complete the last four rows.

$$1 + 3 = 4, \text{ or } 2^2.$$
$$1 + 3 + 5 = 9, \text{ or } 3^2.$$
$$1 + 3 + 5 + 7 = 16, \text{ or } 4^2.$$
$$1 + 3 + 5 + 7 + 9 = ?$$
$$1 + 3 + 5 + 7 + 9 + 11 = ?$$
$$1 + 3 + 5 + 7 + 9 + 11 + 13 = ?$$
$$1 + 3 + 5 + \cdots + (2n - 1) = ?$$

2. What is the reason behind the pattern exhibited in Problem 1?

*3. Take a piece of notebook paper and fold it in half. Then fold it in half again and cut off a corner that does not involve an edge of the original piece of paper. Your paper, when unfolded, should look like the accompanying sketch. Note that with two folds we produced one hole. Repeat the same process but this time make three folds before cutting off an edge. Try to predict the number of holes that will be produced. How many holes will be produced with four folds? With *n* folds?

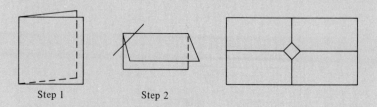

Step 1   Step 2

4. At the age of ten, the famous mathematician Gauss (1777–1855) is said to have found the sum of the first 100 counting numbers,

$$1 + 2 + 3 + \cdots + 98 + 99 + 100,$$

by the following method: He reasoned that there would be 50 pairs of numbers, each with a sum of 101 (1 + 100, 2 + 99, 3 + 98, etc.). Thus, the sum would be 50 × 101 or 5,050. Use this method to find:
(a) The sum of the first 80 counting numbers.
(b) The sum of the first 200 counting numbers.
(c) The sum of all the odd numbers from 1 through 49.
(d) The sum of all the odd numbers from 1 through 199.
(e) The sum of all the even numbers from 2 through 400.

*5. Use the results obtained in Problem 4 to try to find a formula for the sum of:
(a) The first *n* counting numbers

$$[\text{i.e., } 1 + 2 + 3 + \cdots + (n - 1) + n = ?].$$

(b) The first *n* odd numbers

$$[\text{i.e., } 1 + 3 + 5 + \cdots + (2n - 3) + (2n - 1) = ?].$$

6. Try to find the pattern in each of the following sequences, and then write down the next two numbers.
(a) 1, 2, 3, 4, ...   (d) 2, 5, 8, 11, ...
(b) 1, 3, 6, 10, ...   (e) 1, 1, 2, 3, ...
(c) 1, 2, 6, 24, ...   (f) 2, 1, 3, 4, ...

7. How would you describe the property of the numbers in the following square? Can you find another arrangement of these numbers which has the same property?

$$
\begin{array}{ccc}
4 & 9 & 2 \\
3 & 5 & 7 \\
8 & 1 & 6
\end{array}
$$

8. Consider n given points such that no three are on the same line. How many line segments are there with both end points at these given points if n is (a) 3, (b) 4, (c) 5, °(d) n?

*9. Find the sum:

$$\frac{1}{2} + \frac{1}{2^2} + \frac{1}{2^3} + \frac{1}{2^4} + \cdots + \frac{1}{2^n}.$$

To help you discover this sum, complete these partial sums and search for a pattern.

(a) $\dfrac{1}{2} + \dfrac{1}{2^2} = \dfrac{1}{2} + \dfrac{1}{4} = \,?$

(b) $\dfrac{1}{2} + \dfrac{1}{2^2} + \dfrac{1}{2^3} = \dfrac{1}{2} + \dfrac{1}{4} + \dfrac{1}{8} = \,?$

(c) $\dfrac{1}{2} + \dfrac{1}{2^2} + \dfrac{1}{2^3} + \dfrac{1}{2^4} = \dfrac{1}{2} + \dfrac{1}{4} + \dfrac{1}{8} + \dfrac{1}{16} = \,?$

*10. An infinite series is one in which the terms go on without end. Some of these series approach numbers as limits. Consider this series:

$$\frac{1}{2} + \frac{1}{4} + \frac{1}{8} + \frac{1}{16} + \frac{1}{32} + \cdots.$$

Consider the sum of the first two terms, the first three terms, the first four terms, etc. Then conjecture an answer for the sum of the series as the terms go on without end. (**HINT:** See Problem 9.)

*11. Use the result of the preceding problem to explain the following paradoxes of Zeno. [These paradoxes, which were devised by the philosopher Zeno of Elea (born about 490 B.C.), have had a profound influence on mathematics. It should be noted that the paradoxes, as given below, have been modified by changing the units of distance and time.]

(a) Zeno argued that a man cannot reach a point a mile away as follows: "He first has to traverse the first half mile, then he would have to traverse the next quarter of a mile, then the next eighth of a mile, etc.—and since performing an infinite succession of acts should take an infinite length of time, the man can never reach his goal."

(b) Zeno argued that Achilles (who runs 20 yards per second) could never overtake the Tortoise (who runs 10 yards per second) if the Tortoise is given a handicap of 20 yards and they start at the same instant—for by the time Achilles had run 20 yards the Tortoise would have run 10 yards, by the time Achilles had run the next 10 yards, the Tortoise would have run 5 yards, etc.; and since the Tortoise will always be ahead of Achilles, he will never be caught.

12. Use the procedure suggested in Problem 10 to determine the sums, if any, of the following series:

(a) $1 + 2 + 4 + 8 + 16 + 32 + \cdots$.

°(b) $\dfrac{1}{3} + \dfrac{1}{9} + \dfrac{1}{27} + \dfrac{1}{81} + \cdots$.

°13. Try to find a formula for

$$1^3 + 2^3 + 3^3 + \cdots + n^3$$

by first considering the sum of the first two terms, the first three terms, etc. Can you prove your formula works when n is *any* counting number? How?

14. Write the decimal representations for $\frac{1}{7}, \frac{2}{7}, \frac{3}{7}, \frac{4}{7}, \frac{5}{7}$, and $\frac{6}{7}$. See if you can discover a relationship among the sequences of repeating digits.

CHAPTER 2

What Is Mathematics?

2.1 Abstract Mathematical Structures

Some students who enjoyed working the problems in the last chapter may have thought that chapter should be entitled "Fun with Math," and some may have asked, "If you can solve all these problems, do you know mathematics?"—or even wondered, "What is mathematics?"

Anyone who becomes involved in the study of mathematics will at some time be confronted with the question, "What is at the foundation of mathematics?" If you were asked this question, what would your answer be? What are the building blocks of mathematics? You may find this a difficult question to answer—for you may feel you really know the answer but just cannot put it into words. It is true that the right words can be of great assistance at a time like this, and the "right words" we have in mind are *Abstract Mathematical Structures*. So you reply, "That sounds fine . . . , but what are Abstract Mathematical Structures?"

Before giving an answer, we will consider the following problem: "Suppose you were studying ordinary plane geometry and wanted to manufacture its 'basic parts', how would you begin?" Before answering this, you should first answer, "What sort of things do we study in geometry?" Well, some place along the way we would want to talk about triangles. This may lead us to the following dialogue:

> WE: What is a triangle?
> YOU: A triangle is a set of three line segments arranged in a certain way. For example, ...
> WE: What is a line segment?
> YOU: A set of points arranged in a certain way. For example, ...
> WE: What is a point?
> YOU: Everyone knows what a point is—it is a dot!

[9

If we are now persistent enough to continue this questioning and ask you, "What is a dot?" you would probably reply, "It is a point." Well, no matter how stubborn you are, you would agree eventually that we cannot define everything, and therefore we must start with *undefined terms*. Now how do these undefined terms acquire properties? Well, you just give them properties by making certain *assumptions* about them. After we have undefined terms and assumptions, what sort of results can we obtain from them? At this point it might seem natural to *guess* which *conclusions* follow from the assumptions. After making a guess, we should attempt to establish that the guess really does follow from the assumptions by trying to give a convincing argument based on "logic." If we are successful in this attempt, the guess is called a *theorem*, the convincing argument based on "logic" is called a *proof*, and the structure formed is called an *Abstract Mathematical Structure* (or AMS). We will now exhibit a diagram which pictures an AMS as described above.

Abstract Mathematical Structure

$$
\begin{bmatrix}
\text{Undefined terms} \\
\text{Assumptions} \\
\cdots\cdots\cdots\cdots \\
\text{Guesses}
\end{bmatrix}
\xRightarrow[\text{("logic")}]{\text{Proof}}
[\text{Theorems}]
$$

We note that the bridge can be crossed only by means of a proof—or convincing argument—based on "logic." We also note that the more standard terms are *postulates* or *axioms* for assumptions, and *conjectures* for guesses.

We shall now illustrate the meaning of an AMS with a simple example.

AMS (1)

UNDEFINED TERMS

x, y, z.

ASSUMPTIONS

1. All x are y.
2. All y are z.

After some consideration, and possibly the drawing of a picture like Fig. 2.1, a natural guess is

Guess 1: All x are z.

Now how can we convince others that this guess actually does follow from the assumptions, or equivalently, how can we convert this guess into a theorem? One way is to draw a picture like that of Fig. 2.1 where all x are represented inside the inner circle, all y are represented inside the middle

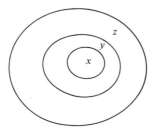

FIGURE 2.1.

circle (so that every x is a y), and all z are represented inside the outer circle (so that every y is a z).[1]

As a result of this picture argument, could anyone in his right mind dispute that all x are z? If someone objected to the drawing of a picture as a proof, we could say, "If you don't agree that we are forced to accept all x are z, then surely you would be able to find some $x = x'$ which is not a z. But since x' must be a y, and every y is a z, x' must be a z."

Presumably he is now convinced, and so we have

THEOREM 1 *All x are z.*

Since this AMS is so limited, we will not attempt any further guesses. Instead, we will consider the question, "Can meanings be given to x, y, and z that will make both assumptions true?" Before considering any examples, we will find it convenient to have the following.

NOTATION

The words *represents* and *is represented by* will often be designated by the symbol : , as shown in the following examples:

EXAMPLE 1
x : boys; y : humans; z : animals.

EXAMPLE 2
x : triangles; y : polygons; z : geometric figures.

EXAMPLE 3
x : universities; y : schools; z : institutions.

---

[1] Diagrams in which geometric figures are used to represent sets of points are called either *Euler circles* or *Venn diagrams*—in honor of the Swiss mathematician Leonhard Euler (1707–1783), who introduced this idea in the eighteenth century, and the British logician John Venn (1834–1923), who in the nineteenth century extended the idea to include more complicated figures.

Clearly all these examples give concrete interpretations to the undefined terms which make both assumptions true. We also note the important fact that Theorem 1 must hold in each case.

We now have the equipment for answering the following questions.

(1) What is pure mathematics?

(2) What is applied mathematics?

(3) What is mathematics?

The answers are, respectively:

(1) Pure mathematics consists of all AMS.

(2) Applied mathematics consists of all concrete interpretations of AMS.

(3) Mathematics consists of both pure and applied mathematics.

Lord Bertrand Russell (1872–1970) once described mathematics as "the subject in which we never know what we are talking about nor whether what we are saying is true." Many people accept this statement—but for a variety of reasons. We can now see that it is a valid description of pure mathematics, for in this subject we never know what we are talking about (since our structure rests on undefined terms) and we never know whether what we are saying is true (since our assumptions have no relationship to reality).

From our discussion the reader may have concluded that the meaning of *logic* is commonly accepted as clear to all, since we have not made any attempt to explain it. However, we shall soon see that logic itself can be considered either an AMS (pure logic) or a concrete interpretation of an AMS (concrete logic).

Problem Set 2.1

1. Make up an example of an AMS and
   (a) Give two different concrete interpretations.
   (b) Find as many theorems as you can.

2.2 Boolean Arithmetic

The example of the previous section was given to illustrate the meaning of AMS and is admittedly trivial and unfruitful. We will now proceed to give a more interesting example.

AMS (2)

UNDEFINED TERMS

$\overline{0}, \overline{1}; \ \oplus, \otimes$

[where $\overline{0}$ and $\overline{1}$ (read "zero-bar" and "one-bar") are called *elements*; $\oplus$ and $\otimes$ (read "plus-circle" and "cross-circle") are called *operations*].

ASSUMPTIONS

a	b	$a \oplus b$
$\overline{0}$	$\overline{0}$	$\overline{0}$
$\overline{0}$	$\overline{1}$	$\overline{1}$
$\overline{1}$	$\overline{0}$	$\overline{1}$
$\overline{1}$	$\overline{1}$	$\overline{1}$

a	b	$a \otimes b$
$\overline{0}$	$\overline{0}$	$\overline{0}$
$\overline{0}$	$\overline{1}$	$\overline{0}$
$\overline{1}$	$\overline{0}$	$\overline{0}$
$\overline{1}$	$\overline{1}$	$\overline{1}$

The assumptions are written in the form of tables where a, b represent either $\overline{0}$ or $\overline{1}$ and, for example, the first row in the first table means $\overline{0} \oplus \overline{0} = \overline{0}$, the second row means $\overline{0} \oplus \overline{1} = \overline{1}$, etc.

The reader may observe that all the table entries look reasonable with the exception of the last row in the first table (i.e., $\overline{1} \oplus \overline{1} = \overline{1}$) and ask, "Why?" At this point we simply say there is no reason why the assumptions should look reasonable, since we are dealing with meaningless symbols (although admittedly they do look like symbols we are all familiar with). Thus at this stage there is no reason to justify our assumptions in any way.

Now that the assumptions are given, what conclusions can you draw? You might want to see if these creatures (i.e., $\overline{0}$ and $\overline{1}$) behave like ordinary numbers. For example, you may want to investigate the following questions:

(1) Does $a \oplus b = b \oplus a$?

(2) Does $a \oplus (b \oplus c) = (a \oplus b) \oplus c$?

(3) Does $a \otimes b = \overline{0}$ imply $a = \overline{0}$ or $b = \overline{0}$?

NOTE: Unless otherwise indicated, we shall interpret "or" to mean "and/or."

In order to determine the answers to these questions, we merely study the assumptions. This is not difficult, since there are so few entries. By considering all possible cases, we conclude that the answer to each of the questions is yes, and therefore we have the following theorems in AMS (2).

THEOREM 1 $a \oplus b = b \oplus a$.

THEOREM 2 $a \oplus (b \oplus c) = (a \oplus b) \oplus c$.

THEOREM 3 $a \otimes b = \overline{0}$ implies $a = \overline{0}$ or $b = \overline{0}$.

We next extend our horizon somewhat by seeing if we can obtain more interesting-looking results. We may proceed by just writing down expressions and then seeing whether they can be simplified. For example, we may want to see whether the following questions make any sense, and if so, what are the answers.

(4) $a \oplus a = ?$

(5) $a \oplus (a \otimes b) = ?$

One way of obtaining answers to these questions is by constructing tables. Since $\bar{0} \oplus \bar{0} = \bar{0}$ and $\bar{1} \oplus \bar{1} = \bar{1}$, the following table results

a	$a \oplus a$
$\bar{0}$	$\bar{0}$
$\bar{1}$	$\bar{1}$

and therefore we have a theorem corresponding to (4).

THEOREM 4 $a \oplus a = a.$

For question (5), the table can be written as follows

a	b	$a \otimes b$	$a \oplus (a \otimes b)$
$\bar{0}$	$\bar{0}$	$\bar{0}$	$\bar{0}$
$\bar{0}$	$\bar{1}$	$\bar{0}$	$\bar{0}$
$\bar{1}$	$\bar{0}$	$\bar{0}$	$\bar{1}$
$\bar{1}$	$\bar{1}$	$\bar{1}$	$\bar{1}$

After comparing the first and last columns we obtain the following theorem corresponding to (5).

THEOREM 5 $a \oplus (a \otimes b) = a.$

We next rewrite the $\otimes$ table of AMS (2) as follows: First, write the rows in reverse order so that they appear as

a	b	$a \otimes b$
$\bar{1}$	$\bar{1}$	$\bar{1}$
$\bar{1}$	$\bar{0}$	$\bar{0}$
$\bar{0}$	$\bar{1}$	$\bar{0}$
$\bar{0}$	$\bar{0}$	$\bar{0}$

and then interchange $\bar{0}$ with $\bar{1}$ so that we now have

a	b	$a \oslash b$
$\bar{0}$	$\bar{0}$	$\bar{0}$
$\bar{0}$	$\bar{1}$	$\bar{1}$
$\bar{1}$	$\bar{0}$	$\bar{1}$
$\bar{1}$	$\bar{1}$	$\bar{1}$

After studying this last table we notice the familiar pattern of the $\oplus$ table—and thus if we also convert $\otimes$ to $\oplus$, the process described above converts the $\otimes$ table into a $\oplus$ table. A similar procedure will convert the $\oplus$ table into the $\otimes$ table. (Try it and see!)

The results just obtained can be useful. For example, they can be used to convert Theorem 3 into the equally true statement:

THEOREM 3' $a \oplus b = \bar{1}$ implies $a = \bar{1}$ or $b = \bar{1}$.

Similarly we can assert

THEOREM 1' $a \otimes b = b \otimes a$.

since it is the "dual" of Theorem 1.

We will now formally state the procedure justifying the "duality" proofs of Theorems 3' and 1' by means of a *Duality Theorem*.

DUALITY THEOREM   *If in AMS (2) statement p is converted into statement q by interchanging $\bar{0}$ with $\bar{1}$ and $\oplus$ with $\otimes$, then statement q is true if and only if statement p is true.*

Thus the Duality Theorem provides us with a method for obtaining new theorems from old theorems—free of charge.

In order to discover a concrete interpretation for AMS (2) we must find a situation in which only two things can happen. A simple example occurs in electricity where a light can be on or off, or, equivalently, a switch can be closed or open. If the switch is closed, as in Fig. 2.2*a*, current will flow and the light will be on (assuming current, etc.); if the switch is open, as in Fig. 2.2*b*, no current flows and the light will be off.

(a)   (b)

FIGURE 2.2.

We note that there are two basic electrical networks, parallel as indicated in Fig. 2.3*a* and series as indicated in Fig. 2.3*b*.

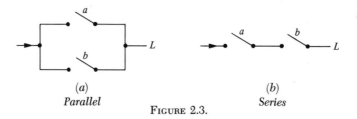

(a)   (b)
Parallel   Series
            FIGURE 2.3.

We next gather this information together into the following tables, where

N : no current flows to L;
C : current flows to L;
aSb : a is in series with b.
aPb : a is in parallel with b;

a	b	aPb
N	N	N
N	C	C
C	N	C
C	C	C

a	b	aSb
N	N	N
N	C	N
C	N	N
C	C	C

These tables look similar to those for $\oplus$ and $\otimes$. In fact, if N is replaced by $\bar{0}$, C by $\bar{1}$, P by $\oplus$, and S by $\otimes$, these two tables become identical with the previous ones, and we do in fact have a concrete interpretation for AMS (2).

Practical applications can now be obtained by using theorems in AMS (2) to simplify electrical networks. Since Theorem 5 $[a \oplus (a \otimes b) = a]$, for example, becomes converted to $aP(aSb) = a$, the network of Fig. 2.4a can be replaced by that of Fig. 2.4b.

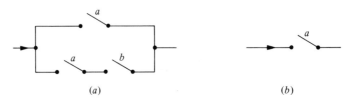

FIGURE 2.4.

It turns out that AMS (2) has other interesting concrete interpretations (some of which are included in the exercises), and is often called *Boolean arithmetic* in honor of the English mathematician George Boole (1815–1864).

Problem Set 2.2

1. Determine which of the following are theorems in AMS (2) and prove your answers.
(a) $a \oplus \bar{1} = \bar{1}$.
(b) $a \otimes \bar{0} = \bar{0}$.
(c) $a \otimes (b \otimes a) = a$.
(d) $a \otimes (b \otimes a) = b$.
(e) $a \otimes (b \otimes a) = b \otimes a$.

   (f) $a \oplus (b \oplus a) = b \oplus a$.
   (g) $a \otimes (b \oplus c) = (a \otimes b) \oplus (a \otimes c)$.
   (h) $a \oplus (b \otimes c) = (a \oplus b) \otimes (a \oplus c)$.

2. Draw an electrical network to illustrate each part of Problem 1 that is a theorem.

3. Use the Duality Theorem to write duals of (a) Theorem 2, (b) Theorem 4, (c) Theorem 5, (d) each part of Problem 1 that is a theorem, (e) a theorem of your own for AMS (2).

4. If AMS (2) is extended to AMS (2♯) by introducing the new undefined term $a^{\sharp}$ (read "a-sharp"), with assumptions given in the table

a	$a^{\sharp}$
$\bar{0}$	$\bar{1}$
$\bar{1}$	$\bar{0}$

   so that $\overline{0^{\sharp}} = \bar{1}$ and $\overline{1^{\sharp}} = \bar{0}$, find
   (a) $(a^{\sharp})^{\sharp}$.
   *(b) $(a \oplus b)^{\sharp}$ in terms of $a^{\sharp}$ and $b^{\sharp}$.
   *(c) Another theorem involving ♯.
   (d) An interpretation of ♯ for electrical networks.

*5. Write the dual of your result in Problem 4(b). Is it a theorem? Why?

6. Suppose the last row in the $\oplus$ table of AMS (2) is changed so that $\bar{1} \oplus \bar{1} = \bar{0}$.
   (a) Which theorems of AMS (2) remain true?
   (b) Find a theorem in this converted AMS (2) which was not a theorem for AMS (2).
   *(c) Find a concrete interpretation for this converted AMS (2).

7. Let T : true and F : false. If $\bar{0} : F$, $\bar{1} : T$, $\oplus$: or, $\otimes$: and, prove that the system of logic [F, T; or, and] is a concrete interpretation of AMS (2). Use this system to give new interpretations to some of the theorems in AMS (2).

*8. Convert AMS (2♯) into "logic" by use of Problem 7 and by giving ♯ the "proper" concrete interpretation. Use this system to give new interpretations to some of the theorems in AMS (2♯).

*9. Let AMS (3) be defined as follows:

$S = \{a, b, c, \ldots\}$, *.

ASSUMPTIONS
(1) If a is in S and b is in S, then $(a * b)$ is in S.
(2) If $a * b = c$, then $b * c = a$.
(3) There exists a special element e in S such that $a * e = a$ for each a in S.

Which of the following are theorems in AMS (3)? *Prove* your answers.
(a) $e * a = a$.
(b) $a * a = e$.
(c) $b * (a * b) = a$.
(d) $a * b = b * a$.
(e) If $a * b = e$, then $a = b$.
(f) If $a * b = c$, then $c * a = b$.
(g) If $a * b = c * b$, then $a = c$.
(h) If $b * a = b * c$, then $a = c$.
(i) $a * (b * a) = (a * b) * a = b$.
(j) $a * (b * c) = (a * b) * c$.
(k) If $(a * b) * c = d$, then $a * b = c * d$.

*10. Let an *associative* AMS (3) be defined to be an AMS (3) with the following property:
(4) $a * (b * c) = (a * b) * c$ for all a, b, c in S.
Prove that the following are theorems for an associative AMS (3).
(a) $a * b = b * a$.
(b) $(a * b) * (a * c) = b * c$.

11. Find a concrete interpretation for AMS (3) with two elements.

*12. Find a concrete interpretation for AMS (3) with more than two elements.

13. Let AMS (4) be the "abstract finite geometry" defined by:

UNDEFINED TERMS
$P = \{P_1, P_2, \ldots\}$, $L = \{l_1, l_2, \ldots\}$
[where $P_1, P_2, \ldots$ are called points and $l_1, l_2, \ldots$ are called lines].

ASSUMPTIONS
(1) A line contains points.
(2) Every pair of points is on exactly one line.

(3) Every line contains exactly three points.

(4) Every pair of lines has exactly one point in common.

(5) There are exactly seven points.

    (a) Can the following figure be used to obtain a concrete interpretation of AMS (4)? *Explain.*

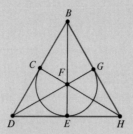

    (b) Describe the concrete interpretation of AMS (4) obtained when "points" are replaced by "people" and "lines" are replaced by "committees."

    (c) What happens to AMS (4) when "points" and "lines" are interchanged?

    °(d) Can you use AMS (4) to obtain a concrete interpretation of AMS (3)?

    °(e) If AMS (4) is modified by omitting Assumption 5, what can you say about the number of points in *P*?

    °(f) Find as many concrete interpretations of AMS (4) as you can.

    °(g) Find as many concrete interpretations as you can for the modified AMS (4) described in part (e).

14. Make a new attempt at Problem 1 of Problem Set 2.1.

CHAPTER 3

Logic

3.1 Introduction

In Chapter 2, we assumed that the meaning of "logic" is clear to all. Since "Logic" is the title of this chapter, one may surmise that it should be investigated—and it should!

For our purposes it will be convenient to think of logic as a tool of reasoning. More concretely it deals with reasoning about *statements*, where a statement is a sentence that can be labeled true or false—but not both. (By *sentence* we mean an ordered set of words or symbols, and our experience dictates whether a sentence can be identified as true or false. For example, "Water is wet" is true, and "Abraham Lincoln was the first president of the United States" is false.) We shall use symbols such as p, q, r, s to designate statements.

Some examples of statements (assuming that the meaning of all words and symbols used are known) are the following.

p : The earth is flat.
$q : 1 + 1 = 1$.
r : All birds fly.
s : Some boys are intelligent.
Some examples of nonstatements are
(1) Come here!
(2) $7 + 3$.
(3) If I live in Wisconsin.
(4) Then I will be happy.

When reasoning about statements, we often want to know whether certain statements imply certain other statements. If an argument forces us to accept a particular conclusion once we have accepted certain assumptions, we say the argument is *valid*. Thus an argument is valid if and only if the conclusion is inescapable. If the conclusion is not inescapable, we say the argument is *not valid* or is *invalid*.

20]

EXAMPLE 1

Consider the argument: "All undergraduates are freshmen and all freshmen are beautiful. Therefore, all undergraduates are beautiful." If we let U: "undergraduates," F: "freshmen" and B: "beautiful," and we draw a Venn diagram like that of Fig. 3.1 to illustrate the two assumptions (All U are F and all F are B), then it should be clear that the conclusion (All U are B) is inescapable, and therefore the argument is *valid*. It should be emphasized that we do not care about the truth of the statements involved—only their implications. The reader may have observed that this example is essentially the same as AMS (1).

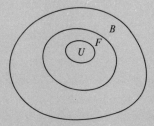

FIGURE 3.1.

EXAMPLE 2

Consider the argument: "Some freshmen are clever and all girls are clever. Therefore some freshmen are girls." If we let F: "freshmen," C: "clever," and G: "girls," then we find that both assumptions (Some F are C and all G are C) are satisfied in each part of Fig. 3.2. We observe that the conclusion (Some F are G) holds in Fig. 3.2a, c, d, and f but not in Fig. 3.2b

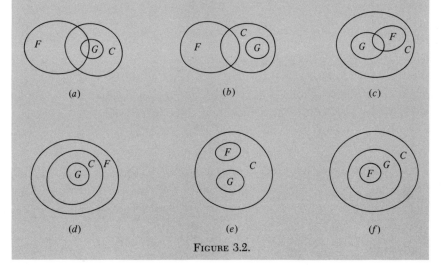

FIGURE 3.2.

or *e*. Since we have found at least one case in which the assumptions hold, but not the conclusion (e.g., Fig. 3.2*b*), the conclusion is not escapable, and therefore the argument given in this example is *not valid*. We want to emphasize that the word *some* means "at least one"—and conceivably could be "all." Also, just because we assume "some freshmen are clever" we need not conclude that "some freshmen are not clever."

Problem Set 3.1

1. Determine which of the following are statements (indicate any stipulations that may be needed).
   (a) There are a billion stars in the universe.
   (b) Are you there?
   (c) $3 + 1 = 6$.
   (d) Hello.
   (e) The collection of all bicycles.
   (f) Let us have faith that right makes might.
   (g) If today is Monday.
   (h) Everyone is able to bring pleasure in some way.
   (i) Then I shall return.
   (j) Australia is part of New Zealand.
   (k) $(2 + 2 = 4)$ and $(3 + 1 = 7)$.
   (l) $(2 + 2 = 4)$ or $(3 + 1 = 7)$.
   (m) $(2 + 2 = 4)$ or $(3 + 1 = 4)$.
   (n) $(2 + 2 = 4)$ and $(3 + 1 = 4)$.
   (o) He knows everything.
   (p) Freedom to ask questions.
   (q) If the problem can be solved, then Tom will solve it.
   (r) Go fly a kite.
   (s) He lost all his marbles.
   (t) Ping pong in Hong Kong.
   (u) The University of Otago is in New Zealand.
   (v) This statement is false.
   (w) $x + 2 = 5$.
   (x) 1984.
   (y) Incompetence is no obstacle.
   (z) There was an old woman who lived in a shoe.

2. Make up your own example of (a) a statement, (b) a nonstatement.

Determine which of the following arguments are *valid*.

3. All Wisconsinites are Martians.
   All Martians are residents of the U.S.A.
   Therefore, all Wisconsinites are residents of the U.S.A.

4. All juniors are brilliant.
   All brilliant people love mathematics.
   Therefore, if you are a junior then you love mathematics.

5. All freshmen are clever.
   All girls are clever.
   Therefore, all freshmen are girls.

6. All a's are b's.
   Some a's are c's.
   Therefore, some c's are b's.

7. All students love mathematics.
   David is a student.
   Therefore, David loves mathematics.

8. All girls are clever.
   All clever people like this course.
   Therefore, if you like this course, then you are a girl.

9. All mathematics teachers are delightful.
   Some Ph.D's are delightful.
   Therefore:
   (a) Some mathematics teachers have Ph.D's.
   (b) Some delightful people have Ph.D's.

10. All juniors are clever.
    Some juniors are males.
    Therefore:
    (a) Some males are clever.
    (b) Some males are juniors.
    (c) Some clever people are males.
    (d) Some males are not juniors.

11. All boys are handsome.
    Some boys are athletes.
    Therefore, some athletes are handsome.

12. All mathematics teachers are interesting.
All attractive individuals are interesting.
Some mathematics teachers are kind.
Therefore:
(a) Some interesting people are kind.
(b) Some mathematics teachers are attractive.
(c) All mathematics teachers are attractive.
(d) Some mathematics teachers are not kind.
(e) Some kind individuals are attractive.
(f) No mathematics teachers are attractive.
(g) No attractive individuals are interesting.

13. All x's are y's.
Some y's are z's.
Therefore:
(a) Some x's are z's.
(b) Some z's are y's.

14. All a's are b's.
All b's are c's.
Some d's are not c's.
Therefore:
(a) All a's are c's.
(b) Some d's are not b's.
(c) Some d's are not a's.
(d) Some c's are not d's.
(e) All not c's are not a's.

15. All zorks are korks.
Some zorks are morks.
Some yorks are zorks.
Therefore:
(a) Some korks are zorks.
(b) Some yorks are korks.
(c) Some korks are morks.
(d) No mork is a york.
(e) Some yorks are kork-morks.

3.2 AMS (Logic)

In the previous section we drew diagrams to help us "reason." The reader may have become aware that this procedure can be confusing and difficult on occasion. Our next objective is to develop a simple set of rules to aid us in our reasoning, and these rules should help us to avoid the drawing of complicated diagrams.

We shall first consider methods of forming new statements from old ones. One way is to negate statements. For example, the negation of "the world is flat" is "it is false that the world is flat" or "the world is not flat," and the negation of "all birds fly" is "it is false that all birds fly" or "some birds do not fly" (*not* "all birds do not fly"). The negation of $p : \sim p$, and this symbol will be read "it is false that p" or "not p."

Another way of forming new statements from old ones is to consider pairs of statements. For example, with each pair of statements p, q we can form the following new statements,

"p and q" : $p \wedge q$.

"p or q" : $p \vee q$ (here "or" means "and/or").

"p implies q" : $p \rightarrow q$ (i.e., if p, then q).

"p is equivalent to q" : $p \leftrightarrow q$ (i.e., p if and only if q, which will often be abbreviated as p iff q).

Before developing logic as a tool, we will find it convenient to use the preceding discussion to help us develop AMS (Logic)—and then later we shall establish its natural concrete interpretation called *applied logic*, or *concrete logic* or just plain *logic* to serve as the desired tool of reasoning about statements. Hence, we will need to justify all our assumptions in AMS (Logic).

AMS (LOGIC)

UNDEFINED TERMS

$\{p, q, r, \ldots\};$ statement; $\{T, F\}, \sim, \wedge, \vee, \rightarrow, \leftrightarrow$

[where p, q, r, . . . will be called statements, T : true, F : false, $\sim$: it is false that (or *not*), $\wedge$: and, $\vee$: or, $\rightarrow$: implies, $\leftrightarrow$: is equivalent to. It is understood that *all* of these terms are now *undefined*, but the assumptions will be based on their usual meanings].

ASSUMPTIONS

"p is a statement" means (p is T) or (p is F)—but *not* both.

Negation	
p	$\sim p$
T	F
F	T

And		
p	q	$p \wedge q$
T	T	T
T	F	F
F	T	F
F	F	F

Or		
p	q	$p \vee q$
T	T	T
T	F	T
F	T	T
F	F	F

Implication		
p	q	$p \rightarrow q$
T	T	T
T	F	F
F	T	T
F	F	T

Equivalence		
p	q	$p \leftrightarrow q$
T	T	T
T	F	F
F	T	F
F	F	T

NOTE: The symbol $\wedge$ is often called *conjunction* and the symbol $\vee$ is often called (inclusive) *disjunction*.

Since the truth tables that serve as defining axioms for AMS (Logic) will be used to prove theorems involving the expected concrete interpretations of the undefined terms, all entries in these tables probably seem reasonable, with the possible exception of the last two rows in the Implication Table.

We shall now make an attempt to justify all of the entries in all of the preceding tables.

NEGATION

Since every statement is either T or F (but not both), it should be clear that the Negation Table must have exactly two horizontal lines—and that if p is T, then $\sim p$ must be F and if p is F, then $\sim p$ must be T.

NOTE: In the remaining four tables it should be noted that all logical possibilities are represented. For if p is T, then q can be either T or F (giving us the first and second lines), and if p is F, then q can be either T or F (giving us the third and fourth lines).

AND & OR

If p : "it is snowing" and q : "it is windy," then p and q are both true (i.e., $p \wedge q$ is T) iff it is both snowing and windy. On the other hand, p or q is true (i.e., $p \vee q$ is T) when (1) it is both snowing and windy, or (2) it is snowing but not windy, or (3) it is not snowing but it is windy—and p or q is false (i.e., $p \vee q$ is F) only when it is not snowing and not windy. Thus it is reasonable that the And Table should state that $p \wedge q$ is F unless p and q are both T, and the Or Table should state that $p \vee q$ is T unless p and q are both F.

IMPLICATION

Since we translate $p \rightarrow q$ as "p implies q" or "if p, then q," it follows that $p \rightarrow q$ can be interpreted to mean "if we have p, then we must also have q." Therefore, $p \rightarrow q$ means "*it is not possible* to have both p and $\sim q$," which permits us to replace $p \rightarrow q$ with $\sim[p \wedge (\sim q)]$. If we now construct the truth table for $\sim[p \wedge (\sim q)]$, using the results of the Negation and And Tables, we find

p	q	$\sim q$	$p \wedge (\sim q)$	$\sim[p \wedge (\sim q)]$
T	T	F	F	T
T	F	T	T	F
F	T	F	F	T
F	F	T	F	T

If we now compare the last column in this truth table with the last column in the Implication Table, we find identical entries, and thus it is reasonable that $p \rightarrow q$ is F iff p is T and q is F. We will now introduce some examples to reaffirm the reasonableness of the Implication Table.

EXAMPLE 1

Suppose that a candidate for mayor states, "I promise you that if I am elected, then there will be a decrease in crime." If we let p : "I am elected," and q : "there will be a decrease in crime," then strictly speaking the candidate is saying "$p \rightarrow q$ is T." Therefore, if he is elected (i.e., p is T), then he keeps his promise only if there is a decrease in crime (i.e., q is T). However, if he does not get elected (i.e., p is F), then he cannot break his promise—and therefore $p \rightarrow q$ cannot be F!

EXAMPLE 2

Let $p : 3 = 7$ and $q : 10 = 10$. Thus p is F and q is T. Granting that if equals are added to equals the results are equal, we can show that $p \rightarrow q$ is true as follows:

$$\text{If } 3 = 7, \text{ then } 7 = 3.$$

But

$$3 = 7$$
$$7 = 3$$
$$\overline{}$$

yields
$$3 + 7 = 7 + 3$$

Hence $10 = 10$, and it is true that $p \rightarrow q$.

EXAMPLE 3

Let $p : 3 = 7$ and $q : 6 = 14$. Thus p and q are both F. Granting that if equals are multiplied by equals the results are equal, we can show that $p \rightarrow q$ is true as follows:

Since $(3 = 7)$ yields $(3 \times 2 = 7 \times 2)$, it follows that $(6 = 14)$. Hence it is true that $p \rightarrow q$.

Finally we observe that if you start with a true *hypothesis* (also called *assumption* or *premise*) and end with a false conclusion, then your reasoning cannot be valid, which means that the implication must be false. It would be sad indeed if logic could be used to convert a true statement into a false one!

EQUIVALENCE

If "p is equivalent to q" (i.e., $p \leftrightarrow q$ is T), then we would expect p and q to have identical truth values (i.e., p and q are both T or both F). Thus the Equivalence Table faithfully represents the meaning of logical equivalence.

Now that we have justified all the assumptions, we are ready to proceed with the development of AMS (Logic). That is, we should try to find theorems in AMS (Logic) which are based exclusively on the assumptions (i.e., truth tables). In order to make "judicious" guesses, one may decide to interpret the undefined terms in the expected way.

An initial guess may be

FIRST GUESS: $(p \wedge q) \leftrightarrow (q \wedge p)$.
We will now proceed to investigate this guess with the aid of a truth table.

p	q	$p \wedge q$	$q \wedge p$	$(p \wedge q) \leftrightarrow (q \wedge p)$
T	T	T	T	T
T	F	F	F	T
F	T	F	F	T
F	F	F	F	T

Since the last column is T in *all* cases, our guess is now established as a theorem in AMS (Logic).

The next guess may be

SECOND GUESS: $[(p \rightarrow q) \rightarrow (q \rightarrow p)]$.
We again proceed by constructing a truth table.

p	q	$p \rightarrow q$	$q \rightarrow p$	$(p \rightarrow q) \rightarrow (q \rightarrow p)$
T	T	T	T	T
T	F	F	T	T
F	T	T	F	F
F	F	T	T	T

Since the third row in the last column contains an F, it should be clear that this Second Guess is *not* a theorem. We also note that since it is *not* a theorem, only *one* line (i.e., the third) is needed to show this. The reader should try to find a "real-life" example in which $(p \rightarrow q)$ is T and $(q \rightarrow p)$ is F.

NOTE: The symbols T and F are sometimes used to represent statements that are always true and always false, respectively.

Problem Set 3.2

1. If r: "some boys are intelligent," does $\sim r$ mean (a) some boys are not intelligent, (b) all boys are not intelligent, (c) no boys are intelligent, (d) all boys are intelligent, (e) none of these?

2. If r: "all girls are intelligent," does $\sim r$ mean (a) no girls are intelligent, (b) all girls are not intelligent, (c) some girls are not intelligent, (d) some girls are intelligent, (e) none of these?

3. If r: "he is both a gentleman and a scholar," does $\sim r$ mean (a) he is not a gentleman and he is not a scholar, (b) he is a gentleman but not a scholar, (c) he is not a gentleman but is a scholar, (d) he is not a gentleman or he is not a scholar, (e) none of these?

4. If r: "he is talking or he is sleeping," does $\sim r$ mean (a) he is not talking or he is not sleeping, (b) he is not talking and he is not sleeping, (c) he is talking or he is not sleeping, (d) he is not talking or he is sleeping, (e) none of these?

5. If r: "if you press the button, then the bell rings," does $\sim r$ mean (a) if you do not press the button, then the bell does not ring; (b) if you do not press the button, then the bell rings; (c) if you press the button, then the bell does not ring; (d) you press the button and the bell does not ring; (e) you do not press the button and the bell rings; (f) none of these?

6. In Problem 2, r can also be stated as "If x is a girl, then x is intelligent." Therefore if we let p: "x is a girl" and q: "x is intelligent," then r becomes converted to $p \rightarrow q$. In Problems 3, 4, and 5 give interpretations to p and q so that r can be stated using the symbols of AMS (Logic). Then translate each part of Problems 3, 4, and 5 (except "none of these") into AMS (Logic).

7. Make up some guesses for AMS (Logic), and then use the Assumptions to prove or disprove them.

8. True-False. In AMS (Logic)
   (a) $p \wedge q$ is T iff p and q are both T.
   (b) $p \vee q$ is F iff $p \wedge q$ is F.
   (c) $p \rightarrow q$ is F iff p is T and q is F.
   (d) $p \rightarrow q$ is F iff $p \wedge (\sim q)$ is T.
   (e) $p \rightarrow q$ is T iff $p \wedge (\sim q)$ is F.

(f) $p \rightarrow q$ is T iff p is F or q is T.

(g) $p \rightarrow (\sim p)$ is always F.

(h) If $p \rightarrow q$ is T, then $p \rightarrow (\sim q)$ is F.

(i) $[(p \rightarrow q) \wedge (q \rightarrow r)] \rightarrow [p \rightarrow r]$ is always T.

(j) $p \rightarrow (p \vee q)$ is always T.

(k) $p \rightarrow (p \wedge q)$ is always T.

9. Determine which of the following are always true [i.e., are theorems in AMS (Logic)]. *Prove* your answers, and *translate* each theorem into words.

(a) $[p \wedge p] \leftrightarrow p$.

(b) $[p \vee p] \leftrightarrow p$.

(c) $[p \wedge q] \leftrightarrow [q \wedge p]$.

(d) $[p \vee q] \leftrightarrow [q \vee p]$.

(e) $[p \wedge (q \wedge r)] \leftrightarrow [(p \wedge q) \wedge r]$.

(f) $[p \vee (q \vee r)] \leftrightarrow [(p \vee q) \vee r]$.

(g) $[p \wedge (q \vee r)] \leftrightarrow [(p \wedge q) \vee (p \wedge r)]$.

(h) $[p \vee (q \wedge r)] \leftrightarrow [(p \vee q) \wedge (p \vee r)]$.

(i) $\sim(\sim p) \leftrightarrow p$.

(j) $[\sim(p \wedge q)] \leftrightarrow [(\sim p) \vee (\sim q)]$.

(k) $[\sim(p \vee q)] \leftrightarrow [(\sim p) \wedge (\sim q)]$.

(l) $[\sim(p \rightarrow q)] \leftrightarrow [p \wedge (\sim q)]$.

(m) $(p \rightarrow q) \leftrightarrow (q \rightarrow p)$.

(n) $(p \rightarrow q) \leftrightarrow [(\sim q) \rightarrow (\sim p)]$.

(o) $(p \leftrightarrow q) \leftrightarrow [(p \rightarrow q) \wedge (q \rightarrow p)]$.

(p) $[p \wedge (\sim p)] \leftrightarrow F$.

(q) $\sim[p \wedge (\sim p)] \leftrightarrow T$.

(r) $[p \vee (\sim p)] \leftrightarrow T$.

(s) $[p \wedge T] \leftrightarrow p$.

(t) $[p \vee T] \leftrightarrow T$.

(u) $[p \wedge F] \leftrightarrow F$.

(v) $[p \vee F] \leftrightarrow p$.

(w) $[p \wedge q] \rightarrow p$.

(x) $[p \vee q] \rightarrow q$.

(y) $[r \leftrightarrow s] \leftrightarrow [(\sim r) \leftrightarrow (\sim s)]$.

(z) $[(p \rightarrow q) \wedge (q \rightarrow r)] \rightarrow [p \rightarrow r]$.

10. Consider the following implications: (a) $p \rightarrow q$, (b) $q \rightarrow p$, (c) $(\sim p) \rightarrow (\sim q)$, (d) $(\sim q) \rightarrow (\sim p)$. If we assume that (a) is T, can we be sure that (i) (b) is T, (ii) (c) is T, (iii) (d) is T? Explain and give examples.

11. Let p : "the moon is made of Swiss cheese" and q : "John is my friend." Consider the following argument: "Since p is F, it follows from the

truth table that $p \rightarrow q$ is T. Therefore John must be my friend." Do you agree? Explain.

12. Do you agree with the statement: Logic cannot force us to accept a statement unless we have previously accepted another statement? Explain.

13. If you accept someone's argument and his conclusion, are you forced to accept his assumption? Explain and give examples.

14. If you accept someone's assumption and his argument, are you forced to accept his conclusion? Explain and give examples.

15. Can you find a relationship between AMS (Logic) and AMS ($2\sharp$) (defined in Problem 4 of Section 2.2)?

16. Let $p \veebar q$: "p or q but not both" (i.e., "exclusive or")
    (a) Construct a truth table for $p \veebar q$.
    °(b) Define $p \veebar q$ in terms of the symbols of AMS (Logic).
    °(c) Can you use $\veebar$ to find an interpretation for AMS (3) [defined in Problem 9 of Section 2.2]?

3.3 Methods for Proving Theorems in AMS (Logic)

NOTE: In the remainder of this chapter we shall refer to the problems of Problem Set 3.2 by means of their numbers alone. For example, 9j or Problem 9j will mean Problem 9j of Problem Set 3.2.

In attempting to prove the "guesses" in Problem 9 the reader may have set up a truth table, such as the following, for the proof of 9j.

EXAMPLE 1
Prove 9j : $\{[\sim(p \wedge q)] \leftrightarrow [(\sim p) \vee (\sim q)]\}$.

Proof:

p	q	$p \wedge q$	$\sim(p \wedge q)$	$\sim p$	$\sim q$	$(\sim p) \vee (\sim q)$	9j
T	T	T	F	F	F	F	T
T	F	F	T	F	T	T	T
F	T	F	T	T	F	T	T
F	F	F	T	T	T	T	T

Now Problem 9k can be proved in a similar way, or by judiciously using 9j and some of the other results as follows.

EXAMPLE 2
Prove 9k : $\{[\sim(p \lor q)] \leftrightarrow [(\sim p) \land (\sim q)]\}$ from 9j and other results from Problem 9 (i.e., without using a truth table.)

Proof:
By 9j we have

(1) $$[(\sim p) \lor (\sim q)] \leftrightarrow [\sim(p \land q)].$$

Using 9y, (1) becomes converted into

(2) $$\sim[(\sim p) \lor (\sim q)] \leftrightarrow \sim[\sim(p \land q)].$$

If we now apply 9i to the right-hand member of (2) three times, we obtain

(3) $$\sim[(\sim p) \lor (\sim q)] \leftrightarrow [\sim(\sim p) \land \sim(\sim q)].$$

Since $\sim p$ and $\sim q$ can represent any statements, we now have the desired result.

The method used in the preceding example can also be used to establish 9d from 9c, 9f from 9e, 9h from 9g, . . . , and vice versa.

EXAMPLE 3
Prove

$$9d : [(p \lor q) \leftrightarrow (q \lor p)]$$

from

$$9c : [(p \land q) \leftrightarrow (q \land p)]$$

and other results from Problem 9.

Proof:
By 9c we have

(1) $$(p \land q) \leftrightarrow (q \land p).$$

Problem 9y can be used to convert (1) into

(2) $$\sim(p \land q) \leftrightarrow \sim(q \land p).$$

If we now apply 9j to each member of (2) we obtain

$$[(\sim p) \lor (\sim q)] \leftrightarrow [(\sim q) \lor (\sim p)].$$

Now since $\sim p$ and $\sim q$ represent any statements, the desired result is obtained.

The list of statements in Problem 9 contains some basic theorems. The following theorem incorporates these theorems together with some of their standard names.

THEOREM 3.3.1   If p, q, r are any statements in AMS (Logic), then

(a) $[p \wedge p] \leftrightarrow p.$ ⎫
(b) $[p \vee p] \leftrightarrow p.$ ⎭   Idempotent Laws

(c) $[p \wedge q] \leftrightarrow [q \wedge p].$ ⎫
(d) $[p \vee q] \leftrightarrow [q \vee p].$ ⎭   Commutative Laws

(e) $[p \wedge (q \wedge r)] \leftrightarrow [(p \wedge q) \wedge r].$ ⎫
(f) $[p \vee (q \vee r)] \leftrightarrow [(p \vee q) \vee r].$ ⎭   Associative Laws

(g) $[p \wedge (q \vee r)] \leftrightarrow [(p \wedge q) \vee (p \wedge r)].$ ⎫
(h) $[p \vee (q \wedge r)] \leftrightarrow [(p \vee q) \wedge (p \vee r)].$ ⎭   Distributive Laws

(i) $\sim(\sim p) \leftrightarrow p.$ Double Negation Law

(j) $[\sim(p \wedge q)] \leftrightarrow [(\sim p) \vee (\sim q)].$ ⎫
(k) $[\sim(p \vee q)] \leftrightarrow [(\sim p) \wedge (\sim q)].$ ⎭   Laws of De Morgan

(l) $[\sim(p \rightarrow q)] \leftrightarrow [p \wedge (\sim q)].$
(m) $[p \rightarrow q] \leftrightarrow [(\sim q) \rightarrow (\sim p)].$
(n) $[p \leftrightarrow q] \leftrightarrow [(p \rightarrow q) \wedge (q \rightarrow p)].$
(o) $[(p \rightarrow q) \wedge (q \rightarrow r)] \rightarrow [p \rightarrow r].$
(p) $[p \leftrightarrow q] \leftrightarrow [(\sim p) \leftrightarrow (\sim q)].$

Problem Set 3.3

1. Use the methods of Examples 2 and 3 to prove (a) 9c from 9d, (b) 9f from 9e, (c) 9h from 9g.

*2. Try to prove some other results in Problem 9 without using truth tables.

*3. Try to find a theorem in AMS (Logic) that is not included in Problem 9, and prove your answer.

3.4 Converse and Contrapositive

In examining the results obtained from Problem 9 the reader should have found that $9m : [(p \rightarrow q) \leftrightarrow (q \rightarrow p)]$ was *not* a theorem, but that $9n : [(p \rightarrow q) \leftrightarrow [(\sim q) \rightarrow (\sim p)]]$ was a theorem—and may have been surprised by both of these results. These results are important, and the following terminology is commonly used.

DEF 3.4.1
The *converse* of $(p \rightarrow q) : q \rightarrow p.$

DEF 3.4.2
The *contrapositive* of $(p \rightarrow q) : (\sim q) \rightarrow (\sim p).$

Thus, from the preceding discussion, if we know that $(p \rightarrow q)$ is true, then the contrapositive of $(p \rightarrow q)$ *must* be true—but the converse of $(p \rightarrow q)$ *can be* false! The following example may help to convince the nonbeliever that this is really so.

EXAMPLE 1
Let p : "I go to school" and q : "I wear shoes." Suppose we assume that "I" is a teacher. Then it is probably reasonable to agree that $(p \rightarrow q)$ is *T*, so let us do so. However, $(q \rightarrow p)$ need not be true (and probably is not), and therefore the converse of a true statement can be false. However, $[(\sim q) \rightarrow (\sim p)]$ must be *T* [if we have accepted $(p \rightarrow q)$ is *T*], since the situation which occurs when "I do not wear shoes" and "I go to school" is an impossible one—because it is impossible for "I" to not wear shoes and to wear shoes at the same time.

A more convincing argument (or proof) can be given by means of truth tables. To prove that the converse of a true statement need not be true, we need only observe that when $(p$ is $F)$ and $(q$ is $T)$, then $(p \rightarrow q)$ is *T* but $(q \rightarrow p)$ is *F*. In order to prove that the contrapositive of a true statement must be true, we must establish that $[(\sim q) \rightarrow (\sim p)]$ is *T* whenever $(p \rightarrow q)$ is *T*. The following table reveals this.

p	q	$p \rightarrow q$	$\sim q$	$\sim p$	$(\sim q) \rightarrow (\sim p)$
T	T	T	F	F	T
T	F	F	T	F	F
F	T	T	F	T	T
F	F	T	T	T	T

This truth table establishes the following theorem.

THEOREM 3.4.1 $[p \rightarrow q] \leftrightarrow [(\sim q) \rightarrow (\sim p)].$

Problem Set 3.4

1. Make up an example of a true statement with a (a) true converse, (b) false converse.

2. For each of the following implications, write (i) the converse and (ii) the contrapositive.
   (a) If it goes up, then it goes down.
   (b) If he tells the truth, then they will be surprised.
   (c) If you are in New Zealand, then you are in the Southern Hemisphere.

(d) If today is Monday, then tomorrow is Tuesday.

(e) If you are a monkey, then you can think.

(f) If he is over 30, then he cannot be trusted.

(g) If he knows, then he tells.

(h) If the President is not accountable, then the country will decline.

(i) If good men do nothing, then evil will triumph.

(j) If he lives in Wisconsin, then he lives in the U.S.A.

(k) If you proceed correctly, then you will obtain the correct answer.

(l) If he comes early, then he leaves early.

(m) If it does not exist, then Ed cannot find it.

(n) If it is an atmosphere hospitable to rational thought, then justice will prevail.

(o) If it is winter in the Northern Hemisphere, then it is summer in the Southern Hemisphere.

(p) If Humpty Dumpty sits on the wall, then Humpty Dumpty has a great fall.

(q) If it is a square, then it has four sides.

(r) If I see it, then I believe it.

(s) If I won't see you again, I wish you a happy holiday.

(t) All football players are strong.

(u) A happy student is a productive student.

(v) A sad instructor will have sad students.

(w) Every time I pitched for the Dodgers, they won.

3. Which of the implications in Problem 2 have true converses?

3.5 Concrete Logic

NOTE: In this section the symbol $(p \rightarrow q)$ should be interpreted to mean $(p \rightarrow q$ is $T)$.

We now have all the equipment needed for using logic as a tool of reasoning. Since we will be mainly concerned about the implications of statements, we will now re-examine the Implication Table and list the following two important results which are direct consequences of this table.

THEOREM 3.5.1 *If $(p \rightarrow q)$ and $(p$ is $T)$, then $(q$ is $T)$.*

THEOREM 3.5.2 *If $(p \rightarrow q)$ and $(q$ is $F)$, then $(p$ is $F)$.*

We are now ready to use AMS (Logic) in a practical way by giving the expected concrete interpretations to the undefined terms (noting that all assumptions hold for these interpretations) to obtain *concrete logic*—or the logic which is used to prove certain statements (i.e., conclusions) from certain other statements (i.e., assumptions). The following examples illustrate some ways in which concrete logic can be used.

EXAMPLE 1

Consider the argument: "If Linda is a junior, she is taking history. Linda is a junior. Therefore, Linda is taking history." If we let p : "Linda is a junior," q : "she is taking history," then the argument becomes converted to

$$[(p \rightarrow q) \wedge (p \text{ is } T)] \rightarrow [q \text{ is } T].$$

Since this statement is equivalent to Theorem 3.5.1, the conclusion is inescapable and the argument is *valid*.

EXAMPLE 2

Consider the argument: "If you worked hard, then you passed the course. You passed the course. Therefore, you worked hard." If we let p : "you worked hard," q : "you passed the course," then the argument becomes

$$[(p \rightarrow q) \wedge (q \text{ is } T)] \rightarrow [p \text{ is } T].$$

If we examine the Implication Table, we find that $[(p \rightarrow q) \wedge (q \text{ is } T)]$ is true when $(p \text{ is } F)$ and $(q \text{ is } T)$, and therefore the conclusion is not inescapable. The argument is therefore *invalid*. How does the argument of this example relate to the concept of *converse*?

EXAMPLE 3

Consider the argument: "If x is even, then x^2 is even. We know that x^2 is not even. Therefore x is not even." If we let p : "x is even," q : "x^2 is even," then the argument can be expressed as

$$[(p \rightarrow q) \wedge (q \text{ is } F)] \rightarrow [p \text{ is } F].$$

Since this statement is equivalent to Theorem 3.5.2, the conclusion is inescapable and the argument is *valid*. How does the argument of this example relate to the concept of *contrapositive*?

EXAMPLE 4

Consider the argument: "If you brush your teeth with CHALK, then you will have no cavities. Therefore, if you do not brush your teeth with CHALK, then you will have cavities." If we let p : "you brush your teeth with CHALK," q : "you will have no cavities," then the argument can be written as

$$[(p \rightarrow q)] \rightarrow [(\sim p) \rightarrow (\sim q)].$$

If $(p \text{ is } F)$ and $(q \text{ is } T)$, then $(p \rightarrow q)$ is T but $[(\sim p) \rightarrow (\sim q)]$ is F. Therefore the implication is false, and hence the argument is *invalid*.

EXAMPLE 5

Consider the argument: "If you like this course, then you like mathematics. If you like mathematics, then you are intelligent. Therefore if you like this course, then you are intelligent." If we let p : "you like this course," q : "you like mathematics," r : "you are intelligent," then the argument becomes

$$[(p \rightarrow q) \wedge (q \rightarrow r)] \rightarrow [p \rightarrow r].$$

The validity of this argument can be established by use of a truth table. Another approach is the following. First, note that the only way this implication could be false is if $(p \rightarrow r)$ is F and $[(p \rightarrow q) \wedge (q \rightarrow r)]$ is T. But then $(p$ is $T)$ and $(r$ is $F)$; $(p \rightarrow q)$ is T [which requires that $(q$ is $T)$ since $(p$ is $T)$] and $(q \rightarrow r)$ is T [which requires that $(q$ is $F)$ since $(r$ is $F)$]. Since we cannot have $(q$ is $T)$ and $(q$ is $F)$ at the same time, the implication given in the argument cannot be false. Therefore it must be true, which means that the argument is *valid*. Can you conclude from the given argument that, "If you are not intelligent, then you do not like this course"?

Problem Set 3.5

1. Use a truth table to prove that the argument of Example 5 is valid.

Determine which of the following arguments are *valid* by using *both* Venn diagrams and AMS (Logic):

2. *Given:* If Michael is a freshman, then he takes mathematics.
           Michael is a freshman.
   Conclusion: Michael takes mathematics.

3. *Given:* If you worked hard, then you passed the course.
           You did not pass the course.
   Conclusion: You did not work hard.

4. *Given:* If you worked hard, then you passed the course.
           You did not work hard.
   Conclusion: You did not pass the course.

5. If the Yanks win the game, then they win the pennant.
   They do not win the pennant.
   Therefore, they do not win the game.

6. If you like mathematics, then you like this book.
   You do not like mathematics.
   Therefore, you do not like this book.

7. If her lawn looks like a golf course, then she is happy.
She is not happy.
Therefore, her lawn does not look like a golf course.

8. If Frances joins the Women's Liberation movement, then she will promote justice.
Frances does not join the Women's Liberation movement.
Therefore, Frances will not promote justice.

9. If clothes are made for people, then they serve some practical purpose.
These clothes do not serve any practical purpose.
Therefore, these clothes are not made for people.

10. If Frank is in Antarctica, then he wears ear muffs.
Frank wears ear muffs.
Therefore, Frank is in Antarctica.

11. If you work hard, then you will pass the course.
If you pass the course, then your teacher will be surprised.
Therefore, if you work hard, then your teacher will be surprised.

12. If you like this book, then you like mathematics.
If you like mathematics, then you are intelligent.
Therefore, if you are intelligent, then you like this book.

13. If a polygon is a square, then it has 3 sides.
If a polygon has 3 sides, then it has 4 angles.
Therefore, if a polygon is a square, then it has 4 angles.

14. If a polygon is a square, then it has 4 sides.
If a polygon has 4 sides, then it has 3 angles.
Therefore, if a polygon is a square, then it has 3 angles.

15. If he is stupid, then he will tell all.
If he tells all, then there will be no trouble.
Therefore, if there is trouble, then he is not stupid.

Supply the conclusions that make the following arguments *valid*.

16. If you drink milk, then you will be healthy.
You are not healthy.
Therefore, ...

17. If Charles rides on a train, then he is happy.
Charles rides on a train.
Therefore, ...

18. If you like to exercise, then you enjoy swimming.
If you enjoy swimming, then you are a mathematician.
Therefore, ...

19. If you do not work hard, then you will not pass.
If you do not pass, then your parents will be unhappy.
Therefore, ...

20. If he knows, then he tells.
He tells.
Therefore, ...

21. If he knows, then he tells.
He does not know.
Therefore, ...

22. If he is a hippie, then he has long hair.
He has long hair.
Therefore, ...

23. If he is riding a bicycle, then he is happy.
He is not happy.
Therefore, ...

24. If he smokes, then he pollutes the air.
He does not smoke.
Therefore, ...

25. If he is under 30, then he knows it all.
If he is not wise, then he does not know it all.
If he is wise, he says nothing.
He is under 30.
Therefore, ...

26. If he fears the protests of the BADS, he will not oppose them.
If he does not oppose them, there will be a disaster.
He fears the protests of the BADS.
Therefore, ...

27. The following sign appeared in a restaurant: "Credit will be granted to those over 85, if they are accompanied by their parents."

   (a) If p : "credit will be granted to those over 85" and q : "they are accompanied by their parents," translate this sign into the symbols of AMS (Logic).

   (b) Is the statement on the sign contradicted if credit is granted to a 92-year-old man who is not accompanied by his parents? Use AMS (Logic) to explain your answer.

28. Miss Longbottom told Mr. Flathead, "I will marry you only if I lose my mind."

   (a) If p : "I will marry you" and q : "I lose my mind," convert Miss Longbottom's promise into the symbols of AMS (Logic).

In each of the following, justify your answer by means of AMS (Logic).

   (b) If Miss Longbottom loses her mind but refuses to marry Mr. Flathead, has she broken her promise?

   (c) If Miss Longbottom keeps her promise and marries Mr. Flathead, can we be sure that she lost her mind?

   (d) If Miss Longbottom doesn't marry Mr. Flathead and doesn't lose her mind, has she kept her promise?

CHAPTER 4

Sets and Paradoxes

4.1 What Is a Set?

Now that we have completed our study of logic and have become aware that logic can be interpreted either as an abstract mathematical structure or as a concrete interpretation which serves as a tool of reasoning about statements, we will consider the question, "What sort of things are involved in statements?" If we return to our examples in Chapter 3, we find that the following things were involved: birds, boys, undergraduates, freshmen, etc. Thus there were collections of things all of which had—or did not have—certain properties. This leads us to the study of sets.

In recent years set theory has become an important area of investigation because of the way in which it permeates so much of contemporary mathematical thought. The subject of set theory as we know it today may be considered as originating in the late nineteenth century with Georg Cantor, who attempted to organize collections of objects into a structure which could serve as a basis for a mathematical theory of the infinite.

In 1914 Felix Hausdorff wrote in his *Fundamentals of the Theory of Sets,* "Geometry and analysis, differential and integral calculus deal continually, even though perhaps in disguised expression, with infinite sets." It turns out that a genuine understanding of the various branches of mathematics requires a knowledge of the theory of sets—for it is their common foundation.

David Hilbert said that Cantor "created one of the most fertile and powerful branches of mathematics; a paradise from which no one can drive us out." The theory of sets stands as one of the boldest and most beautiful creations of the human mind; its concepts have revitalized just about every branch of mathematics. In fact, the theory of sets reflects Cantor's statement, "The essence of mathematics lies in its freedom."

One way of exercising this freedom is by asking "simple-minded" questions such as,

(1) Are there more whole numbers than there are even numbers?

[41

(2) Does an unbounded straight line contain more points than a line segment?

(3) Does a plane contain fewer points than all of space?

(4) What is the exact meaning of "infinity"?

People refrained from discussing these questions publicly since such inquiries seemed naive or stupid, and also because they appeared to have no answers. However, the theory of sets gives clear answers to all these questions—when the questions are properly phrased.

The general theory of sets has now been established for over seventy years. To understand it calls for hardly any prerequisite technical knowledge. All that is necessary is an interest in establishing some harmless-looking concepts regarding the "infinite." Even though the theory of sets starts out at a concrete level, it soon climbs to a very high degree of abstraction.

We are now ready to consider the question, "What is a set?" One would expect to find an authentic answer in the work of Cantor. He wrote, "A set is a bringing together into a whole of definite well-distinguished objects of our perception or thought—which are to be called elements of the set." (Please note that this is a literal translation from the German.) After reading this "definition" one may get the feeling that it could be stated more simply and more clearly. Our initial attempt appears in the following.

DEF 4.1.1
A *set* is a well-defined collection of objects.

One may object to this definition as well, for the words *collection* and *well-defined* may not be entirely clear to every reader. We shall attempt to clarify this by giving examples of sets and nonsets.

EXAMPLES OF SETS
(1) The collection of counting numbers from 1 to 5 [which can be represented symbolically as $\{1, 2, 3, 4, 5\}$].
(2) The collection of counting numbers greater than 5 [i.e., $\{6, 7, 8, \ldots\}$ or $\{x \mid x$ is a counting number and $x > 5\}$, which is literally translated "the set of all x such that x is a counting number and x is greater than 5"].
(3) The collection of points inside the curve 🗋 .
(4) The collection of points on the line segment _____.
(5) $\{$All counting numbers between 1 and 2$\}$.
(6) $\{$All college students under two years old$\}$.
(7) $\{$All boys that are cows$\}$.

Since it is possible to determine whether a given element belongs to any of the preceding collections, the collections are "well defined," which justifies our calling them sets. On the other hand, the following "collections" do not have this distinguishing property.

EXAMPLES OF NONSETS
   (1) {Nice numbers}.
   (2) {Large numbers}.
   (3) {Beautiful people}.

Although Def 4.1.1 may now appear to be clear and practical, we shall not use it—except for intuitive purposes. Instead, we shall develop set theory as an AMS and regard *set* as an undefined term.

AMS (SETS)

UNDEFINED TERMS

$$\{A, B, C, \ldots .\}, \{a, b, c, \ldots , x, y, \ldots \}, \in, \notin,$$

[where $A, B, C, \ldots$ are called *sets*; $a, b, c, \ldots , x, y, \ldots$ are called *elements*; $\in$ is translated "is an element of"; and $\notin$ is translated "is not an element of"].

ASSUMPTION (AXIOM FOR SETS)
Given any element x and any set A, either $(x \in A)$ or $(x \notin A)$ but *not* both.

The reader should now return to the preceding examples and see how this axiom distinguishes sets from nonsets.

There are two kinds of sets that play special roles and we shall now give them special names and special symbols.

DEF 4.1.2
A *universal set* is a set that contains all elements under discussion. The symbol U will denote a universal set.

DEF 4.1.3
A *null set* (or *empty set*) is a set that contains no elements. The symbol $\varnothing$ will denote a null set, and is read "fee."

Some null sets are given in the preceding Examples 5, 6, and 7. Can you find others?

4.2 Some Relations for Sets

Thus far our development of AMS (Sets) includes four undefined terms (set, element, $\in$, $\notin$), one axiom, and two definitions. We shall now extend this structure by adding some basic definitions.

The first of these definitions involves the "equality of sets." We would expect to say that sets A and B are "equal" if they contain exactly the same elements—and this we shall do.

DEF 4.2.1

$A = B$ iff each element of A is an element of B, and each element of B is an element of A.

If every element of A is also an element of B, we would expect to say "A is a subset of B," and we shall.

DEF 4.2.2

$A \subseteq B$ (to be translated "A is a *subset* of B") iff each element of A is also an element of B.

The preceding definition, which is illustrated in Fig. 4.1, gives rise to questions such as,

(1) Is $A \subseteq A$?

(2) Is $\varnothing \subseteq A$?

(3) How many subsets are there in a set with n elements?

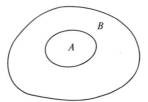

FIGURE 4.1.

Since each element in A is also an element in A, the answer to the first question is yes. In fact, from this simple-minded observation we can conclude that $[A = B]$ iff $[(A \subseteq B)$ and $(B \subseteq A)]$. This first question now leads us to a new definition. For although $A \subseteq B$ when $A = B$, this subset A does not sound like a "proper" one. Therefore we will want the following.

DEF 4.2.3

$A \subset B$ (to be translated "A is a *proper subset* of B") iff $[(A \subseteq B$ and $(A \neq B)]$. Note: This means that A is a subset of B, but there is at least one element in B that is *not* in A.

The second question can also be answered in the affirmative, since surely every element in $\varnothing$ is also in A. If you are not convinced, see if you can find an element in $\varnothing$ which is *not* in A!

The third question cannot be handled quite so easily. We will approach it by considering special values for n, and then leave it to the reader to find the answer for the general case. If $n = 2$, we let $A_2 = \{1, 2\}$ and observe that the subsets are $\emptyset$, $\{1\}$, $\{2\}$, $\{1, 2\}$; and therefore A_2 has four subsets. If $n = 3$, we let $A_3 = \{1, 2, 3\}$ and find that the subsets are $\emptyset$, $\{1\}$, $\{2\}$, $\{3\}$, $\{1, 2\}$, $\{1, 3\}$, $\{2, 3\}$, $\{1, 2, 3\}$; and therefore A_3 has eight subsets. Before finding the subsets of a set with four elements, we may be tempted to guess what the answer will be. Since A_2 has 2^2 subsets and A_3 has 2^3 subsets, we would naturally expect A_4 to have 2^4 subsets—and in general A_n should have 2^n subsets. But does it?

EXERCISE
Determine the number of subsets in a set with n elements, and prove your answer.

4.3 What Is a Number?

The exercise at the end of the last section was "Determine the number of subsets in a set with n elements. . . ." This question apparently assumes that the reader knows the meaning of the word *number*. What is a number? For example, what is the meaning of the symbol 3? This question is easy to ask—but not easy to answer! Before attempting an answer, we shall relate a situation where the need for a concept of number is vital.[1]

Suppose that you are the leader of an expedition of forty-three people, traveling in an uncivilized country where the vocabulary of number words is limited to "one," "two," "three," "four," and "many." (The existence of savage tribes whose number vocabulary is so limited is well known.) Suppose further that you have gone on ahead to a village where you expect to spend the night, and that you are trying to make the village chief understand that you want food prepared for forty-three people. Assuming that he understands you want food, how will you put over the idea of "forty-three"? Very likely you will do it by making marks on a piece of paper, or on the ground—one mark corresponding to each member of the party. If a plate of food corresponding to each mark is then prepared, you can be sure that each member of the party will be fed.

Thus the chief, with no word whatever for the number "forty-three," is able to count the number of people in the party, and the number of plates of food. To describe the process in somewhat more precise terms, you set up what is called a "one-to-one correspondence" between the members of your party and the marks on the paper. The correspondence is "one-to-one" because corresponding to each person there is one mark; and, conversely, corresponding to each mark there is one person. The chief then sets up a one-to-one correspondence between the marks and the plates of food.

---

[1] This illustration is taken from *Riddles in Mathematics* by Eugene P. Northrop. © 1944 by Litton Educational Publishing, Inc. Reprinted by permission of Van Nostrand Reinhold Company.

Here is counting in its simplest and most fundamental form—the setting up of a one-to-one correspondence between the members of two classes. The child who counts on his fingers, the Chinese laundryman who reckons his accounts on the abacus, the billiards player who keeps score by means of counters—all of them, consciously or unconsciously, are counting by means of one-to-one correspondences.

Thus we can say that two sets have the same "number" iff their elements can be put into one-to-one correspondence. For example, we say that the set $\{a, b, c\}$ has the same "number" of elements as the set $\{x, y, z\}$, and often use the symbol 3 or III to represent this "number." We will now convert these concepts into formal definitions.

DEF 4.3.1
$A \sim B$ (to be translated "*A* is equivalent to *B*") iff there exists a one-to-one correspondence between the elements of A and the elements of B.

EXAMPLE 1
If $A = \{a, b, c\}$ and $B = \{x, y, z\}$, then $A \sim B$ since $[(a \leftrightarrow y), (b \leftrightarrow x), (c \leftrightarrow z)]$ establishes a one-to-one correspondence between the elements of A and B.

EXAMPLE 2
If $N = \{1, 2, 3, \ldots\}$, $B = \{2, 4, 6, \ldots\}$, $C = \{1, 3, 5, \ldots\}$, $D = \{1, \frac{1}{2}, \frac{1}{3}, \ldots\}$, $E = \{10, 10^2, 10^3, \ldots\}$, then $N \sim B$, $N \sim C$, $N \sim D$, $N \sim E$, $B \sim C$, $B \sim D$, etc. Thus each of these five sets is equivalent to each of the others. We can show that $N \sim B$ by exhibiting the following one-to-one correspondence: $[(1 \leftrightarrow 2), (2 \leftrightarrow 4), (3 \leftrightarrow 6), \ldots, (n \leftrightarrow 2n), \ldots]$. The others can be exhibited in a similar way.

EXAMPLE 3
If $L_1 = \{$points on a line segment 1 inch long$\}$ and $L_2 = \{$points on a line segment 2 inches long$\}$, then each of the following figures can be used to show that $L_1 \sim L_2$, since they each establish a one-to-one correspondence between the elements of L_1 and the elements of L_2.

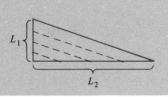
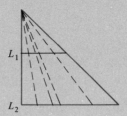

The results of Examples 2 and 3 may appear strange at first—for they reveal that a set can be equivalent to a proper subset of itself (e.g., in Example 2, $B \subset N$ and $N \sim B$). It is clear that such a strange phenomenon cannot occur in "finite" sets; for if $A = \{a, b, c\}$ and $B \subset A$, then surely A cannot be equivalent to B. This observation is an important one because it distinguishes "infinite" sets from "finite" sets, and thus helps to provide us with the following two definitions.

DEF 4.3.2

Set A is an *infinite set* (or is *infinite*) iff A is equivalent to some proper subset of itself.

DEF 4.3.3

Set A is a *finite set* (or is *finite*) iff A is not infinite.

EXAMPLE 4

In Example 2, set N (and therefore each set equivalent to N) is an infinite set. In Example 3, set L_2 (and therefore set L_1) is an infinite set.

A natural question which now arises is, "Is $N \sim L_1$ (where N and L_1 are given as in Examples 2 and 3)?" The answer to this question is *no*—and this can be proved by labeling each point on L_1 with the decimal that represents its distance from one of the end points of L_1, and then showing that any attempt to establish a one-to-one correspondence between the elements of N and the points of L_1 is bound to result in failure. [For a convincing argument see Kasner and Newman, *Mathematics and the Imagination*, pp. 49–53—but before reading this argument the reader should try to prove the result for himself.]

Now that we have seemingly strayed a bit, we are ready to give a partial answer to the question, "What is a number?"

DEF 4.3.4

$n(A) = n(B)$ (to be translated "the *cardinal number of A equals the cardinal number* of B") iff $A \sim B$.

DEF 4.3.5

If A is an infinite set, $n(A)$ is called a *transfinite cardinal number*.

DEF 4.3.6

If A is a finite set, $n(A)$ is called a *natural number*.

EXAMPLE 5

If $A = \{a, b, c\}$ and $B = \{x, y, z\}$, then $n(A) = n(B)$, and the symbol (or numeral) 3 is ordinarily used to represent this cardinal number. Hence $n(A) = n(B) = 3$.

EXAMPLE 6

If $N = \{1, 2, 3, \ldots\}$, then the cardinal number $n(N)$ is often symbolized by $\aleph_0$ (read "aleph-nought") since this symbol was used by Cantor and "aleph," or $\aleph$, is the first letter of the Hebrew alphabet. Using the sets of Example 2, we note that

$$n(N) = n(B) = n(C) = n(D) = n(E) = \aleph_0.$$

We also note that $\aleph_0$ is a transfinite cardinal number.

EXAMPLE 7

Using the symbols of Example 3, the cardinal number $n(L_1)$ is often symbolized by c, and is called the *cardinal number of the continuum*. Thus, we can say $n(L_1) = n(L_2) = c$ and that $c \neq \aleph_0$ (by virtue of Examples 3 and 6, and the remarks following Example 4).

The following definition provides terminology which is commonly used when referring to infinite sets.

DEF 4.3.7

A set is called *denumerable* if it is equivalent to the set of all natural numbers. A set is called *countable* if it is either finite or denumerable. An infinite set that is not denumerable is called *nondenumerable* or *uncountable*.

Using the notation and discussion in the preceding examples, we observe that N, B, C, D, and E are denumerable and that L_1 and L_2 are nondenumerable.

Problem Set 4.3

1. True-False
   (a) If $A = B$, then A must be equivalent to B.
   (b) If A is equivalent to B, then $A = B$.
   (c) The symbol 0 represents a natural number.

2. Show a one-to-one correspondence between
   (a) The set of counting numbers greater than 100 and the set of all counting numbers.

(b) The set of even counting numbers and the set of all counting numbers.

(c) The set of odd counting numbers and the set of even counting numbers.

3. How many one-to-one correspondences are there between $\{a, b, c\}$ and $\{x, y, z\}$? List them.

*4. How many one-to-one correspondences are there between $\{a_1, a_2, \ldots, a_n\}$ and $\{b_1, b_2, \ldots, b_n\}$? Prove your answer.

5. Prove that all the sets in Example 2 have cardinal number $\aleph_0$.

*6. If we define $n(A) > n(B)$ (to be translated: "$n(A)$ *is greater than* $n(B)$") as follows: "B is equivalent to a subset of A *but* A is not equivalent to *any* subset of B," prove $\mathbf{c} > \aleph_0$.

4.4 Some Operations for Sets

We shall often be interested in forming new sets from old sets. For example, if A and B are any two sets (such as those in Fig. 4.2), we can form a new set by uniting these two sets (as in the shaded area) so that the new set or *union* consists of those elements that are in A or in B or in both A and B.

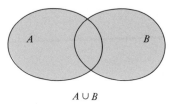

$A \cup B$

Figure 4.2.

We shall use the symbol $A \cup B$ [to be translated "A union B"] to represent this new set. More formally we have

DEF 4.4.1
$A \cup B \equiv \{x \mid (x \in A) \vee (x \in B)\}$.

Thus we can say

$$[x \in (A \cup B)] \text{ iff } [(x \in A) \vee (x \in B)].$$

EXAMPLE 1
If $A = \{1, 2, 3, 5\}$ and $B = \{3, 4, 5\}$, then $A \cup B = \{1, 2, 3, 4, 5\}$.

If A and B are any two sets (such as those in Fig. 4.3), another way of forming a new set from them is by considering the elements they have in common—or their intersection (as in the shaded area)—so that this new set or *intersection* consists of those elements that are in both A and B.

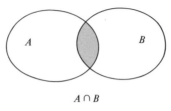

$A \cap B$

FIGURE 4.3.

We shall use the symbol $A \cap B$ (to be translated "A intersection B") to represent this new set. More formally we have

DEF 4.4.2
$A \cap B \equiv \{x \mid (x \in A) \wedge (x \in B)\}$.

Thus we can say

$$[x \in (A \cap B)] \text{ iff } [(x \in A) \wedge (x \in B)].$$

EXAMPLE 2
If $A = \{1, 2, 3, 5\}$ and $B = \{3, 4, 5\}$, then $A \cap B = \{3, 5\}$.

EXAMPLE 3
If $A = \{1, 2, 3\}$ and $B = \{4, 7\}$, then $A \cap B = \emptyset$.

If $A \cap B = \emptyset$, then A and B are called *disjoint*. We note that Example 3 provides us with an example of disjoint sets.

If A is any set, we can form a new set from A by considering those elements that are not in A. Since every element under consideration is in the universal set U, we can picture those elements that are not in A by means of the shaded area in Fig. 4.4.

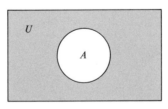

A'

FIGURE 4.4.

We shall use the symbol A' (to be translated "the complement of A" or "A complement") to represent this new set. More formally we have

DEF 4.4.3
$A' \equiv \{x \mid x \notin A\}.$

Thus we can say

$$(x \in A') \text{ iff } (x \notin A)$$

or

$$(x \in A') \text{ iff } \sim(x \in A).$$

EXAMPLE 4
If $U = \{1, 2, 3, 4, 5\}$ and $A = \{1, 2, 3\}$, then $A' = \{4, 5\}$.

Now that we have some new definitions, one might expect to find some interesting relationships. The following example helps to reveal some of them.

EXAMPLE 5
If $U = \{1, 2, 3, 4, 5\}$, $A = \{1, 2, 5\}$ and $B = \{2, 4\}$, then $A \cup B = \{1, 2, 4, 5\}, (A \cup B)' = \{3\}, A \cap B = \{2\}, (A \cap B)' = \{1, 3, 4, 5\}, A' = \{3, 4\}, B' = \{1, 3, 5\}, A' \cup B' = \{1, 3, 4, 5\}$ and $A' \cap B' = \{3\}$.

On the basis of Example 5, one may guess that

$$(A \cup B)' = A' \cap B'$$

when A and B are any sets whatsoever. In order to determine whether this guess is really a theorem in AMS (Sets), one may attempt Venn diagrams such as in Fig. 4.5. Note that $(A \cup B)'$ is represented by light red shading in Fig.

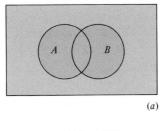

(a)

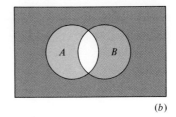

(b)

$A \cup B$: ▨

$(A \cup B)'$: ▨

A' : ▨

B' : ▨

$A' \cap B'$: ▨

FIGURE 4.5.

4.5a and that $A' \cap B'$ is represented by the dark red shading in Fig. 4.5b—and since these two shadings correspond, we have established

$$(A \cup B)' = A' \cap B'$$

for this illustration at least. Some readers may now be convinced that

$$(A \cup B)' = A' \cap B'$$

is a theorem in AMS (Sets); but others may object, and rightfully so, since there are other ways in which A and B can be represented. To satisfy these skeptics, we will now use the definitions and a truth table to establish that $(A \cup B)' = A' \cap B'$ as follows.

$x \in A$	$x \in B$	$x \in (A \cup B)$	$x \in (A \cup B)'$	$x \in A'$	$x \in B'$	$x \in (A' \cap B')$
T	T	T	F	F	F	F
T	F	T	F	F	T	F
F	T	T	F	T	F	F
F	F	F	T	T	T	T

Since the results in the fourth and last columns are identical, the desired result [called a Law of De Morgan for AMS (Sets)] is now proved.

Problem Set 4.4

1. For each of the following, list the elements in (i) $A \cup B$ and (ii) $A \cap B$.
   (a) $A = \{1, 2, 3\}$; $B = \{1, 3, 5, 7\}$.
   (b) $A = \{1, 3, 5, \ldots\}$; $B = \{2, 4, 6, \ldots\}$.
   (c) $A = \emptyset$; $B = \{1, 2, 3, \ldots\}$.
   (d) $A = \{1, 2, 3, \ldots\}$; $B = \{1, 3, 5, \ldots\}$.

2. For each of the given universal sets list the elements in (i) A', (ii) B', (iii) $A' \cup B'$, (iv) $A' \cap B'$, (v) $(A \cup B)'$, (vi) $(A \cap B)'$,
   (a) $U = \{1, 2, 3, 4, 5\}$; $A = \{1, 2\}$; $B = \{1, 3, 5\}$.
   (b) $U = \{1, 2, 3, \ldots, 10\}$; $A = \{1, 3, 5, 7, 9\}$; $B = \{2, 4, 6, 8, 10\}$.
   (c) $U = \{1, 2, 3, \ldots\}$; $A = \{1, 3, 5, \ldots\}$; $B = \{2, 4, 6, \ldots\}$.
   (d) $U = \{1, 2, 3, 4, 5, 6, 7\}$; $A = \emptyset$; $B = \{1, 2, 3, 4, 5, 6, 7\}$.
   (e) $U = \{1, 2, 3\}$; $A = \{1\}$; $B = \{3\}$.

3. If $A \subseteq B$, describe (a) $A \cap B$; (b) $A \cup B$; (c) $A \cap B'$; (d) $A' \cup B$; (e) $B' \cap A'$.

4. If $A \subseteq B$ and $B \subseteq A$, describe (a) $A \cup B$; (b) $A \cap B$; (c) $A \cap B'$; (d) $A' \cup B$.

⁎5. Make some guesses involving relationships for (a) ∪; (b) ∩; (c) ′; (d) joint use of ∪ and ∩; (e) joint use of ∪, ∩, and ′; (f) ⊆ together with some other symbols of AMS (Sets).

⁎6. Try to prove or disprove your guesses in Problem 5.

⁎7. Can you find a relationship between theorems in AMS (Logic) and theorems in AMS (Sets)?

8. Use AMS (Sets) to solve Problems 1 and 2 of Problem Set 3.2. **HINT:** In Problem 1, let $A = \{boys\}$ and $B = \{those \ who \ are \ intelligent\}$. Then observe that $r : A \cap B \neq \varnothing$.

9. Which of the following are theorems in AMS (Sets)? *Prove* your answers.
(a) $A \cup B = B \cup A$.
(b) $A \cup (B \cup C) = (A \cup B) \cup C$.
(c) $A \cap (B \cup C) = (A \cap B) \cup C$.
(d) $A \cup (B \cap C) = (A \cup B) \cap (A \cup C)$.
(e) $A \cap (A \cup B) = A$.
(f) $(A \cap B)' = A' \cup B'$.
(g) $A \cup A' = U$.
(h) $A \cap A' = \varnothing$.

4.5 The Star Product

In this section we shall create a new operation for sets which will be defined in terms of the basic operations of the last section.

DEF 4.5.1
$A \star B \equiv (A \cup B) \cap (A \cap B)'$, and is read "$A$ star B".

If sets A and B intersect, as in Fig. 4.6, then $A \star B$ can be represented by the shaded area in this figure. The reader should now use shading to represent $A \star B$ when $A \subseteq B$, $A = B$, $B = \varnothing$, $B = A'$, etc.

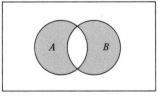

$A \star B$

FIGURE 4.6.

Problem Set 4.5

1. Find simple expressions for each of the following: (a) $A \star A$, (b) $A \star \emptyset$, (c) $A \star A'$, (d) $A \star U$.

2. Is $A \star B = B \star A$? Prove your answer.

*3. Is $A \star (B \star C) = (A \star B) \star C$? Prove your answer.

4. If $A \subseteq B$, how would you describe $A \star B$?

*5. Does $(A \star B)' = A \star B'$? Prove your answer.

*6. If $A \star B = C$, find $B \star C$.

*7. Use the algebra of sets to find another expression for $A \star B$.

*8. Make some guesses concerning properties of the star product, and then prove or disprove them [e.g., consider $A \star (B \star A)$].

*9. Prove that the system $[\{A, B, \ldots\}, \star]$ is a concrete interpretation of AMS (3).

*10. In comparing AMS (Sets) with AMS (Logic), you may have observed that $\cup$ "behaves like" $\vee$, $\cap$ "behaves like" $\wedge$, A' "behaves like" $\sim p$, etc. Try to find out what $\star$ "behaves like."

4.6 Addition of Cardinal Numbers

Now that we have cardinal numbers and some operations for sets, what should we do with them? Since one ordinarily wants to be able to add numbers, we should decide on a reasonable definition for adding cardinal numbers. First let us consider an example.

EXAMPLE 1

If $n(A) = 2$ and $n(B) = 3$, then our experience dictates that

$$n(A) + n(B) = 2 + 3 = 5.$$

Thus we are intuitively led to suspect that $n(A) + n(B)$ should be defined as $n(A \cup B)$. But does it always follow that $n(A \cup B) = 5$ when $n(A) = 2$ and $n(B) = 3$? If $A = \{x, y\}$ and $B = \{x, y, z\}$, then

$n(A \cup B) = n(B) = 3$—which is not the desired result. If, on the other hand, $A = \{x, y\}$ and $B = \{a, b, c\}$, then $n(A \cup B) = 5$ and we have the desired result. In the second case we observe that $A \cap B = \varnothing$, and suspect that this criterion is needed for a reasonable definition.

DEF 4.6.1
$n(A) + n(B) = n(A \cup B)$ iff $A \cap B = \varnothing$.

We note that the condition $A \cap B = \varnothing$ is no real obstacle since sets A_1 and B_1 can always be chosen so that $A_1 \sim A$, $B_1 \sim B$ and $A_1 \cap B_1 = \varnothing$, and these relations provide us with

$$n(A) + n(B) = n(A_1) + n(B_1) = n(A_1 \cup B_1).$$

EXAMPLE 2
If $n(A) = 1$, $n(B) = \aleph_0$, and we let $A = \{0\}$ and $B = \{1, 2, 3, \ldots\}$, then $A \cap B = \varnothing$ and $n(A) + n(B) = n(A \cup B)$. Hence, $1 + \aleph_0 = \aleph_0$—which may at first look strange.

Problem Set 4.6

Let $n(A) = a$, $n(B) = b$, $n(C) = c$.

1. Use Def. 4.6.1 to prove:
   (a) $a + b = b + a$.
   (b) $(a + b) + c = a + (b + c)$.
   (c) $\aleph_0 + 2 = \aleph_0$.
   (d) $\aleph_0 + 3 = \aleph_0$.
   (e) $\aleph_0 + m = \aleph_0$, where m is any natural number.
   (f) $\aleph_0 + \aleph_0 = \aleph_0$.

2. Give a reasonable definition for $a + b + c$.

3. Prove: $\aleph_0 + \aleph_0 + \aleph_0 = \aleph_0$.

*4. Prove or disprove the following:
   (a) $n(A \cup B) = n(A) + n(B) - n(A \cap B)$.
   (b) $n(A \star B) = n(A \cap B') + n(A' \cap B)$.

*5. Give a reasonable definition for the product ab.

4.7 A Practical Application

Suppose we have a group of 45 students and know that 20 are (enrolled) in algebra, 22 are in geometry, 14 are in trigonometry, 11 are in both algebra and geometry, 8 are in both geometry and trigonometry, 5 are in both algebra and trigonometry, and 3 are in all three of these courses. If we want to know how many of these students are enrolled in

(1) only algebra
(2) none of these courses
(3) algebra and trigonometry but not geometry

we can proceed as follows. Draw a Venn diagram as in the following figure, with the rectangular region designating the universe.

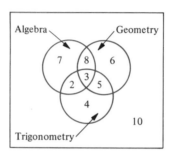

It is best to start with the information that there are 3 students in all three courses. We then write the number 3 in the region that is the intersection of all three circles. Then we work backward; since 5 are in algebra and trigonometry, there must be 2 in the region representing algebra and trigonometry but not geometry. Continuing in this manner, we enter the given data in the figure. Since the sum of the numbers in the three circles is 35, there must be 10 students not enrolled in any of these courses. Also, reading directly from the figure, we find that there are 7 students taking algebra only; and 2 students are in algebra and trigonometry but not geometry.

We will now restate the entire problem using the symbolism of AMS (Sets). We are given $n(U) = 45$, $n(A) = 20$, $n(G) = 22$, $n(T) = 14$, $n(A \cap G) = 11$, $n(G \cap T) = 8$, $n(A \cap T) = 5$, and $n(A \cap G \cap T) = 3$. We want to know

(1) $n[A \cap (G \cup T)']$.
(2) $n[(A \cup G \cup T)']$.
(3) $n[(A \cap T) \cap G']$.

As above, from the diagram we find

Solution to (1)

$$n[A \cap (G \cup T)'] = 7,$$

and note that

$$n[A \cap (G \cup T)'] = n[A \cap G' \cap T'], \qquad \text{(using a Law of De Morgan)}.$$

Solution to (2)

$$n[(A \cup G \cup T)'] = 10,$$

and note that

$$n[(A \cup G \cup T)'] = n[A' \cap G' \cap T'], \quad \text{(using a Law of De Morgan twice)}.$$

Solution to (3)

$$n[(A \cap T) \cap G'] = 2.$$

Problem Set 4.7

1. In a survey of 50 students, the following data were collected: There were 19 taking biology, 20 taking chemistry, 19 taking physics, 7 taking physics and chemistry, 8 taking biology and chemistry, 9 taking biology and physics, and 5 taking all three subjects.
   (a) How many of the group are not taking any of the three subjects?
   (b) How many are taking only chemistry?
   (c) How many are taking physics and chemistry, but not biology?

2. A survey was taken of 30 students enrolled in three different clubs: *A*, *B*, and *C*. Show that the following data that were collected are inconsistent: 18 in *A*, 10 in *B*, 9 in *C*, 3 in *B* and *C*, 6 in *A* and *B*, 9 in *A* and *C*, 2 in *A*, *B*, and *C*.

4.8 The Relationship Between AMS (Sets) and AMS (Logic)

The reader may have become aware of the similarities between AMS (Logic) and AMS (Sets) and wonder whether there is any basic relationship between their structures. That is, you may ask whether there is a correspondence between the symbols of these structures which could be used to convert one of the structures into the other. If there is, it seems likely to be as follows:

AMS (Logic)	AMS (Sets)
$\{p, q, \ldots\}$	$\{A, B, \ldots\}$
$\{T, F\}$	$\{U, \varnothing\}$
$\sim p$	A'
$\wedge$	$\cap$
$\vee$	$\cup$
$\rightarrow$	$\subseteq$
$\leftrightarrow$	$=$

It turns out that we can establish this correspondence by first extending AMS (Logic) so that it includes *open sentences* and *truth sets,* and then using these concepts to define set operations and relations in terms of the corresponding ones for logic. The following seven definitions provide us with this equipment.

DEF 4.8.1

An *open sentence* is a "variable statement" which becomes a statement (i.e., T or F) when a specific element of U is substituted for the variable. Symbols such as p_x, q_x, r_x, s_x will be used to represent open sentences when $x \in U$.

> **EXAMPLE**
> Let $U = \{1, 2, 3, 4, 5\}$.
> $p_x : x$ is odd.
> $q_x : x < 3$ (read "x is less than 3").
> $r_x : x > 5$ (read "x is greater than 5").
> $s_x : x \leq 5$ (read "x is less than or equal to 5").

DEF 4.8.2

The *truth set* of $p_x \equiv P \equiv \{x \mid p_x$ is $T\} \equiv \{x \mid p_x\}$.

> **NOTE:** Every set can be converted into a truth set by selecting an appropriate open sentence. For example, the set $P = \{a, b, c\}$ is the truth set of the open sentence
> $$p_x : [(x = a) \lor (x = b) \lor (x = c)].$$

> **EXAMPLE**
> Referring to the preceding example we have
> $$P = \{1, 3, 5\}, \qquad Q = \{1, 2\}, \qquad R = \varnothing, \qquad S = U.$$

DEF 4.8.3

$P \cap Q \equiv \{x \mid p_x \land q_x$ is $T\} = \{x \mid p_x \land q_x\}$.

> **EXAMPLE**
> Referring to the preceding examples, $P \cap Q = \{1\}$.

DEF 4.8.4

$P \cup Q \equiv \{x \mid p_x \lor q_x$ is $T\} = \{x \mid p_x \lor q_x\}$.

> **EXAMPLE**
> Referring to the preceding examples, $P \cup Q = \{1, 2, 3, 5\}$.

DEF 4.8.5

$P' \equiv \{x \mid \sim p_x \text{ is } T\} = \{x \mid \sim p_x\}$.

EXAMPLE

Referring to the preceding examples, $Q' = \{3, 4, 5\}$.

DEF 4.8.6

$P \subseteq Q$ iff $[\forall_x : p_x \rightarrow q_x]$, where $\forall_x$ is translated "for all x"
  NOTE: $(P \subseteq Q)$ is a statement!

EXAMPLE

$p_x : x > 3$ and $q_x : x > 2$, so that $P = \{4, 5\}$ and $Q = \{3, 4, 5\}$. Thus $[p_x \rightarrow q_x]$ is equivalent to $[(x \in P) \rightarrow (x \in Q)]$.

DEF 4.8.7

$P = Q$ iff $[\forall_x : p_x \leftrightarrow q_x]$ iff $\{x \mid p_x\} = \{x \mid q_x\}$.
  NOTE: $(P = Q)$ is a statement!

EXAMPLE

$p_x : x < 4$ and $q_x : x \leq 3$, so that $P = Q = \{1, 2, 3\}$.

The preceding definitions reveal the sense in which AMS (Sets) corresponds to AMS (Logic). Since these two structures are essentially the same, theorems in AMS (Logic) can be used to obtain corresponding theorems in AMS (Sets). The following examples illustrate this.

EXAMPLE 1
In AMS (Logic)
$$\forall_x : [p_x \wedge p_x] \leftrightarrow p_x.$$

Therefore
$$\{x \mid p_x \wedge p_x\} = \{x \mid p_x\}$$
by Def. 4.8.7, and hence $P \cap P = P$ by Def. 4.8.3.

EXAMPLE 2
In AMS (Logic)
$$\forall_x : [\sim(p_x \wedge q_x)] \leftrightarrow [(\sim p_x) \vee (\sim q_x)].$$

Therefore
$$\{x \mid \sim(p_x \wedge q_x)\} = \{x \mid (\sim p_x) \vee (\sim q_x)\}$$

by Def. 4.8.7, and hence

$$(P \cap Q)' = P' \cup Q'$$

by Defs. 4.8.5, 4.8.3, 4.8.4.

EXAMPLE 3
In AMS (Logic)

$$\forall_x : [p_x \wedge (q_x \wedge r_x)] \leftrightarrow [(p_x \wedge q_x) \wedge r_x].$$

Therefore

$$\{x \mid p_x \wedge (q_x \wedge r_x)\} = \{x \mid (p_x \wedge q_x) \wedge r_x\}$$

by Def. 4.8.7, and hence

$$P \cap (Q \cap R) = (P \cap Q) \cap R$$

by repeated use of Def. 4.8.3.

*Problem Set 4.8

Use the following theorems in AMS (Logic) to establish corresponding theorems for AMS (Sets) by means of the definitions in this section.

1. $\forall_x : (p_x \wedge q_x) \leftrightarrow (q_x \wedge p_x).$

2. $\forall_x : [p_x \wedge (q_x \vee r_x)] \leftrightarrow [(p_x \wedge q_x) \vee (p_x \wedge r_x)].$

3. $\forall_x : [\sim(\sim p_x)] \leftrightarrow p_x.$

4. $\forall_x : [p_x \rightarrow q_x] \leftrightarrow [(\sim q_x) \rightarrow (\sim p_x)].$

5. $\forall_x : (p_x \leftrightarrow q_x) \leftrightarrow [(p_x \rightarrow q_x) \wedge (q_x \rightarrow p_x)].$

6. $\forall_x : [p_x \wedge (\sim p_x)] \leftrightarrow F.$

7. $\forall_x : [p_x \vee (\sim p_x)] \leftrightarrow T.$

8. $\forall_x : (p_x \wedge T) \leftrightarrow p_x.$

9. $\forall_x : (p_x \vee T) \leftrightarrow T.$

10. $\forall_x : (p_x \wedge F) \leftrightarrow F.$

11. $\forall_x : (p_x \vee F) \leftrightarrow p_x.$

12. $\forall_x : (p_x \wedge q_x) \to p_x.$

13. $\forall_x : p_x \to (p_x \vee q_x).$

14. $\forall_x : [(p_x \to q_x) \wedge (p_x \text{ is } T)] \to \forall_x : [q_x \text{ is } T].$

15. $\forall_x : [(p_x \to q_x) \wedge (q_x \text{ is } F)] \to \forall_x : [p_x \text{ is } F].$

4.9 Some Paradoxes

After seeing the logical and reasonable development of sets, one cannot help but feel that it is built on a solid foundation that could never be toppled. For if the development of sets itself does not give sufficient reassurance, its intimate relationship with "God-given" logic should convince even the nonbeliever.

Since the reader should now be convinced that no inconsistency could arise in either sets or logic, he is invited to explain the following situations, which will, for the present, be called *paradoxes*.

RUSSELL'S PARADOX [1]

(1) Let U be the set of all sets.
(2) Let $R = \{X | X \in X\}$ (for example, $U \in R$).
(3) Let $N = \{Y | Y \notin Y\}$ (for example, $\emptyset \in N$).

Now clearly every set is in either R or N— and therefore $(N \in R)$ or $(N \in N)$. We observe

$$(N \in R) \to (N \in N) \to (N \notin R)$$

and

$$(N \in N) \to (N \notin N).$$

Since both of these situations violate the Axiom of AMS (Sets) it follows that $(N \notin R)$ and $(N \notin N)$. Can it be that the set N is not really a set?

BASKET-BALL PARADOX [2]

Let us assume that we have two "very large" baskets which will be called basket A and basket B, and that balls numbered $1, 2, 3, \ldots$ are placed in basket A. We now perform the following acts in order.

---

[1] The English philosopher and mathematician Lord Bertrand Russell proposed this paradox in 1903, and it caused serious doubts concerning the validity of the theory of sets.

[2] In recent years this paradox has been popularized in lectures and on film by Professor Hartley Rogers, Jr., of M.I.T. He heard it from a fellow graduate student at Princeton University, but the original source appears to be a mystery.

(1) Remove balls 1 and 2 from basket *A* and put them into basket *B*.
(2) At 1/2 hour before noon remove the highest numbered ball from basket *B*, so that ball 1 remains.
(3) Remove balls 3 and 4 from basket *A* and put them into basket *B*.
(4) At 1/4 hour before noon remove the highest numbered ball from basket *B*, so that balls 1 and 3 remain.
(5) Remove balls 5 and 6 from basket *A* and put them into basket *B*.
(6) At 1/8 hour before noon remove the highest numbered ball from basket *B*, so that balls 1, 3, and 5 remain; etc.

If this procedure is continued indefinitely, then at noon basket *B* will contain all the odd balls.

We now modify steps (2), (4), (6), . . . by replacing "highest numbered ball" with "lowest numbered ball," so that

At step (2), ball 2 remains.
At step (4), balls 3 and 4 remain.
At step (6), balls 4, 5, and 6 remain; etc.

Then if basket *B* contains any balls at noon, it undoubtedly contains a lowest-numbered one. What is the number on this lowest-numbered ball? If you cannot answer this question, do you believe that basket *B* is completely empty at the noon hour?

4.10 Formalism vs. Intuitionism

In Section 4.9 we noted that set theory was not as pure as we had expected—for some paradoxes raised their ugly heads. It turns out that the paradoxes of set theory were the direct cause of the outbreak of a strong disagreement between *formalists* and *intuitionists*. The disagreement was concerned not only with these paradoxes, but with the question, "What is the correct system of logic?"

FORMALISM

The most outstanding advocates of formalism were David Hilbert (1862–1943) and Georg Cantor (1845–1918). We shall now outline their major doctrines.

(1) Formalists believe that all of mathematics should be developed from Abstract Mathematical Structures (i.e., the axiomatic method).
(2) Formalists interpret mathematical existence to mean freedom from contradiction. (For example, the set of all sets led to a contradiction in Russell's Paradox and therefore it is nonexistent.)
(3) Formalists believe in the *law of the excluded middle* [i.e., (*p* is *T*) or (*p* is *F*)—but not both] and therefore the *indirect method* for proving theorems is legitimate.

EXAMPLE 1
In proving "$\sqrt{2}$ is irrational," formalists say, "Since assuming $\sqrt{2}$ is rational leads to a contradiction, $\sqrt{2}$ must be irrational." (See Section A.1 for the meaning of *rational* and *irrational*.)

EXAMPLE 2
In proving "$(0, 1)$ is nondenumerable" formalists say, "Since assuming $(0, 1)$ is denumerable leads to a contradiction, it follows that $(0, 1)$ is nondenumerable." [$(0, 1)$ represents the set of all points between 0 and 1 on the real number line, and hence $(0, 1) \sim L_1$—where L_1 is defined in Example 3 of Section 4.3].

(4) Formalists believe in the decidability of every mathematical problem. To the early formalist every mathematical problem was decidable, even if at the time it had not been decided. According to Hilbert, every mathematician shares "the conviction that every mathematical problem must necessarily be capable of a rigorous settlement—through the use of pure thought."

EXAMPLE 1
The number 299,909 is either a prime or a nonprime. In a finite number of steps it can be proved prime. (A positive integer p, greater than 1, is called a *prime* if its only positive integral divisors are 1 and p; for example, 2, 3, 5, 7 are primes but 4, 6, 8, 9 are nonprimes.)

EXAMPLE 2
There are either a finite number or an infinite number of twin primes ($p, p + 2$ is a *twin prime* if p and $p + 2$ are both primes; for example, 5, 7 is a twin prime). This problem is still unsolved.

EXAMPLE 3
Every even number greater than 4 is the sum of two odd primes (*Goldbach Conjecture*), or there exists an even number greater than 4 that is not the sum of two odd primes. This problem is still unsolved.

EXAMPLE 4
It is easy to show that there are positive integers x, y, z for which $x^2 + y^2 = z^2$ (e.g., 3, 4, 5); but are there positive integers x, y, z such that $x^n + y^n = z^n$ when $n > 2$? Formalists say, "either there are or there are not." [Fermat's Last Theorem states that $x^n + y^n = z^n$ has no solution in which x, y, z are positive integers whenever n is an integer greater than 2. Pierre de Fermat (1601–1665) wrote in his book that he had

"discovered a truly remarkable proof which this margin is too small to contain," but no one to this day has been able to prove it or disprove it. It has now been verified for all n up through 25,000 (at least). In 1908 a German professor of mathematics (Paul Wolfskehl) left 100,000 marks to be awarded to the first person who proves Fermat's Last Theorem. The inflation after World War I reduced this prize to a fraction of a cent—and interest among the mercenaries was correspondingly reduced!]

EXAMPLE 5
There are either finitely or infinitely many perfect numbers (a *perfect number* is equal to the sum of its proper divisors; for example, 6 is perfect since $6 = 1 + 2 + 3$). This is still unsolved. [Since ancient times magic properties have been associated with certain numbers. Some of the more favored numbers have been 6 (the number of days needed for the creation of the world) and 28 (the length of the lunar cycle), both of which are perfect numbers. Numerology has been taken with the utmost seriousness by some people at all times in human history. For example, in the eighth century Alcuin concluded that the second creation was inferior to the first creation because the second creation was associated with the non-perfect number 8 (the number of souls on Noah's Ark), whereas the first creation was associated with the perfect number 6. (We note that 8 is called a *deficient number* because the sum of its proper divisors is less than 8.)]

EXAMPLE 6
Formalists say either there exists an odd perfect number or there does not. To this day no one knows.

The strength of the formalistic method—its rigor and its elegance—appeared to give mathematics an immovable permanence, until about 1900, when the intuitionists broke this firm foundation wide open.

INTUITIONISM

The foremost intuitionists have been Leopold Kronecker (1823–1891), Hermann Weyl (1885–1965), and Luitzen Egbertus Jan Brouwer (1881–1966). We will now outline their doctrines.

(1) The intuitionists received their name by viewing the natural numbers as *original intuition*. They consider the natural numbers as something originally given, for which no further foundation is necessary, whereas the formalists insist that even the natural numbers must be built from an Abstract Mathematical Structure. Kronecker said, "The natural numbers were made by God, all else is the work of man." The intuitionists have focused sharp criticism on "the work of man."

(2) Intuitionists interpret *mathematical existence* to mean constructability in a finite number of steps.

EXAMPLE 1

The intuitionists consider the *well-ordering theorem* (i.e., "Every nonempty subset of an ordered set has a first element") of no value because it merely establishes the existence of well-ordering without indicating how well-ordering can be achieved.

EXAMPLE 2

The digits x_i in the decimal $x = 0.x_1x_2x_3 \ldots$ can be assigned from the digits of $\pi = 3.14159265\ldots$ as follows. First, separate the digits after the decimal point in π into groups of ten. If the ith group consists of ten equal digits, all 7's, let $x_i = 1$; otherwise let $x_i = 0$. For example, the first group of ten digits is certainly not all 7's, and hence $x_1 = 0$. It is now impossible, in a finite number of steps, to determine the value of x. At this time we do not even know whether $x = 0$ or $x \neq 0$. The formalists say, "Clearly x exists, for it is determined uniquely and without contradiction." The intuitionists say, "At no time do we know the value of x. We cannot construct x in a finite number of steps, and therefore x has no mathematical existence." As a matter of fact, Kronecker asserted that π does not exist since there is no way of constructing it from the natural numbers in a finite number of steps. (We will discuss the meaning of π in Section 5.2.)

(3) Intuitionists forbid the use of the law of the excluded middle (except for finite sets). To the intuitionist the law of the excluded middle is an "unfounded prejudice." He contends that this law arose from the study of finite sets and has been given to infinite sets without proper authority. Also, the statement "either (p is T) or (p is F)" need not always be true—for there is a third possibility, namely, that p is undecidable.

(4) The intuitionists contend that some mathematical problems are undecidable. Thus an intuitionist can be considered a *mathematical agnostic*.

EXAMPLE 1

Intuitionists answer the question, "Is Fermat's Last Theorem true?" by saying, "Maybe yes, maybe no, or maybe it is undecidable." If the answer is yes, it might turn out to be true only by accident in the sense that it just happens to be true but a proof is logically impossible; and hence no one will ever know for sure that it is true. On the other hand, if the answer is no, it might turn out to be false for such large numbers that not even the fastest electronic computer could reach them in a million years.

EXAMPLE 2

When an intuitionist is asked, "Is the sum of the angles of a triangle equal to 180°?" he would answer, "Maybe yes, maybe no, or maybe I don't know." Of course, this is correct since the answer is yes in Euclidean geometry, no in the non-Euclidean geometries, and undecidable in absolute geometry. The reason for this discrepancy is that the sum of the angles of a triangle is directly linked to a parallel postulate. If we assume the basic postulates of geometry without any parallel postulate, we have *absolute geometry*; if in addition to the basic postulates we assume the Euclidean parallel postulate (i.e., given a line l and a point P not on l, there is exactly one line through P parallel to l), we have *Euclidean geometry*; if in addition to the basic postulates we assume a non-Euclidean parallel postulate (i.e., given a line l and a point P not on l, there is *not* exactly one line through P parallel to l), we have a *non-Euclidean geometry*. In the last case, if we assumed no parallels (i.e., elliptic geometry), then the sum of the angles would be greater than 180°; and if we assumed more than one parallel (i.e., hyperbolic geometry), then the sum of the angles would be less than 180°. To this day no one knows whether we live in a Euclidean or a non-Euclidean world—for our measuring instruments are not accurate enough to reveal whether the sum of the angles in a concrete triangle is precisely 180°.

EXAMPLE 3

If an intuitionist is asked, "Is there a cardinal number between $\aleph_0$ and c?" he will answer (as in the case of "the sum of the angles of a triangle") "Maybe yes, maybe no, or maybe I don't know." The reason for this strange-sounding answer is similar to that used for the triangle. It was justified in 1963, when the mathematician Paul Cohen proved that it is just as consistent to have yes as to have no. Therefore the status of set theory is comparable to that of absolute geometry; for an additional postulate is needed to obtain a definite reply, either affirmative or negative. Cantor had conjectured that the answer to this question would be negative, and his conjecture is known as the *continuum hypothesis*. The solutions to many mathematical problems have been based on this hypothesis. (It should be noted that the pure intuitionist would not even consider the question of this example to be meaningful—for he does not accept the existence of the cardinal number c because it originated from an argument requiring the law of the excluded middle. Hence the existence of c may be undecidable!)

The rigorous criticism of intuitionism makes some rather severe demands on the present-day theory of sets; for example, (1) the abolition of everything beyond the denumerable, and in particular the removal of the transfinite cardinal number **c**, and (2) the elimination of the well-ordering theorem.

Intuitionists have created difficulties for the formalists, but they have also revitalized them. For a time the conflict of the two ideologies was violent. Cantor wrote, "There is inherent here to a certain measure, a question of power. . . . It is asked, 'Which ideas are the stronger, more embracing and fruitful ones, Kronecker's or mine?' Time only will decide the outcome of our battle."

And how did the battle turn out? From the quiet distance of several decades and thousands of miles, a mathematician and historian (E. T. Bell) wrote, "It was a battle of life and death between Hilbert's formalism and Brouwer's intuitionism for the possession of mathematics. It does not seem to have occurred to either combatant that while he was engaged in trying to extermi- nate his enemy, some ragged camp follower might make off with the prize; or that it might not make the slightest difference to mathematics whether the battle for him was won, lost, or drawn."

There will probably always be formalists and intuitionists, and most mathe- maticians will follow the paths of both.

We conclude this chapter with a statement by Hilbert, "Let us be glad that we can enter into the theory of sets, into that paradise from which no one can drive us out"—a statement that reflects the enthusiasm and spirit of a mathematician.

CHAPTER 5

Geometry

5.1 The Origin of Geometry

One may wonder how geometry originated and also who invented it. The answer is given in the following document which is a "translation of a manuscript recently found in an ancient wine vessel in a cave in the mountains of Iraq. There are missing sections because of the fragmentary nature of the manuscript."[1]

GENESIS

CHAPTER 1

1. In the beginning Euclid created space.
2. And space was without structure, and void; and darkness was upon the face of deep space. And the spirit of Euclid moved.
3. And Euclid said let there be lines: and there were lines.
4. And Euclid saw the lines, that they were good: and Euclid divided the lines with points.
5. And Euclid called these lines rays. And the extent of the line was the first axiom.
6. And Euclid said let there be planes, and let them divide the points from the points.
7. And Euclid made planes and they divided the points which were under the planes from the points which were above the planes: and it was so.
8. And Euclid called the planes flat. And the evening and the morning were the second axiom.
9. And Euclid said let the points be gathered together unto one place, and let solids appear: and it was so.
10. And Euclid called the solids real; and the gathering together of the points he called space; and Euclid saw that it was good.

[1] Reprinted from *American Mathematical Monthly*, Vol. 77, (Feb., 1970), pp. 189–191, by permission of the Mathematical Association of America and the author (who prefers to remain publicly anonymous).

11. And Euclid said, let the space bring forth segments, the segments yielding fruit after their kind whose seed is in itself: and it was so.

12. And space brought forth segments, yielding segments upon segments to make number lines: and Euclid saw that it was good.

13. And the evening and the morning were the third axiom.

14. And Euclid said let there be orbs in the firmament of space to divide the inside from the outside and let them be signs for the seasons, and for days, and for years.

15. And let them be for gems in the firmament of space to give delight upon the earth: and it was so.

16, 17, 18. And Euclid made two great orbs the greater orb to rule the firmament and the lesser orb to rule the planes: he made the triangles also: and Euclid saw that it was good.

19. And the evening and the morning were the fourth axiom.

20, 21. And Euclid said let the points bring forth abundantly parallels so that alternate interiors are forever equal. And Euclid created great cubes, and squares, and every parallelogram that cometh, which the points brought forth abundantly, after their kind one upon another: and Euclid saw that it was good.

22. And Euclid blessed them, saying, be fruitful and multiply and with parallelograms and parallelepipeds fill the planes and space.

23. And the evening and the morning were the fifth axiom.

26. And Euclid said let us make a Mathematician in our image, after our likeness; and let him have dominion over triangles and over circles, and over spheres and over cubes, and over all of space, and every constructable subset that is constructed out of space.

27. So Euclid created a Mathematician in his own image, in the image of Euclid created he him; great and small created he them.

28. And Euclid blessed them, and Euclid said unto them, be fruitful, and multiply and prove theorems and subdue them: and have dominion over triangles, and over spheres, and over every set of points that cometh out of space.

29. And Euclid said Behold, I have given you every set bearing proof, which is on the face of all of space, and every set which is the fruit of a set yielding proof; to you it shall be for theorems.

31. And Euclid saw everything that he had made, and, behold, it was very good. And the evening and the morning were the sixth day.

CHAPTER 2

Thus space and all its subsets were finished, and all the uncountable host of them.

2. And on the seventh day Euclid ended the theory which he had made; and he rested on the seventh day from all the sets which he had made.

4. These are the generations of the sets and points and of the space when they were created, in the day that the Greek Euclid made the space and its subsets.

8. And Euclid builded a library eastward in Erewhon; and there he put the Mathematician whom he had formed.

9. And out of the points made the Greek Euclid to grow every set that is pleasant to the sight, and good for proof; the set of logic also in the midst of the library, and the set of knowledge of the excluded middle.

15. And Euclid took the Mathematician, and put him in the library to read it and keep it.

16. And Euclid commanded the Mathematician, saying, of every set in the library thou may freely partake:

17. But of the set of the knowledge of the excluded middle, thou shalt not partake of it: for the day that thou partake thereof thou shalt surely die.

18. And Euclid said it is not good that the Mathematician should be alone; I will make a help meet for him.

21. And Euclid caused a deep sleep to fall on the Mathematician, and he slept; and he took one of his brains, and closed up the flesh instead thereof;

22. And the brain which the Greek Euclid had taken from Mathematician, made he a Subman and brought him unto the Mathematician.

23. And the Mathematician said, this is now bone of my bones, and flesh of my flesh; he shall be called Subman because he was taken out of man.

24. Therefore shall a man leave his mentors, and shall cleave to his student: and they shall be one mind.

25. And they were both stupid, the man and his student, and were not ashamed.

CHAPTER 3

Now the Uncountable was more subtle than any set of the space which the Greek Euclid had made. And he said unto the Subman, Yea, hath Euclid said, Ye shall not partake of every set in the library?

2. And the student said to the Uncountable, We may partake of all sets in the library:

3. But of the fruit of the set which is in the midst of the library, Euclid hath said, Ye shall not partake of it, neither shall ye touch it, lest ye die.

4. And the Uncountable said unto the student, Ye shall not surely die:

5. For Euclid doth know that in the day thou partake thereof, then your eyes shall be opened, and ye shall be as gods, knowing consistency and contradiction.

6. And when the student saw that the set was good for thought, and that it was pleasant to the mind, and a set to be desired to make one wise, he partook of the set thereof, and did think, and gave also unto his master with him; and he did partake.

7. And the eyes of both of them were opened, and they knew that they were stupid; and they invented classes and made systems.

8. And they heard the voice of Euclid walking in the library; and the Mathematician and his student hid themselves from the presence of Euclid amongst the footnotes in the library.

9. And Euclid called to the Mathematician and said unto him, Where art thou?

10. And he said, I heard thy voice in the library and I was afraid because I was stupid; and I hid myself.

11. And he said, Who told thee that thou wast stupid? Hast thou partaken of the set, whereof I forbade thee?

12. And the Mathematician said, The Subman whom thou gavest to be with me, he gave me of the set, and I did think.

13. And the Greek Euclid said unto the Subman, What is this that thou hast done? And the Subman said, the Uncountable beguiled me and I did think.

14. And Euclid said unto the Uncountable, Because thou hast done this thou art cursed above all other sets. To the foundations must thou go for all the days of thy life.

15. And I will put enmity between thee and the student, and between thy subsets and his subsets; it shall bruise thy pride and thou shalt bruise his mind.

16. Unto the student he said, I will greatly multiply thy sorrow, in sorrow shalt thou bring forth lemmas; and thy desire shall be to thy master, and he shall rule over thee.

17. And unto the Mathematician he said, Because thou hast hearkened to the voice of thy student, and has thought of the set, of which I commanded thee, saying, Thou shalt not think of it: cursed is the structure for thy sake; in sorrow shalt thou think of it all the days of thy life.

22. And the Greek Euclid said, Behold, the Mathematician is become as one of us, to know consistency and contradiction: and now lest he put forth his hand and partake of the set of logic, and think, and prove theorems forever:

23. Therefore Euclid set him forth from the library of Erewhon, to prove, without a library card, the theorems from whence he was taken.

24. So he drove out the Mathematician; and he placed at the east of the library of Erewhon Cher-u-bims Kronecker, and Hilbert, and Brouwer, with flaming words which turn every way, to keep the way of the set of logic.

5.2 Concrete Geometry in the Plane

Now that the origin of geometry has been revealed to us, one may ask, "Is geometry an abstract mathematical structure, or is it concrete?" We can answer this by saying, "It could be either, since if we consider *point* and *line* as undefined terms and investigate the assumptions made about these words (without considering the usual concrete interpretation of *smudge* for *point* and *streak* for *line*), we are dealing with an AMS. But if we are concerned with the drawings of concrete pictures of point and line, we are then involved in concrete geometry. In this chapter we shall be concerned with smudges and streaks, and therefore we shall be dealing with concrete geometry.

LENGTH

If we draw a concrete line segment, someone may want to know its *length*. Before we can find its length, we must define a unit of length. The most common unit of length is a line segment with *unit length*, and the familiar names of inch, foot, mile, centimeter, etc. have been given to some of the standard units. After we have a unit of length, we can find the length of a line segment by counting the number of units. We observe that the line segment in Fig. 5.1 is 5 units long.

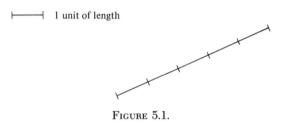

FIGURE 5.1.

We can now find (at least approximately) the length (or perimeter) of any geometric figure which consists of a finite number of line segments.

EXAMPLE 1

If the length of a rectangle is l units and its width is w units, then its perimeter p can be found by use of the formula

(1) $$p = (2l + 2w) \text{ units} = 2(l + w) \text{ units}.$$

The reader should check to see how this formula can be used to show that the perimeter of the rectangle in Fig. 5.2 is 20 units.

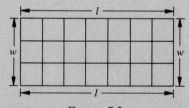

FIGURE 5.2.

EXAMPLE 2

Since a circle does not consist of a finite number of straight line segments, finding its perimeter (called *circumference*) provides some difficulty. If we use an intuitive approach, we observe that a circle can be considered to be a regular polygon (i.e., a plane figure whose sides are equal line segments and whose interior angles are all equal) with infinitely many "small" sides. With this interpretation, a limiting process (or the calculus) can be used to prove that if a circle has a radius of r units, then its circumference is $2\pi r$ units; where π (read "pie") is the number of units in the circumference of a circle with unit diameter and is slightly more than 3. Hence, if C represents the circumference of a circle with radius r units, then

(2) $C = 2\pi r$ units.

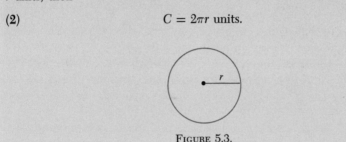

FIGURE 5.3.

ON FINDING π

The reader is probably familiar with the Greek symbol π, but may not be aware of its distinguished history or interesting features. In ancient times various crude methods were used for obtaining π. In the Old Testament (i.e., in I Kings 7 : 23 and II Chron. 4 : 2) π was estimated at 3. In 1897 the Indiana State Legislature (with vigorous support from the State Superintendent of Public Instruction) attempted to legislate the value of π in a simple-minded but erroneous way. The bill passed the House, but not the Senate.

One method for estimating the value of π is to draw a circle with unit diameter and then successively approximate the circumference of this circle by means of regular polygons with more and more sides, all of which are inscribed (or circumscribed) about the given circle. Some men have spent a large part of their lives computing π in this way. For example, in the seventeenth century Ludolph van Ceulen of Germany computed π to 32 decimal places by using a regular polygon with 2^{62} sides—and since 2^{62} (which represents the product of 62 2's) is more than a billion billions, one may guess that this computation took several years.

Some odes to π have served as aids for remembering the digits in its decimal. For example, the number of letters in the successive words of "See I have a rhyme assisting my feeble brain its tasks ofttimes resisting" leads to the decimal 3.141592653589. This mnemonic appeared in the *Scientific American* in 1914.

The calculus has provided the method of infinite series for establishing the decimal representation, and electronic computers have now been used to find

π to over 500,000 places. Two interesting infinite series relations that can be used to evaluate π are

$$\frac{\pi}{4} = 1 - \frac{1}{3} + \frac{1}{5} - \frac{1}{7} + \cdots$$

and

$$\frac{\pi^2}{6} = \frac{1}{1^2} + \frac{1}{2^2} + \frac{1}{3^2} + \frac{1}{4^2} + \cdots.$$

AREA

In addition to finding the perimeter, one may want to find the *area* of a geometric figure. Before we can determine the area, we must define a *unit of area*. Since the most common unit is the *square unit*, which consists of a square with 1 unit for each side, this is what we shall use. If we now want to find the area of a geometric figure, we merely count the number of square units it contains.

Since the rectangle in Fig. 5.2 has been partitioned into unit squares, its area is easily found to be 21 square units. If we are lazy and do not want to count all the squares, we need only note that there are 7 square units in the top layer and 3 layers, and therefore there must be $7 \cdot 3$, or 21 square units.

If A_R represents the area of a rectangle whose length is l units and whose width is w units, we can generalize the observation just made by noting that there are l square units in the top layer and w layers, and hence we obtain the formula

(3) $A_R = lw$ square units.

If we now want to find the area of a parallelogram with base b units and height h units, as in Fig. 5.4, we can transplant the shaded triangle to the right, as indicated. Since the rectangle $ABCD$ has the same area as the parallelogram, the formula for the area of a parallelogram is found to be

(4) $A_P = bh$ square units.

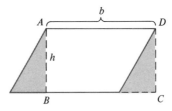

FIGURE 5.4.

In order to find the area of a triangle with base b units and height h units, as in Fig. 5.5, we can draw the dotted lines, as indicated, to obtain a parallelogram. Since the area of the triangle is one half that of the parallelogram, the formula for the area of a triangle is found to be

(5) $A_T = \frac{1}{2}bh$ square units.

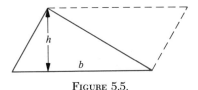

FIGURE 5.5.

The formula for the area of a circle which has a radius of r units is given by

(6) $A_C = \pi r^2$ square units.

This formula can be found by means of a limiting process (or the calculus). However, if we tried to find the area of the circle by using the formula for the area of a triangle (with *base* equal to the circumference of the circle and *height* equal to the radius of the circle), we would have

$$A = \tfrac{1}{2}bh = \tfrac{1}{2}(2\pi r)r = \pi r^2 \text{ square units,}$$

which is the correct formula! But why should this procedure give us the correct answer?

Problem Set 5.2

1. Find (i) the perimeter of and (ii) the area of
   (a) A rectangle with length 6 feet and width 4 feet.
   (b) A square with side 5 inches.

2. Find the area of the following:
   (a) Parallelogram with base 2 feet and height 7 inches.
   (b) Triangle with base 4 yards and height 5 feet.
   °(c) Trapezoid with bases 10 feet and 7 feet and height 4 feet.

3. A circle has a radius of 3 inches. Find its (a) circumference, (b) area.

4. True-False
   (a) $\pi = \frac{22}{7}$.
   (b) Every square is a regular polygon.
   (c) A circle with unit radius has an area of π square units.
   (d) The diameter of a circle is equal to twice its radius.
   (e) A point is a circle with zero radius.

5.3 Geometry and Algebra

The formula for the area of a rectangle can be used to obtain some basic formulas in algebra.

EXAMPLE 1
The diagram in Fig. 5.6 can be used to establish the formula

(1) $a(x + y) = ax + ay,$

which is called the *distributive law*, since the number a is being distributed. Formula (1) follows from the fact that the area of the large rectangle is equal to the sum of the areas of the two smaller rectangles.

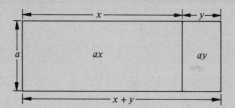

FIGURE 5.6. *Distributive Law:* $a(x + y) = ax + ay$

EXAMPLE 2
The area of the square in Fig. 5.7 is equal to $(a + b)(a + b) = (a + b)^2$. If we now find the area of each component of this square, we obtain

(2) $(a + b)^2 = a^2 + 2ab + b^2.$

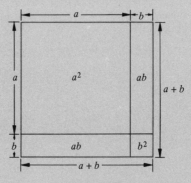

FIGURE 5.7.

EXAMPLE 3
In Fig. 5.8 the region that contains gray shading represents $a^2 - b^2$, since it is the area of the large square with the area of the small square removed.

If we now move the wide gray rectangle at the bottom to the vertical position at the right, we obtain a rectangle (shown with red shading) whose area is $(a + b)(a - b)$. Since this area equals the original area, we have

$$(3) \qquad a^2 - b^2 = (a + b)(a - b).$$

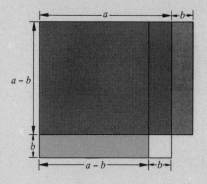

FIGURE 5.8.

EXAMPLE 4

Consider the equal squares in Fig. 5.9, each of which contains four equal right triangles (with legs whose lengths are a and b units and with hypotenuse whose length is c units). If the corresponding triangles (designated by I, II, III, and IV) are removed, we obtain

$$(4) \qquad c^2 = a^2 + b^2,$$

and this formula is called the *Pythagorean theorem*.

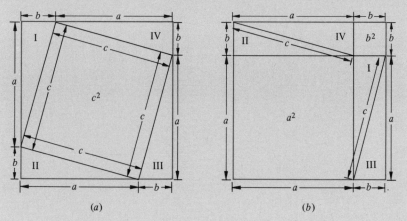

(a)   (b)

FIGURE 5.9. *Pythagorean Theorem:* $c^2 = a^2 + b^2$

Problem Set 5.3

1. Use geometric figures to find expansions for each of the following:
   (a) $(a + b)(c + d)$.
   (b) $(a + b + c)^2$.
   °(c) $(a - b)^2$.

2. Prove the Pythagorean theorem by use of Formula (2) and Fig. 5.9a.

3. Use the result of Formula (3) as a shortcut to find
   (a) $100^2 - 99^2$.   (e) 31×29.
   (b) $23{,}432^2 - 23{,}431^2$.   (f) 41×39.
   (c) $21^2 - 19^2$.   (g) 42×38.
   (d) $57^2 - 43^2$.   (h) 53×47.

5.4 Concrete Geometry in Space

In this section we will investigate the *surface areas* and *volumes* of some basic geometric figures in space.

SURFACE AREA

The surface area of a rectangular solid is easily found, since each of its six faces is a rectangle. If a rectangular solid has length l units, width w units, and height h units (as indicated in Fig. 5.10), its surface area is found to be

(1) $$S_R = (2lw + 2hw + 2lh) \text{ square units,}$$

by virtue of Formula (3) in Section 5.2.

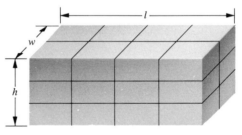

FIGURE 5.10.

Since a rectangular piece of paper can be used to construct the lateral (or side) face of a cylinder whose base is a circle with radius r units and whose height is h units, the lateral area (i.e., the area of the lateral face) of the cylinder is the area of a rectangle whose length is the circumference of the circular base and whose width is the height of the cylinder (as indicated in

Fig. 5.11). Hence, if L_{CL} represents this lateral area, we have the formula

(2) $L_{CL} = 2\pi rh$ square units.

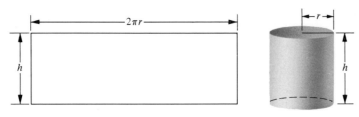

FIGURE 5.11.

In order to find the surface area of a sphere, we need to use a limiting process, or the calculus. However, if we assume that the surface area of a sphere with radius r units is the same as the lateral area of a cylinder whose base is a circle with radius r units and whose height is $2r$ units, we obtain the formula

(3) $S_S = 2\pi r(2r) = 4\pi r^2$ square units,

which happens to be the correct formula! Why should this be?

VOLUME

It is often useful to know the capacity or volume of a solid. But before we are able to determine any volume, we must decide on a unit of volume. We shall let the *unit cube* serve in this role. Then to find the volume of a geometric figure we merely count the number of cubic units in that figure. For example, in the rectangular solid of Fig. 5.10 there are 8 cubic units in the top layer (or base) and there are 3 layers, and therefore the volume of this rectangular solid is 24 cubic units. We can now guess that the volume of a figure with uniform thickness (e.g., one which goes straight up and down) can be found by multiplying the area of the base B by the height h. Hence, the volume of a rectangular solid with length l, width w, and height h is

(4) $V_R = Bh = lwh$ cubic units

and the volume of the cylinder in Fig. 5.11 is

(5) $V_{CL} = Bh = \pi r^2 h$ cubic units.

In order to find the volume of a geometric figure such as a pyramid or a cone (i.e., one which goes uniformly to a point), we will consider Fig. 5.12. Since this figure shows that a cube can be partitioned into three equal pyramids (i.e., *A-BCDE, A-DEFG, A-BEFH*), one may guess that the volume of any pyramid is one third the area of the base times the height, and it is! Since a cone can be thought of as a pyramid with infinitely many "small" sides, it turns out that the volume of a cone is also one third the area of the base times the height (actually, a limiting process, or the calculus, is needed to establish this fact). Therefore a cone of height h whose base is a circle with radius r is

(6) $$V_{CN} = \tfrac{1}{3}Bh = \tfrac{1}{3}\pi r^2 h \text{ cubic units.}$$

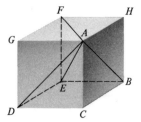

FIGURE 5.12.

In order to find the volume of a sphere, a limiting process, or the calculus, is again needed. However, we shall now "perform" an experiment to try to convince the reader that the volume of a sphere can be found by assuming it has the same volume as a cone whose base has an area equal to the surface area of the sphere, and whose height is the radius of the sphere—so that the volume of a sphere with radius r is

(7) $$V_S = \tfrac{1}{3}(4\pi r^2)r = \tfrac{4}{3}\pi r^3 \text{ cubic units.}$$

Before the experiment can be performed, we need to acquire a special cone and special cylinder (both hollow, but with the cylinder closed at the bottom) corresponding to a sphere with radius r, as indicated in Fig. 5.13. These three figures are constructed so that their diameters and their heights are all equal to $2r$. The experiment consists of the following steps:

(1) Pour water into the cone so that it reaches the top.
(2) Pour all this water from the cone into the cylinder (so that the cylinder now contains the "volume of the cone").
(3) Place the sphere inside the cylinder so that it just touches the bottom.
(4) Observe that the water in the cylinder now reaches to its top.

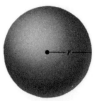

FIGURE 5.13.

If this experiment reflects the precise situation which occurs (and we know that *true* precision is impossible in practical experiments), then it would follow that

$$V_{\text{cone}} + V_{\text{sphere}} = V_{\text{cylinder}}.$$

But since

$$V_{\text{cone}} = \tfrac{1}{3}\pi r^2 h = \tfrac{1}{3}\pi r^2(2r) = \tfrac{2}{3}\pi r^3,$$

and

$$V_{\text{cylinder}} = \pi r^2 h = \pi r^2(2r) = \tfrac{6}{3}\pi r^3,$$

it would follow that

$$V_{\text{sphere}} = \tfrac{4}{3}\pi r^3,$$

which happens to be the correct formula for the volume of a sphere with radius r.

Problem Set 5.4

1. Find (i) the surface area of and (ii) the volume of
   (a) A rectangular solid with length 7 feet, width 5 feet, and height 3 feet.
   (b) A cube with edge 2 miles.
   (c) A sphere with radius 3 feet.

2. A circular cylinder has a diameter of 8 feet and a height of 2 yards. Find its (a) lateral area, (b) total surface area, (c) volume.

3. A circular cone has a radius of 10 inches and a height of 1 foot. Find its (a) volume, *(b) lateral area.

*4. In Example 2 of Section 5.3 we saw how a square of side $(a + b)$ can be partitioned in order to find the expansion for $(a + b)^2$. Since $(a + b)^3$ represents the volume of a cube with side $(a + b)$, partition a cube to find an expansion for $(a + b)^3$.

5.5 Points and Numbers

Thus far we have considered a geometric figure to be a set of "concrete" points, arranged in some special way. In the remainder of this chapter, we shall identify points with numbers, and then a geometric figure will be able to be identified as an equation in algebra.

A need for establishing a relationship between points and numbers arose from a concrete problem in the Town of Purists. Let us first consider how this town was formed. The early Purists built a monument, which was to become the center of the town. Then a long street (going left and right) was constructed on either side of the monument. Then equally spaced houses were built on the right side of the monument. Then since the people who lived in these houses wanted their mail delivered, they needed addresses, and at the town meeting it was decided that the house one block from the monument should have address 1, the house two blocks from the monument should have address 2, etc. Then, since the Purists did not want to live too far from the monument, some of them decided to build their houses on the left side of the monument. But this caused a great controversy since the Purist who lived one block to the left of the monument wanted to have address 1, and those on the right side of the monument said that this would confuse the mailman. So, another town meeting was called and it was decided that those on the right side of the monument should have addresses $+1, +2, \ldots$ etc., and those on the left side should have addresses $-1, -2, \ldots$ etc. Then everything was peaceful until the mayor moved into the monument and wanted an address. It was soon decided that the mayor's address should be 0. A few weeks later, another road (avenue) was built perpendicular to the original street (i.e., it went up and down) on either side of the monument. Then equally spaced houses were built on the avenue and the address problem again created a heated controversy. Before a town meeting could be called, equally spaced houses were springing up all over town and there was great confusion concerning mail delivery. Finally, a town meeting was called and it was decreed that the address of each house shall be written as (x, y), where x designates how far it is to the right $(+)$ or left $(-)$ of the monument and y designates how far it is up $(+)$ or down $(-)$ from the monument. After this inspired decision, no more town meetings were needed.

If we now geometrize the addresses of the Town of Purists, we find (as in Fig. 5.14) that a point (or a small smudge) can be regarded as an ordered

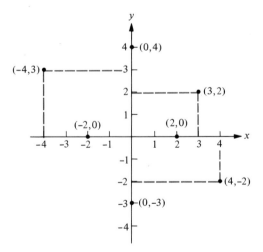

FIGURE 5.14.

pair of numbers, or *coordinates*. For if the original street is renamed *x*-axis and the original avenue is renamed *y*-axis, then each point in the plane can be identified with an ordered pair of numbers, and vice versa. The point where the *x*-axis meets the *y*-axis is called the *origin*.

Now that we have developed a *coordinate system* (usually called a *rectangular* or *Cartesian* coordinate system), we can plot points such as (3, 2), (−2, 0), (4, −2), (0, 4), (0, −3), and (−4, 3) as indicated in Fig. 5.14. This coordinate system is at the heart of the branch of mathematics called *analytic geometry*, which deals with the relationship between numbers and points. It was invented by the famous French mathematician and philosopher René Descartes (1596–1650), and this fact reveals the origin of the name *Cartesian-coordinate-system*.

EXAMPLE 1
If we have a relationship between *x* and *y*, such as $y = x + 1$, then we could find points (x, y) which satisfy this equation by
   (1) Setting up a table.
   (2) Choosing values such as 0, 1, 2, . . . , −1, −2, . . . for *x*.
   (3) Finding the corresponding values of *y*, as indicated below.

x	0	1	2		−1	−2	
y	1	2	3		0	−1	

If we now plot these points (as in Fig. 5.15), we see that they all seem to lie on a straight line. In joining these isolated points by a smooth curve, we are assuming that the curve does not behave erratically between these points. The question of whether this is justified and the question of how many points are needed before the shape of the curve can be determined requires practice, insights, and knowledge of analytic geometry.

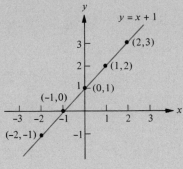

FIGURE 5.15.

After plotting still more points, one should become convinced that all (x, y) that satisfy the equation $y = x + 1$ lie on the line indicated in Fig. 5.15. Thus we see how an equation in algebra can be converted into a curve in geometry.

The set of all points whose coordinates satisfy an equation (i.e., the geometric representation of the equation) is called the *graph* or *picture* of the equation. Figure 5.15 illustrates that the graph of $y = x + 1$ is a straight line.

EXAMPLE 2

If we want to draw the graph of $2x + y = 4$, we could proceed as above. However, if we had some way of knowing that the graph of this equation is a straight line, then we could rapidly draw the graph by selecting any two points (x, y) whose coordinates satisfy the equation—since two points determine a line. For example $(0, 4)$ and $(2, 0)$ meet these requirements (since $2 \cdot 0 + 4 = 4$ and $2 \cdot 2 + 0 = 4$), and therefore we would have the following graph.

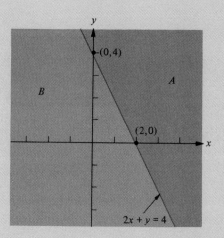

It can be proved that the graph of any equation of the form $ax + by = c$ is a straight line (unless $a = b = 0$). The reader should try to prove this statement, or at least convince himself it is true by verifying it for several values of a, b, and c.

We note that a line divides a plane into three parts: the line itself and two *half-planes*, one on either side of the line. In the preceding figure, the line $2x + y = 4$ divides the plane into half-planes A and B, and the line itself. The reader should observe that the line belongs to neither half-plane and the two half-planes have no points in common (i.e., $A \cap B = \emptyset$).

Since the graph of $y = 4 - 2x$ is the same as that of $2x + y = 4$, we can now conclude that

$$(x, y) \in A \text{ iff } y > 4 - 2x \quad (\text{or } 2x + y > 4)$$

and

$$(x, y) \in B \text{ iff } y < 4 - 2x \quad (\text{or } 2x + y < 4),$$

as can be tested by selecting points *not* on $2x + y = 4$. Therefore

$$A = \{x, y) | y > 4 - 2x\} = \{(x, y) | 2x + y > 4\}$$

is the set of all points above the line, and

$$B = \{(x, y) | y < 4 - 2x\} = \{(x, y) | 2x + y < 4\}$$

is the set of all points below the line.

EXAMPLE 3

NOTE: In this example we will disregard the results of the preceding paragraph.

If we want to draw the graph of the region

$$C = \{x, y) | 2x + y \geq 4\}$$

(i.e., C is the set of all points (x, y) such that $2x + y$ is greater than or equal to 4), we first draw the graph of $2x + y = 4$ (which is the same as the graph of $y = 4 - 2x$). Then since either $y = 4 - 2x$, $y < 4 - 2x$, or $y > 4 - 2x$, it follows that the line $y = 4 - 2x$ separates the plane into the following two half-planes:

$$\{(x, y) | y < 4 - 2x\} = \{(x, y) | 2x + y < 4\}$$

and

$$\{(x, y) | y > 4 - 2x\} = \{(x, y) | 2x + y > 4\}.$$

Hence, we need only test *one* point *not* on the line to see if it satisfies the required relation $2x + y > 4$. If it does (i.e., is a good point), then the half-plane we are now seeking contains that point, and therefore the half-plane of good points is determined. If it does not (i.e., is a bad point), then the half-plane we are now seeking does not contain that point, but the required half-plane is still determined. For example, if we select the point $(0, 0)$, we find that $2 \cdot 0 + 0 < 4$, and therefore $(0, 0)$ is a bad point which lies in the region containing all the bad points—which means that the *other* region consists of the good points.

We can now conclude that $C = A \cup D$, where A is defined in Example 2 and

$$D = \{(x, y) | 2x + y = 4\}$$

(i.e., D is the straight line whose equation is $2x + y = 4$).

The graphing techniques discussed here have useful applications in linear programming, and some of these applications will appear in Section 8.7.

Problem Set 5.5

1. Plot the following points:
   (a) $(2, 3)$.   (d) $(5, -2)$.   (g) $(-2, 3)$.
   (b) $(-4, 0)$.   (e) $(0, -2)$.   (h) $(0, 3)$.
   (c) $(-4, -1)$.   (f) $(0, 0)$.   (i) $(5, 0)$.

2. Graph each of the following curves:
   (a) $y = 2x + 1$.   (e) $y = x^2$.
   (b) $y = 2$.   °(f) $x^2 + y^2 = 25$.
   (c) $x = -3$.   (g) $2x + 3y = 6$.
   (d) $y = 1/x$.

3. Which of the graphs in Problem 2 are straight lines?

4. Graph (or shade) each of the following regions:
   (a) $x \geq 4$.   (e) $2x + y > 6$.
   (b) $y < 3$.   °(f) $x^2 + y^2 < 25$.
   (c) $x \leq y$.   °(g) $x^2 + y^2 \geq 25$.
   (d) $2x + y \leq 6$.   (h) $2x + y \leq 6, x + y \leq 4, x \geq 0, y \geq 0$.

5. Describe the graph of $ax + by = c$ when $a = b = 0$ and (a) $c = 0$, (b) $c \neq 0$.

6. If $a^0 = 1$, $a^{-x} = 1/a^x$, and $(a^{1/x})^x = a$, draw the graphs of (a) $y = 2^x$, (b) $y = 2^{-x}$, °(c) $y = 2^{1/x}$.

5.6 The Straight Line

If you were asked to describe a straight line, what would you say? You may first react by saying, "It is straight"—but then the natural follow-up question is "What do you mean by *straight?*" At this point you may reply, "It keeps going in the same direction," and we now respond with, "What do you mean by *direction?*" An easy way out of this is to say that *direction* is an undefined term—but are we forced to accept direction as an undefined term?

We shall now proceed to provide tools for answering these questions. First, we will find it convenient to assume:

(1) A line is a narrow road.

(2) We are bicycling on this line (or road) from left to right.

With these assumptions we can classify a line as either rising (or uphill), falling (or downhill), horizontal, or vertical.

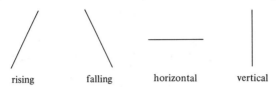

rising   falling   horizontal   vertical

While bicycling uphill one becomes aware of a (positive) obstacle, and the steeper the road the greater the obstacle. Since the bicycle rolls along by itself when going downhill, we can say that there is a negative obstacle—and when the road is steeper it rolls along faster, and hence the obstacle is more negative. When bicycling on a horizontal road we are traveling normally and can say that there is a zero obstacle, but when bicycling on a vertical road the obstacle is insurmountable and travel is impossible.

It would now seem that a reasonable measure for (i.e., a single real number that can be used to describe) the obstacle encountered—or the "steepness"— should have the following five properties:

(1) It should be positive when the line is rising.
(2) It should be negative when the line is falling.
(3) It should be zero when the line is horizontal.
(4) It should not exist when the line is vertical.
(5) It should be numerically larger when the line is steeper.

A measure which has all of these properties is called the *slope* of the line and is defined to be rise/run, where *rise* and *run* are indicated in the following figures.

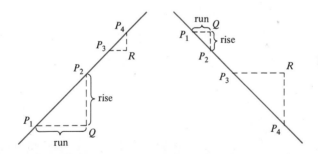

One may now observe that the ratio rise/run was obtained by selecting points P_1 and P_2 on the line, and wonder whether this ratio would be the same if two different points were selected. In order to answer this question, we shall select points P_3 and P_4 (as in the preceding diagram). Then triangle $P_1 Q P_2$ is a magnification of triangle $P_3 R P_4$ (or vice versa), and therefore the corresponding sides are proportional. This means that the ratio rise/run will be the same no matter which two points are selected.

It will now be convenient to install a Cartesian-coordinate system in order to obtain the following more formal definition of slope.

DEF 5.6.1

If points P_1 and P_2 have coordinates (x_1, y_1) and (x_2, y_2), respectively, then the *slope* of the line passing through P_1 and P_2 (i.e., $\overline{P_1P_2}$) is given by

$$m = \frac{y_2 - y_1}{x_2 - x_1} = \frac{\Delta y}{\Delta x}$$

where $y_2 - y_1 = \Delta y$ (read "delta y") is the change in y, or rise, and $x_2 - x_1 = \Delta x$ (read "delta x") is the change in x, or run, as in the following figure.

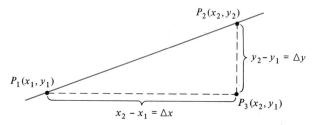

The reader may be interested to know that slope and area are two of the most basic concepts in geometry, and that the calculus serves to establish a close relationship between them.

EXAMPLE 1

If $P_1(2, 5)$, $P_2(7, 3)$, and $P_3(7, 5)$ are points, as in the following figure, then the slope of $\overline{P_1P_2}$ is

$$m = \frac{3 - 5}{7 - 2} = \frac{-2}{5},$$

and is negative, as expected; the slope of P_1P_3 is

$$m = \frac{5 - 5}{7 - 2} = \frac{0}{5} = 0;$$

and the slope of $\overline{P_2P_3}$ is

$$m = \frac{5 - 3}{7 - 7} = \frac{2}{0},$$

which does not exist—as expected.

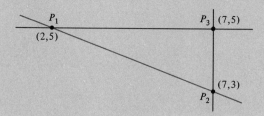

EXAMPLE 2

If we draw the graph of

(1) $$y = 2x + 1$$

as in the following figure (suspecting that it is a straight line) and select any point $P_1(x_1, y_1)$ on the graph [e.g., (x_1, y_1) could be $(0, 1)$, $(1, 3)$, etc.], we know that (x_1, y_1) satisfies Equation (1). That is, we know

(2) $$y_1 = 2x_1 + 1.$$

If we now subtract Equation (2) from Equation (1), we obtain (after using the distributive law)

(3) $$y - y_1 = 2(x - x_1);$$

and hence

(4) $$\frac{y - y_1}{x - x_1} = 2 \qquad \text{if } x \neq x_1.$$

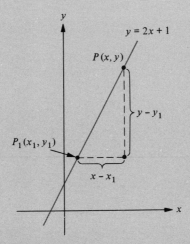

Since Equation (4) reveals that the slope of $\overline{PP_1}$ is 2 when $P \neq P_1$, and P represents any point on the graph of Equation (1), it follows that Equation (1) is indeed the equation of a straight line with a constant slope of 2.

If we are given the equation

(5) $$y = mx + q$$

and we go through the same steps as in Example 2, we find

(6) $$\frac{y - y_1}{x - x_1} = m \qquad \text{if } x \neq x_1;$$

and therefore an argument similar to the one used in the preceding example leads us to the conclusion that Equation (5) represents a straight line with slope m.

It should now be clear that Equation (5) can be used to represent any line with slope m; and that any line without slope is vertical and can therefore be represented by an equation of the form

$$(7) \qquad\qquad\qquad\qquad x = r.$$

Since any given line either has slope or does not have slope, it follows that every line can be represented by an equation of the form of either (5) or (7). If we now observe that both of these equations can be written in the form

$$(8) \qquad\qquad\qquad\qquad ax + by + c = 0,$$

where a and b are not both zero, we can conclude that every straight line has an equation of the form (8). It can also be shown that every equation of the form (8), where a and b are not both zero, represents a straight line. Hence, we can now define a *straight line* to be the set of all points (x, y) that satisfy an equation of the form $ax + by + c = 0$, where a and b are not both zero.

A *straight line with slope m passing through the point* $P_1(x_1, y_1)$ can be defined as the path of a point $P(x, y)$ which moves so that the slope of $\overline{PP_1}$ is m when $P \neq P_1$. Using the definition of slope, we find that the equation of the line with slope m passing through $P_1(x_1, y_1)$ is

$$(9) \qquad\qquad\qquad\qquad y - y_1 = m(x - x_1).$$

EXAMPLE 3
Problem:
Find the equation of the line which passes through the point $(1, 3)$ and has slope 2.

Solution:
Using Equation (9) we obtain the answer

$$(10) \qquad\qquad\qquad\qquad y - 3 = 2(x - 1);$$

and after applying the distributive law and some algebra, Equation (10) can be written as

$$(11) \qquad\qquad\qquad\qquad y = 2x + 1$$

or

$$(12) \qquad\qquad\qquad\qquad 2x - y + 1 = 0.$$

Problem Set 5.6

1. How would you describe a straight line?

2. Find the slope of $\overline{P_1P_2}$ if
   (a) $P_1(2, 1)$ and $P_2(5, 6)$.
   (b) $P_1(4, 7)$ and $P_2(5, 2)$.
   (c) $P_1(1, 3)$ and $P_2(5, 3)$.
   (d) $P_1(3, 1)$ and $P_2(3, 5)$.

3. Find the slope of each of the following lines:
   (a) $y = 3x + 4$.   (d) $2y = 6x + 8$.
   (b) $y = 4$.   (e) $x = 7$.
   (c) $y = -x + 2$.   °(f) $3x + 4y + 5 = 0$.

4. Find the equation of the line which passes through $(0, 3)$ and has slope 2.

5. Find the equation of the line passing through
   (a) $(2, 1)$ and $(5, 6)$.   (d) $(3, 1)$ and $(3, 5)$.
   (b) $(4, 7)$ and $(5, 2)$.   (e) $(2, 1)$ and $(0, 0)$.
   (c) $(1, 3)$ and $(5, 3)$.   (f) (a, b) and (c, d).

6. The formula for changing a temperature reading from degrees centigrade C to degrees Fahrenheit F is

   (*) $F = \tfrac{9}{5}C + 32.$

   Find F when $C =$ (a) 0, (b) 100, (c) 10, (d) -10, (e) -20.

7. Is (*) the equation of a straight line? Explain.

5.7 The Conic Sections

When a cone is sliced by a plane (as in Fig. 5.16), the curve formed is called a *conic section*. Since the conic sections are important in both pure and applied mathematics, they have been studied extensively in both mathematics and physics.

Analytic geometry is sometimes described as the branch of mathematics that uses coordinate systems to establish relationships between algebra and geometry (e.g., the graphs of equations), and many courses in analytic geometry devote a great deal of time to the conic sections. A method of analytic geometry, which converts geometric properties into equations in algebra, has

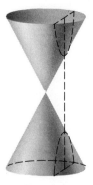

Circle	Ellipse	Parabola	Hyperbola
(plane parallel to base)	(plane cuts all elements obliquely across one nappe)	(plane parallel to an element)	(plane cuts both nappes)

FIGURE 5.16.

been used to show that each conic section can be represented by an equation of the form

$$Ax^2 + Bxy + Cy^2 + Dx + Ey + F = 0,$$

where A, B, C, D, E, and F are constants. More specifically, it is found that $x^2 + y^2 = 25$ represents (or is) a circle, $9x^2 + 16y^2 = 144$ is an ellipse, $y = x^2$ is a parabola, and $x^2 - y^2 = 1$ (also $y = 1/x$) is a hyperbola. The reader should graph these equations to verify these statements. We will now discuss some interesting properties of the conic sections.

CIRCLE

A *circle* can be defined as the path of a point in a plane which moves so that its distance from a fixed point (called *center*) is a constant (called *radius*). If one has a string and wants it to enclose a maximum area, it can be shown[2] that it should be shaped in the form of a circle. Because of this economy feature, the circle is of real practical value.

ELLIPSE

An *ellipse* can be defined as the path of a point in a plane which moves so that the sum of its distances from two fixed points (called *foci*) is a constant. Thus by fixing two points of a string, an ellipse can be constructed. Various positions of the string (where F_1 and F_2 are the foci) are shown in Fig. 5.17.

If you have ever visited the Whispering Gallery in Washington, D.C., you may recall that whispers occurring at one special point of this gallery can

---

[2] For example, see R. Courant and H. Robbins, *What Is Mathematics* (New York: Oxford University Press, 1941) pp. 373–376.

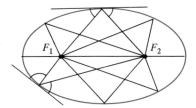

FIGURE 5.17.

be heard at another special point, but not at intermediary points. The reason for this is that it is shaped like an elliptical reflector in which the two special points are the foci of an ellipse. The lines from the foci to any point on an ellipse make equal angles with the tangent at that point (as indicated in Fig. 5.17). Therefore if a source of light or sound is placed at one focus, all the waves will be reflected so as to pass through the other focus. This property is the basis of the Whispering Gallery, as well as of focusing reflectors and elliptical pool tables.

The orbits of the earth and the other planets are elliptical with the sun at one focus, and Halley's comet has an elliptical orbit with the sun at one focus.

PARABOLA

A *parabola* can be defined as the path of a point in a plane which moves so that its distance to a fixed point (called *focus*) is equal to its distance to a fixed line (called *directrix*). If a light source is placed at the focus F of a parabolic reflector, all reflected rays will be parallel to the axis.

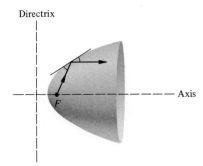

FIGURE 5.18.

The reason for this is that the ray from the focus to any point on a parabola and a ray through that point parallel to the axis of the parabola make equal angles with the tangent at that point (as indicated in Fig. 5.18). Also, all incoming light or sound waves that are parallel to the axis of a parabola will be reflected to the focus. These properties explain the widespread use of parabolic surfaces (i.e., surfaces obtained by revolving a parabola about its axis) in headlamp and searchlight reflectors, reflecting telescopes, sound detectors, etc. The paths of some comets are parabolas with the sun at the focus.

HYPERBOLA

A *hyperbola* can be defined as the path of a point in a plane which moves so that the difference of its distances from two fixed points (called *foci*) is a constant.

The rays from the foci to any point on the hyperbola make equal angles with the tangent at that point. Therefore, if the surface of a reflector is generated by revolving a hyperbola about its principal axis (as indicated in Fig. 5.19), all rays of light converging on one focus from without are reflected toward the other focus. This property is used in some telescopes in conjunction with a parabolic reflector. Also the orbits of some comets are hyperbolas.

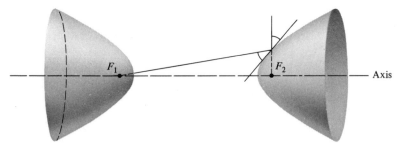

FIGURE 5.19.

CHAPTER 6

Counting and Probability

6.1 Introduction

Many people believe that probability is related to the supernatural, because no ordinary human being can predict the outcome of an experiment that is not entirely understood by human beings—and they are not surprised to learn that the formal study of probability originated from a problem in gambling. As the story goes, the theory of probability is given the birth year 1654 because in that year an aristocratic gambler, Chevalier de Méré, asked the mathematician Blaise Pascal (1623–1662) about a certain dice game that was troubling him in a very concrete way: he was losing money. For some time de Méré had bet that in 4 tosses of a (cubical) die, he would obtain a six at least once. This was a profitable bet, as was attested to by his systematic winnings. Unfortunately he had been so successful that no one wanted to bet with him on this any longer. This led him to change his bet: he now bet that in 24 tosses of a pair of dice, he would obtain a double-six at least once. The Chevalier reasoned that his bet would be as profitable as the previous one (since a die can come up in one of six ways—all equally likely—the chance of getting a 6 in 4 tosses should be $\frac{4}{6}$; and since two dice can come up in 36 ways—all equally likely—the chance of getting a double-six in 24 tosses should be $\frac{24}{36}$; and since $\frac{4}{6} = \frac{24}{36}$, there would be the same likelihood for success.) The change in the bet did provide him with new takers, but to his surprise he began to lose systematically. (The reason for this "change in luck" will be discussed in Section 6.5.) Pascal was interested in this problem and corresponded with the mathematician Pierre de Fermat (1601–1665). The theory of probability stems from the correspondence on this dice game.

It is true that probability spent its early years in gambling casinos. In fact, it still spends part of its time there in the sense that gambling problems provide excellent illustrations when discussing elementary probability. Besides gambling, probability is used in developing insurance rates, for appraising public opinion (e.g., the Gallup Poll), for predicting elections, weather, accidents, financial barometers, etc., as well as in biology, economics, genetics, physics, and sociology. However, in its purest sense probability is a genuine part of pure mathematics.

In this chapter we shall be concerned with the elementary applications of probability in problems related to gambling, because of their general interest. Before becoming involved in probability we shall need to develop some counting techniques.

6.2 Counting Problems

If A, B, and C are the names of three towns, and there are 3 roads from A to B and 2 roads from B to C, how many roads are there from A to C via B? If we draw a figure to represent this, such as Fig. 6.1, we find

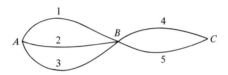

FIGURE 6.1.

If we number the roads as indicated in the figure, we can list the possible routes as

$$14, \quad 15, \quad 24, \quad 25, \quad 34, \quad 35$$

and we count 6, which is our answer. If, on the other hand, we use a *tree diagram* (such as Fig. 6.2) to represent the situation, we have

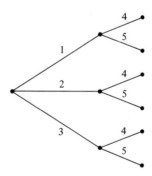

FIGURE 6.2.

and again count 6 different routes.

If there were m roads from A to B and n roads from B to C, then it should be clear (visualizing either a road or a tree diagram) that there would be $m \cdot n$ routes from A to C via B.

Another counting problem related to the preceding one is given as follows: If basket X contains m objects and basket Y contains n objects, in how many ways can we choose an object from basket X and an object from basket Y? Since we can perform the first act in m ways and the second act in n ways, it should be clear that both acts can be performed in $m \cdot n$ ways—just as if roads were being selected, as in the previous example. This consideration now leads us to a fundamental principle.

FUNDAMENTAL PRINCIPLE OF COUNTING

If the first choice can be made in m different ways, and the second choice can be made in n different ways, then both choices can be made in $m \cdot n$ different ways.

Problem Set 6.2

1. Bob has four sport shirts and three pairs of slacks. Assuming that he can wear any combination of these, how many different outfits of one shirt and one pair of slacks can he assemble?

2. How many three-letter "words" may be formed from the set $V = \{a, e, i, o, u\}$ if (a) no letter may be used more than once, (b) repetition of letters is permitted?

3. Florence has five dresses, three hats, and four pairs of shoes. Assuming that she can wear any combination of these, how many different outfits of one dress, one hat, and one pair of shoes can she assemble?

4. If a baseball team has six pitchers and four catchers, how many different batteries consisting of a pitcher and a catcher can be selected?

5. Show, by means of a tree diagram, the number of different methods of traveling from New York to Los Angeles, via Chicago, if you can go from New York to Chicago by one train or one plane and from Chicago to Los Angeles by one train, one plane, or one bus.

6. How many different two-digit numbers may be formed from the set of digits $D = \{1, 2, 3, 4, 5\}$ if repetition of digits is allowed? How many numbers of two different digits can be formed from the set D?

7. The Superior Swim Club has 12 members. How many different sets of officers consisting of a president, vice-president, and secretary-treasurer can it form? (Assume that no member can hold more than one of these three offices.)

8. How many five-digit numbers can be formed using the ten decimal digits if zero is not to be used as the first digit?

9. How many two-digit even numbers can be formed from the set $I = \{1, 2, 3, \ldots, 9\}$?

10. How many license plates can be made using a letter from our alphabet followed by three decimal digits if the first digit must not be zero? How many are possible if the first digit must not be a zero and no digit may be used more than once?

11. In a certain so-called combination lock there are 50 different positions. To open the lock you move to a certain number in one direction, then to a different number in the opposite direction, and finally to a third number in the original direction. What is the total number of such combinations:
    (a) If the first turn must be clockwise?
    *(b) If the first turn may be either clockwise or counterclockwise?

12. If x coins are tossed, in how many ways can they come up if $x =$ (a) 2, (b) 3, (c) 4, (d) 5, (e) m?

13. If x dice are tossed, in how many ways can they come up if $x =$ (a) 2, (b) 3, (c) 4, (d) m?

14. A test consists of ten true-false questions. How many different sets of answers can be given?

15. Consider a situation in which n choices are to be made. If choice 1 can be made in m_1 ways, choice 2 can be made in m_2 ways, . . . , and choice n can be made in m_n ways, in how many different ways can all n choices be made?

6.3 Permutations

The constitution of Club X states that "none of its members is permitted to hold more than one office." If Club X has 5 members and we want to know how many ways a president and vice-president can be chosen, we observe that the president can be chosen in 5 different ways, and after he is chosen the vice-president can be chosen in 4 different ways. Therefore, by the Fundamental Principle of Counting we find that both can be chosen in 5 · 4, or 20 ways. If we call the club members A, B, C, D, E, then the 20 possible selections can be listed as follows:

	BA	CA	DA	EA
AB		CB	DB	EB
AC	BC		DC	EC
AD	BD	CD		ED
AE	BE	CE	DE	

We note that the order is important here, since *AB* means *A* is president and *B* is vice-president—whereas *BA* means *B* is president and *A* is vice-president. An arrangement in which the order is significant is called a *permutation*. We will now state this concept more precisely.

DEF 6.3.1

If we have a set of *n* objects and want to arrange *r* of them in some order on a straight line, then each such arrangement is called a *permutation of the n objects taken r at a time*. The number of permutations of *n* distinct things taken *r* at a time will be denoted by $_nP_r$.

From the preceding example, we observe that the number of ways of selecting a president and vice-president from a club with 5 members is

$$_5P_2 = 5 \cdot 4 = 20.$$

The number of ways of electing a president, vice-president, and secretary from Club *X* is

$$_5P_3 = 5 \cdot 4 \cdot 3 = 60.$$

Similarly, Club *X* can select a president, vice-president, secretary, and treasurer in

$$_5P_4 = 5 \cdot 4 \cdot 3 \cdot 2 = 120$$

ways; and a president, vice-president, secretary, treasurer, and historian in

$$_5P_5 = 5 \cdot 4 \cdot 3 \cdot 2 \cdot 1 = 120$$

ways.

We can now observe that

$$_nP_r = n(n - 1)(n - 2) \cdots (n - r + 1)$$

and

$$_nP_n = n(n - 1)(n - 2) \cdots 1.$$

Since $_nP_n$ occurs frequently in mathematical discussions, a special symbol is given to it. It is written *n*! and is called *n factorial*. Thus

$$n! = {_nP_n} = n(n - 1)(n - 2) \cdots 1.$$

In particular,

$$3! = 3 \cdot 2 \cdot 1 = 6,$$
$$4! = 4 \cdot 3 \cdot 2 \cdot 1 = 24,$$
$$5! = 5 \cdot 4 \cdot 3 \cdot 2 \cdot 1 = 120, \text{ etc.}$$

Problem Set 6.3

1. Evaluate:
   (a) $5!$.
   (b) $\dfrac{8!}{6!}$.
   (c) $\dfrac{11!}{7!}$.
   (d) $_7P_2$.
   (e) $_7P_3$.
   (f) $_{10}P_1$.
   (g) $_{10}P_3$.
   (h) $_{10}P_{10}$.

2. Find the number of different arrangements of the set of letters $V = \{a, e, i, o, u\}$ if they are taken (a) two at a time, (b) five at a time.

3. Find the number of four-digit numbers that can be formed using the digits 1, 2, 3, 4, 5 if no digit may be used more than once. How many of these numbers will be even?

4. Find the number of different signals that can be formed by running up three flags on a flagpole, one above the other, if seven different flags are available.

5. Find the number of different ways that a disc jockey can arrange a musical program of seven selections.

6. Find the number of different ways that a manager of a nine-man baseball team can arrange his batting order.

7. Find:
   $$_nP_r \times (n - r)!$$

*8. Give a reasonable definition for $_nP_0$. **HINT:** See Problem 7.

9. We observe that

   $$4! = 4 \cdot 3 \cdot 2 \cdot 1 = 4 \cdot 3!$$
   $$3! = 3 \cdot 2 \cdot 1 = 3 \cdot 2!$$
   $$2! = 2 \cdot 1 = 2 \cdot 1!.$$

   Thus $1! = 1$. If this procedure is continued, we have $1! = 1 \cdot 0!$. How should $0!$ be defined? Why?

6.4 Combinations

Let us now return to Club X consisting of A, B, C, D, E, and recall that when we were counting the number of ways of choosing a president and vice-president, the selection AB was not the same as BA. Therefore the order of the arrangement was significant, and this led us to the concept of *permutation*. If we now want to find the number of ways in which a committee of two can be selected from Club X, we return to the list we made earlier (in Section 6.3) when we were interested in selecting a president and vice-president, and observe that AB and BA represent exactly the same committee. In fact, each committee is listed twice. Therefore a committee of two can be selected in

$$\frac{5 \cdot 4}{2} = 10$$

ways. We also observe that order has no real significance when we are dealing with committees. When the order of an arrangement is irrelevant, we call the arrangement a *combination*. We will now state this concept in a more formal way.

DEF 6.4.1

If a set of r objects is chosen from a set of n objects, *without regard to order*, the set is called a *combination of n things taken r at a time*. The number of combinations of n distinct things taken r at a time will be denoted by $_nC_r$. (We note that the symbol

$$\binom{n}{r}$$

is commonly used in place of $_nC_r$.)

Now, from the preceding example, we can say that the number of committees of 2 which can be chosen from a club with 5 members is

$$_5C_2 = \frac{5 \cdot 4}{2} = 10.$$

If we want to select a committee of 3, we observe that any such committee (e.g., ACD) can be converted into $3!$ different permutations (e.g., ACD, ADC, CAD, CDA, DAC, DCA) and therefore the committee of 3 can be chosen in

$$_5C_3 = \frac{_5P_3}{3!} = \frac{5 \cdot 4 \cdot 3}{3!} = 10$$

ways. At first one may be surprised that we arrive at the same answer when selecting a committee of 2 or 3, but on further investigation we observe that when we are choosing a committee of 3 we are simultaneously omitting the remaining 2 members—and since we can select 2 in the same number of ways as we can omit 2 (or select 3), it should be clear that the answers to these two seemingly different counting problems must be the same.

We further observe that a committee of 4 can be selected from Club X in

$$_5C_4 = \frac{_5P_4}{4!} = \frac{5 \cdot 4 \cdot 3 \cdot 2}{4!} = 5$$

ways (which is the same as the number of ways of selecting a committee of 1), and that a committee of 5 can be selected from Club X in

$$_5C_5 = \frac{_5P_5}{5!} = 1$$

way.

In order to develop a formula for $_nC_r$, we note that each combination of r objects gives rise to $r!$ permutations and therefore we have

$$_nP_r = [_nC_r] \cdot r!$$

or, equivalently,

$$_nC_r = \frac{_nP_r}{r!},$$

as can be verified in each of the preceding examples.

Problem Set 6.4

In Problems 1 to 9 state whether the question involves a permutation or a combination, and then answer the question.

1. The 20 members of the Smashing Tennis Club are to play on a certain Saturday evening. In how many ways can pairs be selected for playing singles?

2. Students taking a certain examination are required to answer 4 out of 8 questions. In how many ways can a student select the 4 questions that he tries to answer?

3. In how many ways can 7 people line up at a single theater ticket window?

4. How many lines are determined by 10 points if no 3 of these points lie on the same straight line?

5. In how many ways can a group of 9 boys be selected from a class of 20 boys?

6. How many different hands can be dealt from a deck of 52 bridge cards if each hand contains 4 cards?

7. In how many different ways may 5 guests be seated in the 5 seats of a six-passenger car after the driver is seated?

8. In how many ways can 4 pictures be arranged with one in each of 4 given places on the walls of a room?

°9. In how many different ways can 8 students be divided into 2 groups of students?

10. Evaluate the following:

(a) $\dfrac{6!}{4!2!}$.

(b) $\dfrac{10!}{4!6!}$.

(c) $_7C_3$.

(d) $_7C_4$.

(e) $_8C_3$.

(f) $_8C_5$.

(g) $_{11}C_2$.

(h) $_{11}C_9$.

11. List the $_3P_2$ permutations of the elements of the set $\{a, b, c\}$. Then identify the permutations that represent the same combinations and find $_3C_2$.

12. List the $_4P_3$ permutations of the elements of the set $\{p, q, r, s\}$. Then identify the permutations that represent the same combinations and find $_4C_3$.

13. List the elements of each of the $_4C_3$ combinations for the set $\{w, x, y, z\}$. Then match each of these combinations with an appropriate $_4C_1$ combination for the same set; and thereby illustrate the fact that $_4C_3 = {_4C_1}$.

14. True-False
   Let n represent a counting number.
   (a) $_nC_1 = {_nP_1} = n$.
   (b) $_nC_n = 1$.
   (c) $_nP_n = n!$
   (d) If $n > 3$, then $_nC_3 = {_nC_{n-3}}$.
   (e) $_nP_3 = 6 \cdot [_nC_3]$.

*15. If n is any counting number, give a reasonable interpretation for $_nC_0$. What numerical value should be assigned to $_nC_0$?

16. Evaluate $_3C_0$, $_3C_1$, $_3C_2$, $_3C_3$, and check that the sum of these combinations is 2^3, which happens to be the total number of subsets that can be formed from a set of three elements. Is this just a coincidence?

17. Evaluate $_5C_0$, $_5C_1$, $_5C_2$, $_5C_3$, $_5C_4$, $_5C_5$, and then check the sum as in Problem 16.

*18. If n is any counting number, use the results of Problems 16 and 17 to guess the answer to the following question:

$$_nC_0 + {_nC_1} + {_nC_2} + {_nC_3} + \cdots + {_nC_{n-1}} + {_nC_n} = ?$$

Prove your answer.

19. How many sums of money (include the case of no money) can be selected from a set of coins consisting of a penny, a nickel, a dime, a quarter, and a half-dollar?

20. Joe has a penny, a nickel, a dime, a quarter, and a half-dollar in his pocket. In how many different ways can he give a tip if he wishes to use exactly two coins?

21. A class consists of 10 boys and 12 girls. How many different committees of four can be selected from the class if each committee is to consist of two boys and two girls?

22. In how many ways can a hand of 13 cards be selected from a bridge deck of 52 cards?

23. In how many ways can one choose 3 books to read from a set of 7 books?

24. Explain why a so-called *combination* lock should really be called a *permutation* lock.

25. Urn A contains 5 balls and urn B contains 10 balls. In how many ways can 10 balls be selected if 3 are to be drawn from urn A and 7 from urn B?

26. An urn contains 7 black and 3 white balls. In how many ways can 4 balls be selected from this urn? How many of these selections will include exactly 3 black balls?

°27. Give an algebraic proof that $_nC_r = {_n}C_{n-r}$.

°28. Use the definition

$$\binom{n}{r} = \frac{n!}{r!(n-r)!}$$

to prove that

$$\binom{n}{r} = \binom{n-1}{r-1} + \binom{n-1}{r}.$$

29. Try to find a relationship between the combinatorial coefficients $_nC_r$ and the following *Pascal triangle*.

$$
\begin{array}{ccccccccc}
 & & & & 1 & & & & \\
 & & & 1 & & 1 & & & \\
 & & 1 & & 2 & & 1 & & \\
 & 1 & & 3 & & 3 & & 1 & \\
1 & & 4 & & 6 & & 4 & & 1
\end{array}
$$

30. After you guess the pattern in the Pascal triangle given in Problem 29, write down the next two lines.

°31. A basic formula in algebra is the *binomial formula*, which states

$$(a + b)^n = (_nC_0)a^n + (_nC_1)a^{n-1}b + (_nC_2)a^{n-2}b^2 + \cdots + (_nC_n)b^n.$$

(a) Establish the binomial formula when

$$n = 2, 3, \text{ and } 4.$$

(b) Try to prove the binomial formula when n is any counting number by taking the following three steps:
   (1) Note $(a + b)^n = (a + b)(a + b) \cdots (a + b)$, where there are n factors in the right-hand member.
   (2) Observe $(x + y)(z + w) = xz + xw + yz + yw$, and generalize.
   (3) Use the definition for $_nC_r$.

32. Use the binomial formula given in Problem 31 to solve Problem 18.

6.5 Probability

If a normal coin is tossed, there are two possible outcomes: head (H) or tail (T), both of which are equally likely. Therefore, the probability that it comes up H would appear to be 1 out of 2, or $\frac{1}{2}$.

If a normal die (i.e., a cube in which the faces are numbered 1, 2, 3, 4, 5, 6, respectively) is tossed, we recognize that it can come up in six possible

ways, namely, 1, 2, 3, 4, 5, or 6, all of which are equally likely. Therefore
the probability that it comes up

(1) 5 would appear to be 1 out of 6, or $\frac{1}{6}$.
(2) An even number would appear to be 3 out of 6, or $\frac{3}{6} = \frac{1}{2}$.
(3) 7 would appear to be 0 out of 6, or $\frac{0}{6} = 0$.
(4) Less than 7 would appear to be 6 out of 6, or $\frac{6}{6} = 1$.

The preceding illustrations lead us to the following definition.

DEF 6.5.1

Let $U = \{e_1, e_2, \ldots, e_t\}$ be a set of given events, all of which are equally
likely to occur, and let E be any set of events that forms a subset of U(i.e.,
$E \subseteq U$). Then the probability that (an element in) E occurs relative to U
is the ratio of the number of elements in E (which will be denoted by s
for *success*) to t (for *total*). More formally we write

$$P(E) = \frac{n(E)}{n(U)} = \frac{s}{t},$$

where $P(E)$ is called *the probability of E*. Alternatively stated, $P(E)$ is the
ratio of the number of ways in which E can succeed to the total number
of ways in which the event can occur.

We observe that $P(E)$ must always lie between 0 and 1. If $P(E) = 0$, E cannot
occur. For example, the probability of selecting a white ball from a bag of
black balls is zero. If $P(E) = 1$, the success of E is inevitable. For example,
the probability of selecting a black ball from a bag of black balls is 1. Also,
since

$$E \cup E' = U,$$

we have

$$P(E \cup E') = P(U) = \frac{n(U)}{n(U)} = \frac{t}{t} = 1.$$

From this we can conclude that

$$P(E) + P(E') = 1$$

[since

$$P(E) + P(E') = \frac{n(E)}{n(U)} + \frac{n(E')}{n(U)} = \frac{n(E) + n(E')}{n(U)}$$

$$= \frac{n(E \cup E')}{n(U)} = P(E \cup E')].$$

We will now gather the preceding results.

THEOREM 6.5.1   *Using the symbols of Def. 6.5.1,*
(a) $0 \le P(E) \le 1$.
(b) $P(E) = 0$ *iff E cannot occur (i.e., $E = \emptyset$).*

(c) $P(E) = 1$ *iff* E must *occur* (*i.e.*, $E = U$).
(d) $P(E) + P(E') = 1$.

EXAMPLE 1
Problem:
If 3 normal coins are tossed, find the probability of 2 heads and 1 tail.

Solution:
The first coin can fall in 2 different ways, H or T. For each way the first coin falls, the second coin can fall H or T, and for each way the first two coins fall, the third coin can fall H or T. Therefore by the Fundamental Principle of Counting the three coins can fall in $2 \cdot 2 \cdot 2 = 8$ different ways. The following tree diagram can be useful in listing the possible outcomes.

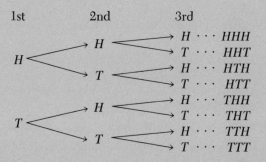

Thus

$$U = \{HHH, HHT, HTH, HTT, THH, THT, TTH, TTT\}$$

and

$$E = \{HHT, HTH, THH\},$$

and therefore

$$P(E) = \frac{n(E)}{n(U)} = \frac{s}{t} = \frac{3}{8},$$

which is the required probability.

EXAMPLE 2   Chevalier de Méré's First Bet
The Chevalier's original bet was that he would obtain at least one six in 4 tosses of a die. Therefore,

$$U = \{\text{outcomes}\,|\,\text{a die is tossed 4 times}\},$$
$$E = \{\text{outcomes}\,|\,\text{at least one six occurs}\},$$
$$E' = \{\text{outcomes}\,|\,\text{no six occurs}\}.$$

Since there are 6 possible outcomes on each toss, there will be $6 \times 6 \times 6 \times 6 = 1{,}296$ possible outcomes when 4 tosses are made (by the Fundamental Principle of Counting). Thus

$$n(U) = t = 1{,}296.$$

We now note that on each toss *no sixes* are obtained in 5 ways (i.e., 1, 2, 3, 4, or 5); hence there will be $5 \times 5 \times 5 \times 5 = 625$ possible ways for *no sixes* to occur in 4 tosses. Therefore $n(E') = 625$ and

$$P(E') = \frac{n(E')}{n(U)} = \frac{625}{1{,}296} \doteq .48$$

(where $\doteq$ is translated "is approximately equal to"). Now by Theorem 6.5.1(d) we have

$$P(E) = 1 - P(E') \doteq 1 - .48 = .52.$$

Thus the Chevalier had better than a 50–50 chance of winning—and he did win!

EXAMPLE 3   Chevalier de Méré's Second Bet
The Chevalier's second bet was that he would obtain at least one double-six in 24 tosses of a pair of dice. Therefore,

$$U = \{\text{outcomes} \mid \text{a pair of dice is tossed 24 times}\},$$
$$E = \{\text{outcomes} \mid \text{at least one double-six occurs}\},$$
$$E' = \{\text{outcomes} \mid \text{no double-six occurs}\}.$$

Since there are $6 \times 6 = 36$ possible outcomes on each toss, there will be 36^{24} possible outcomes when 24 tosses are made (by the Fundamental Principle of Counting). Thus

$$n(U) = t = 36^{24}.$$

We note that on each toss no double-six occurs in 35 ways; hence there are 35^{24} possible ways for no double-six to occur in 24 tosses. Therefore $n(E') = 35^{24}$ and a calculating machine reveals that

$$P(E') = \frac{n(E')}{n(U)} = \frac{35^{24}}{36^{24}} \doteq .51.$$

Now by Theorem 6.5.1(d) we have

$$P(E) = 1 - P(E') \doteq 1 - .51 = .49,$$

which is less than half. Therefore in the long run, the Chevalier *should* lose more often than he wins—and he did! Thus although the two bets sounded equivalent, they were not, and some mathematical analysis would have saved the Chevalier a great deal of money—but, as Pascal pointed out, de Méré was no mathematician!

Problem Set 6.5

1. A single card is selected from a deck of 52 bridge cards. What is the probability that it is (a) a spade, (b) not a spade, (c) an ace, (d) an ace or a spade, (e) a red card?

2. A single die is tossed. What is the probability it will come up
   (a) An even number?
   (b) An odd number?
   (c) A number greater than 3?
   (d) A number less than 5?
   (e) A number different from 5?
   (f) The number 7?
   (g) A number different from 7?
   (h) An even number or a number greater than 3?

3. The probability of obtaining all heads in a single toss of three coins is $\frac{1}{8}$. What is the probability that not all three coins are heads on such a toss?

4. What is the probability that the next person you meet was not born on a Sunday?

5. A box contains 2 red and 3 white balls. If two balls are drawn in succession without replacement, find the probability that
   (a) Both balls are red.
   (b) Both balls are white.
   (c) The first ball is red.
   (d) The first ball is red and the second ball is white.
   (e) One ball is red and the other is white.
   (f) One ball is white and the other is green.

6. If three coins are tossed, find the probability that
   (a) All three coins are heads.
   (b) At least two coins are heads.
   (c) At most one coin is tails.

7. If four coins are tossed, find the probability that
   (a) All four coins are heads.
   (b) At least three coins are heads.
   (c) At most two coins are tails.

8. If a pair of dice is tossed, find the probability that
   (a) The number on the first die is 2.
   (b) The number 2 is on both dice.

(c) The same number is on both dice.
(d) The sum of the numbers obtained is 11.
(e) The sum of the numbers obtained is not 11.
(f) The sum of the numbers obtained is 7.
(g) The sum of the numbers obtained is not 7.
(h) The number on one die is twice the number on the other die.
(i) The number on one die is three more than the number on the other die.
(j) The product of the numbers obtained is 17.
(k) The product of the numbers obtained is less than 40.

*9. Three cards are in a box. One is red on both sides, one is white on both sides, and one is red on one side and white on the other. A card is drawn at random and placed on a table. It has a red side showing. What is the probability that the side not showing is also red? HINT: The answer is not $\frac{1}{2}$.

10. A bag contains 3 red, 2 black, and 5 yellow balls. Find the probability that a ball drawn at random will be red or black.

11. A single die is tossed. What is the probability that either an odd number or a number greater than 3 appears?

12. Urn *A* contains 3 white and 5 red balls. Urn *B* contains 4 white and 3 red balls. One ball is drawn from each urn. What is the probability that they are both red?

13. Two cards are selected in succession, without replacement, from an ordinary bridge deck of 52 cards. What is the probability that they are both aces?

14. A single card is drawn from a deck of 52 bridge cards. Find the probability that the card selected is
(a) An ace or a king.
(b) A spade or a heart.
(c) A spade or a king.
(d) A spade and a king.
(e) A heart or a king or a queen.

15. A coin is tossed 5 times. What is the probability that all 5 tosses are heads?

*16. A coin is tossed 5 times. What is the probability that at least one head is obtained? HINT: First find the probability of getting no heads.

17. A bag contains 3 red balls and 7 white balls. (a) If one ball is drawn at random, what is the probability that it is white? (b) If two balls are drawn at random, what is the probability that they are both white?

18. True-False
    (a) $P(U) = 1$.
    (b) $P(\emptyset) = 0$.
    (c) $P(A \cup B) = P(A) + P(B)$.
    (d) $P(A \cup B) = P(A) + P(B) - P(A \cap B)$.

6.6 Odds and Mathematical Expectation

In games of chance, such as rolling dice or a horse race, the *odds* that a certain event will occur is usually given, rather than the probability. For example, if a single die is tossed, and we want to know, "What are the *odds* in favor of tossing a 4?" we observe that the possibilities include 1 favorable and 5 unfavorable outcomes—and therefore we say *odds in favor* are 1 to 5, or $\frac{1}{5}$, and odds against are 5 to 1, or $\frac{5}{1}$.

DEF 6.6.1

The *odds in favor* of an event is the quotient obtained when the probability that the event will occur is divided by the probability that the event will not occur. (Thus the odds in favor of an event that occurs in equally likely ways is the ratio of the number of favorable ways to the number of unfavorable ways.) The *odds against* an event is the reciprocal of the odds in favor of the event (where the reciprocal of a/b is b/a).

EXAMPLE 1

If two coins are tossed, what are the odds in favor of obtaining two heads? What are the odds against this?

Solution: Since $U = \{HH, HT, TH, TT\}$, $E = \{HH\}$, and $E' = \{HT, TH, TT\}$, we have $P(E) = \frac{1}{4}$ and $P(E') = \frac{3}{4}$. Therefore the odds in favor is $\frac{1}{3}$ and the odds against is $\frac{3}{1}$.

Suppose you are tossing two coins and someone says, "I will give you $3 each time you obtain two heads." How much should you be willing to pay so that you would expect to come out even in the long run? According to the preceding example, you *should* get two heads once every 4 tosses—and therefore should be willing to pay 75 cents for each toss, in order to break even in the long run. In this case, we will call 75 cents the *mathematical expectation*, for it represents the amount you can reasonably expect to win on each toss (i.e., $\frac{1}{4} \times 3$). We will now give a formal definition.

DEF 6.6.2

If an event has n possible outcomes with probabilities $p_1, p_2, \ldots, p_n$ having respective payoff amounts of $a_1, a_2, \ldots, a_n$, then the *mathematical expectation* (or *expectation*) for this event is defined by:

$$\text{M.E.} \equiv p_1 a_1 + p_2 a_2 + \cdots + p_n a_n.$$

EXAMPLE 2

Suppose that you play a game in which you are to toss a coin twice and are to receive 10 cents if two heads are obtained, 5 cents if one head is obtained, and nothing if zero heads are obtained. What is your expected value in this game?

Solution: By virtue of Example 1, we observe that the probabilities of obtaining two, one, and zero heads are $\frac{1}{4}, \frac{1}{2}$, and $\frac{1}{4}$, respectively. Therefore the expected value in cents is given by

$$\text{M.E.} = (\tfrac{1}{4} \times 10) + (\tfrac{1}{2} \times 5) + (\tfrac{1}{4} \times 0) = 5.$$

This solution may be interpreted in different ways. For one thing, it is the price you should be willing to pay for the privilege of playing this game. It may also be interpreted as the average amount of winnings per game that you may expect, if you play a large number of games.

Problem Set 6.6

1. Three coins are tossed. What are the odds in favor of (a) no heads, (b) 1 head, (c) 2 heads, (d) 3 heads, (e) 4 heads?

2. Three coins are tossed. What are the odds against (a) no heads, (b) 1 head, (c) 2 heads, (d) 3 heads, (e) 4 heads?

3. A marble is drawn at random from a sack containing 2 red, 3 green, and 4 blue marbles. What are the odds in favor of (a) red, (b) green, (c) blue?

4. A card is chosen at random from an ordinary bridge deck of 52 playing cards. What are the odds against the card being an ace?

5. If the odds in favor of Porcupine winning the Kentucky Derby are 6 to 5, what is the probability of Porcupine (a) winning, (b) losing?

6. If two coins are tossed, what is the expected number of heads?

7. Phil tosses two coins and receives $1 if both fall heads. What is his M.E.?

8. Five hundred tickets are sold for a raffle in which the grand prize is $1,000. (a) What is a fair price for a single ticket? (b) If Carl buys 10 tickets, what is his M.E.?

9. A test consists of 100 multiple-choice questions, and each question has four answers, only one of which is correct. What is the expected score for a student who is completely unprepared and selects the answers at random if x points are given for each correct answer and y points are given for each incorrect answer when (a) $x = 3$, $y = -1$; (b) $x = 1$, $y = 0$; (c) $x = y = 1$.

*10. Gordon wins the number of dollars equal to the number shown on a die if this number is even, but loses the number of dollars equal to the number on the die if this number is odd. Find his M.E.

*11. Lydia and Ralph are pitching coins. Lydia makes Ralph the following bet, "I will toss 3 coins and will pay you 5 cents every time they all fall heads if you will pay me 1 cent each time they do not." Is this a fair bet? Why?

12. Eugene chooses a marble at random from a box that contains 1 red, 4 green, and 5 blue marbles. He is paid 30 cents for red, 20 cents for green, and 10 cents for blue. (a) What is his M.E.? (b) What is a fair price to pay for playing this game?

13. There are three identical boxes on a table. One is empty, one contains 5 cents, and one contains 25 cents. Don selects one of these boxes and keeps its contents. What is his M.E.?

14. There are 4 pennies, 3 nickels, 2 dimes, and 1 quarter in a sack. If Dick selects a coin from the sack and keeps it, what is his M.E.?

CHAPTER 7

Statistics

7.1 What Is Statistics?

Disraeli said, "There are three kinds of lies: lies, damned lies, and statistics." This statement may prompt some readers to ask, "How is it possible to convert true numbers into anything but the truth?" We shall see.

When one hears the word *statistics* he may visualize a collection of numbers together with one or more special numbers (e.g., "averages") which serve to characterize the collection. Since the appearance of numbers tends to hypnotize many people, they are often accepted without question. For who questions that which looks scientific? However, the curious person may have the courage to ask, "What do the special numbers mean?" or, "How were the special numbers obtained?" or, "Do the special numbers really reflect the true situation?" These questions lie at the heart of statistics, for the primary goal of the applied statistician is to obtain facts from figures and to interpret them.

In our society, statistics has played important roles in the fields of science, education, politics, social science, medicine, government, labor, business, sports, insurance, and agriculture. For example,

(1) Schools must have statistics concerning birth rates in order to plan for the future.

(2) A clothing manufacturer needs to know which sizes will be in most demand.

(3) The government needs to know the distribution of incomes of people in order to estimate income from income taxes.

(4) Graduate schools want to know the credit point averages of all applicants.

(5) Before accepting a pastorate, a minister may want to know the "average" income of people attending the church.

(6) A baseball manager wants to know the earned-run average of a pitcher before deciding to draft him.

114]

(7) Citizens need to know when the air-pollution index has reached a dangerous level.

(8) Pollsters need to be able to correctly predict the outcome of an election by polling a sample of the population. Hence, they must be able to find a "representative sample."

(9) Labor unions are very much concerned about the cost of living index.

(10) Instructors may want to know how grades correlate with I.Q. or some other measure of "intelligence."

(11) A student may want to know the "average" grades given by instructors before deciding which course to take.

We shall now peek into the file of the Chief of The Society of Statistical Affairs in order to become acquainted with some statistical problems (or case studies) that are registered there and to help understand the role of the applied statistician.

PROBLEM 1

A statistician has revealed the following information concerning the average number of passengers per car in the years 1950, 1960, and 1970. In 1950 it was 3.5, in 1960 it was 2.5, and in 1970 it was 1.5. If this trend continues, (a) Will every other car be empty as it goes by in 1980? (b) What will happen in 1990?

PROBLEM 2

Four different therapeutic pills called R, S, T, U, produced by four different companies, were tested by scientists and were found to be equally effective. If these therapeutic pills are the only ones on the market, is it reasonable for the producer of pill U to advertise, "Scientists have proved that there is no therapeutic pill on the market that is more effective than pill U"?

PROBLEM 3

A news bulletin stated, "The rate of increase in crime is tapering off, for this year it is only 11 per cent more than last year." Does this mean that crime is decreasing?

PROBLEM 4

If the cost of clothing is up 30 per cent, the cost of food is up 30 per cent, and the cost of housing is up 40 per cent, can we conclude that the cost of living on these items is up 100 per cent?

PROBLEM 5

A statistician observed, "The class had a 100 per cent increase in enrollment and therefore we can conclude it must be a very large class." Is this conclusion justified?

PROBLEM 6
It has been found that grades for athletic team members at Mystic University are always below average. Can we therefore conclude that these athletic team members do not have enough time to study?

PROBLEM 7
It has been shown that more auto accidents occur in clear weather than in foggy weather. Does this mean that clear-weather driving is more dangerous than foggy-weather driving?

PROBLEM 8
Two groups of students at Bubblegum University are trying to learn how the students feel about the question, "Do you believe that the university should award football scholarships?" Groups A and B both polled several students and returned with very different results. Group A found that 90 per cent of the students favored the idea, whereas group B found that 80 per cent of the students were opposed to the idea. How can this be?

PROBLEM 9
The Phenom Car Co. advertises, "Of all the Phenom Cars sold in the last 50 years, 90 per cent are still on the road." If the Phenom Car is known to have a maximum life expectancy of six months and the advertisement is a legitimate one, how can this situation be explained?

PROBLEM 10
It was reported that all the students failed a certain course. Is this necessarily a serious situation?

PROBLEM 11
In 1936 the *Literary Digest* polled 10 million people (selected mostly from telephone directories or lists of automobile owners) in order to predict the presidential election for that year. On the basis of their poll, they predicted that the Republican candidate Alfred Landon would win with 57 per cent of the vote—but it turned out that the Democratic candidate Franklin D. Roosevelt won an overwhelming victory with more than 62 per cent of the vote. How could this happen?

The Chief was able to find a plausible answer to each of the preceding problems, but we do not want to insult the intelligence of the reader by presenting his solutions here. Instead, we shall challenge the reader to find his own solutions.

Problem Set 7.1

1. Give answers to each of the questions raised in the preceding eleven problems from the Chief's file.

2. Determine which of the following statistical arguments are valid. Explain.

   (a) Last year 576 men and 143 women drivers were involved in auto accidents in the Town of Thistle. Therefore, women were safer drivers than men in Thistle last year.

   (b) Figures showed that retail sales in April of 1971 were higher than those in April of 1970. This is a good sign for business in 1971.

   (c) Fifty years ago there was one hospital bed for every 200 persons, and today the ratio is better than 1 to 100. Therefore, illness has greatly increased in the past 50 years.

   (d) The number of unemployed people in the Village of Wrong Way has been steadily growing smaller. Therefore, business in the Village of Wrong Way has been improving.

   (e) The number of people on welfare in the Town of Tinkers has increased steadily in the past few years. Therefore, business has been steadily getting worse in that town.

   (f) The ratio of people convicted of crimes to the total population has shown a marked rise in the past 20 years. Hence, there is more crime than formerly.

   (g) More money is spent for automobile parts than for new automobiles. Therefore it is cheaper to buy a new automobile than to buy parts for an old automobile.

7.2 Mean, Median, and Mode

Suppose Bill has the following algebra test scores (listed in numerical order):

$$20, 30, 50, 50, 70, 80, 90, 90, 90, 100$$

and we want to find his "average" or "representative" score. One way of proceeding is to add the scores and then divide by the number of scores. We then find that the "average" called the *mean* (or *arithmetic mean*) is 67. However, the reader may observe that the *middle grade* or *median* is 75, since there are five grades above 75 and five grades below 75. Hence 75 is also an "average." A third "average" is obtained by finding the score which occurs most frequently. This "average," called *mode*, is clearly 90.

Since the word *average* can be interpreted in different ways, we must take great care when using and interpreting this term. We shall now give formal definitions for *mean* (which is commonly called *the average*), *median*, and *mode*.

DEF 7.2.1

If $S = \{x_1, x_2, \ldots, x_n\}$ is a set of real numbers arranged in numerical order, then

(a)
$$\bar{x} = \frac{x_1 + x_2 + \cdots + x_n}{n}$$

is called the *mean* or *arithmetic mean* or the *average* of S.

(b) The "middle score" is called the *median* of S (i.e., if n is odd it is the middle score; if n is even it is the average of the two middle scores).

(c) The number x_j is called a *mode* of S if no number occurs more frequently than x_j. (Note that there can be more than one mode.)

EXAMPLE 1

The following problem was taken from the file of the Chief of The Society of Statistical Affairs.

Problem:

A housing development in the Village of Vigilante consists of 20 houses, and 10 of them have now been sold. The promoter of this development has advertised, "The average yearly income here is $50,000." However, a taxpayer's committee that is trying to keep the bus fare down claims that the average income is only $4,000. Then an impartial group of Vigilantes attempts to resolve this matter in a fair way—and after many calculations this group concludes that the average is really $7,000. How can this situation be explained if there have been no errors in arithmetic?

Solution:

If the incomes are (in dollars)

(1) 2,000; 2,000; 3,000; 3,000; 4,000; 4,000; 7,000; 7,000; 7,000; 461,000

then the mean is 50,000, the median is 4,000, and the mode is 7,000; and thus we have a solution which explains the apparent dilemma.

We note that the extreme figure, 461,000, has a marked effect on the mean but not on the median or mode. For if 461,000 were omitted, the mean, median, and mode would be 4,333.33, 4,000, and 7,000, respectively. Thus the mean can be misleading!

The reader may have observed that the mean of the set of incomes in (1) could have been computed by grouping the like figures as follows:

(2) $\bar{x} = \dfrac{2{,}000(2) + 3{,}000(2) + 4{,}000(2) + 7{,}000(3) + 461{,}000(1)}{10}.$

We note that each figure is weighted according to the number of times it appears, and therefore it is reasonable to call (2) a *weighted mean*.

EXAMPLE 2
Last semester Frank was enrolled in calculus, physics, English, history, and art with semester hour credits 5, 4, 3, 3, and 1, respectively. If he received an A in both calculus and physics, F in English, C in history, and B in art, we can compute his *credit point average (CPA)* by letting $A = 4, B = 3, C = 2, D = 1, F = 0$ as follows:

$$CPA = \frac{4(5) + 4(4) + 0(3) + 2(3) + 3(1)}{16} = \frac{45}{16} \doteq 2.8.$$

Hence Frank has almost a B average. We note that the CPA average is a weighted mean in which the semester hours are the weights.

Problem Set 7.2

1. Find the mean and median of $S = \{1, 2, \ldots, n\}$ when $n =$ (a) 1, (b) 2, (c) 3, (d) 4, (e) 5, (f) 6, (g) 7, (h) 8, (i) 9, (j) 10, (k) 25, °(l) x.

2. A score of 100 per cent is obtained by each of 18 students in a class of 30 students. Find (a) median, (b) mode, (c) minimum value of the mean.

3. Find an example of a set in which the mean, median, and mode are all equal to 50.

4. The faculty salaries at Goathead University are as follows:

Position	Number	Yearly Salary
Professor	10	16,000
Associate professor	20	12,000
Assistant professor	30	10,000
Instructor	40	6,000

Find
(a) the modal salary, (b) the median salary, (c) the mean of the salaries in the right-hand column, (d) the weighted mean of the salaries (i.e., the average salary of the faculty at Goathead University).

5. A research scientist has revealed that the normal person finds 52° to be the most comfortable temperature. If Fantastic Village has

an average year-round temperature of 52°, can we conclude that a normal person will be comfortable if he lives in Fantastic Village? Explain.

6. The instructors at Dingaling University are rated by their students as follows: A is excellent, B is good, C is fair, D is poor, and F is terrible. Let us assume that A = 4, B = 3, C = 2, D = 1, F = 0, and that ratings of B, C, or D do not reflect any strong feelings on the part of students. If instructors X and Y both have 20 students, X receives 15 A's and 5 F's, and Y receives 20 B's, how would you judge the relative teaching effectiveness of these two instructors?

7. An instructor tells his class he is going to disregard their lowest grade when computing averages. Will this help all members of the class? Explain.

8. An instructor gives a True-False test with 100 questions and tells his students that they will receive one point for each correct answer and lose one point for each incorrect answer (e.g., 90 correct and 10 incorrect means a grade of 80, 50 correct and 50 incorrect means a grade of 0, 30 correct and 50 incorrect means a grade of −20). Is this a fair grading system? Explain.

9. Is it possible to have a class in which there are no students below average? Explain.

*10. Bernice drives 60 miles at an average speed of 30 mph and returns over the same route at an average speed of 60 mph. Find her average speed for the round-trip. HINT: The answer is *not* 45 mph.

11. If each of the following "averages" is to be found, state (i) the "fairest average," and (ii) the reason for your choice.
   (a) The average bill for electric current.
   (b) The average size of women's shoes sold at The Shoe Store.
   (c) The average size of men's hats sold at The Hat Store.
   (d) The average salary for employees in an industry in which two people have salaries at least 100 times that of any of the others.
   (e) The average donation to a college by 1,000 alumni when two are for 500,000 and the remaining 998 range from 10 to 300.
   (f) The average bacteria count of milk from dairies selling milk in town.

12. True–False
    (a) If each of a set of scores is increased by 7, then the mean,
        median, and mode will each be increased by 7.
    (b) If sets S and T have the same number of elements and the same
        mean, median, and mode, then $S = T$.
    (c) A few abnormal values can have a great effect on the mean.
    (d) A few abnormal values do not disturb the median to an appre-
        ciable extent.
    (e) If a test is given to a class of 30, then 15 students will have
        scores above the median.
    (f) If a test is given to a class of 29, then 14 students will have
        scores above the median.
    (g) If a test is given to a class of 31, then 15 students will have
        scores above the mean.
    (h) In the set {1, 2, 3}, the numbers 1, 2, and 3 are all modes.
   °(i) Mathematical expectation can be interpreted as a weighted
        mean.

7.3 Standard Deviation

Let us assume that the Basketball Shoe Company manufactures special
made-to-order shoes for basketball teams with medium-width feet. If the shoe
sizes of team A are

$$6, 7, 8, 9, 10, 10, 10, 12, 14, 14$$

and those of team B are

$$9, 9, 10, 10, 10, 10, 10, 10, 11, 11,$$

then it should be easier for them to accommodate team B; for although teams
A and B both have the same mean, median, and mode size of 10, the sizes
for team A are more variable. Hence, the mean, median, and mode do not
always tell us what we need to know about a set of numbers. Instead it may
be important to have a measure of variability or *dispersion* from the average.

One reasonable measure of dispersion, called *mean deviation* (or MD), is
the average (or mean) of the numerical deviations from the mean. For team
A, these deviations are

$$4, 3, 2, 1, 0, 0, 0, 2, 4, 4,$$

respectively, and hence the MD for team A is $\frac{20}{10} = 2$. For team B, the
deviations from the mean are

$$1, 1, 0, 0, 0, 0, 0, 0, 1, 1,$$

respectively, and hence the MD for team B is $\frac{4}{10} = .4$. It should come as no
surprise that the MD for team B is much less than that for team A.

Although the MD tells us how much, on the average, the numbers in a set deviate from the mean and is easy to calculate, another measure of dispersion, called *standard deviation* (or SD), is more frequently used because of its theoretical importance (which we shall discuss in the next section). In order to find the SD of the set of numbers $\{x_1, x_2, \ldots, x_n\}$ with mean $\bar{x}$, we perform the following steps:

(1) Find the difference of each number from the mean:

$$x_1 - \bar{x}, x_2 - \bar{x}, \ldots, x_n - \bar{x}.$$

(2) Square each:

$$(x_1 - \bar{x})^2, (x_2 - \bar{x})^2, \ldots, (x_n - \bar{x})^2.$$

(3) Add:

$$(x_1 - \bar{x})^2 + (x_2 - \bar{x})^2 + \cdots + (x_n - \bar{x})^2$$

(4) Divide by n:

$$\frac{1}{n}[(x_1 - \bar{x})^2 + (x_2 - \bar{x})^2 + \cdots + (x_n - \bar{x})^2]$$

(5) Take the square root:

$$\text{SD} = \sqrt{\frac{1}{n}[(x_1 - \bar{x})^2 + (x_2 - \bar{x})^2 + \cdots + (x_n - \bar{x})^2]}$$

We note that step (4) yields the *variance* and step (5) yields the SD [where the square root symbol $\sqrt{y}$ represents a positive number or zero such that $(\sqrt{y})^2 = y$ when $y \geq 0$; e.g., $\sqrt{9} = 3$].

If we perform these five steps on the shoe sizes for team A, we find:
(1) $-4, -3, -2, -1, 0, 0, 0, 2, 4, 4.$
(2) $16, 9, 4, 1, 0, 0, 0, 4, 16, 16.$
(3) $66.$
(4) $6.6.$
(5) $\text{SD} = \sqrt{6.6} \doteq 2.6.$

For team B we find:
(1) $-1, -1, 0, 0, 0, 0, 0, 0, 1, 1.$
(2) $1, 1, 0, 0, 0, 0, 0, 0, 1, 1.$
(3) $4.$
(4) $.4.$
(5) $\text{SD} = \sqrt{.4} \doteq .6.$

Problem Set 7.3

1. Suppose an instructor is given a choice of teaching class X or class Y and is given the following I.Q. scores for these classes:

X: 50, 50, 60, 60, 60, 100, 100, 120, 180, 190
Y: 90, 100, 100, 100, 100, 100, 100, 100, 110, 120.

From these scores, find the following for both classes X and Y: (a) mean, (b) median, (c) mode, (d) MD, (e) variance, (f) SD.

2. On the basis of your answers to Problem 1, determine which class would be more challenging to teach. Explain.

*3. If $\bar{x}$ is the mean of $\{x_1, x_2, \ldots, x_n\}$, prove
   (a) $(x_1 - \bar{x}) + (x_2 - \bar{x}) + \cdots + (x_n - \bar{x}) = 0$.
   (b) $(SD)^2 = \dfrac{1}{n}(x_1{}^2 + x_2{}^2 + \cdots + x_n{}^2) - \bar{x}^2$.

4. True–False
   (a) If the MD of a set is zero, then all numbers in the set must be identical.
   (b) If the SD of a set is zero, then all numbers in the set must be identical.
   (c) A smaller SD indicates that the scores tend to be clustered closer to the mean.
   (d) A larger SD indicates that the scores are more widely scattered about the mean.
   *(e) If the mean, median, mode, and SD of a set of five numbers are given, then these five numbers are uniquely determined.

7.4 The Normal Curve

In our society many people have great respect for the concept of normality, because they are afraid of being labeled abnormal. Thus, happily (?), it turns out that most people fall within the normal range of intelligence, height, weight, income, etc. In order to describe the phenomena of normally distributed items, statisticians have invented the normal curve, and the designation *normal* gives it a somewhat supernatural justification. In this section we shall see how it arises and shall discuss some of its properties, uses, and misuses.

If the heights of a large number of "normal" college students are tabulated, we would probably find that most of the students would be in the "average range"—and that relatively few would be extremely tall or extremely short. If we classify the heights of 6,400 male college students into the following seven categories, we might find an "ideal" distribution such as the following:

$$
\begin{array}{ll}
\text{I Extremely short} & 100 \\
\text{II Very short} & 600 \\
\text{III Average short} & 1{,}500 \\
\text{IV Average} & 2{,}000 \\
\text{V Average tall} & 1{,}500 \\
\text{VI Very tall} & 600 \\
\text{VII Extremely tall} & 100 \\
\end{array}
$$

We can picture this distribution by means of a *histogram* or *step-curve*, as in the following figure.

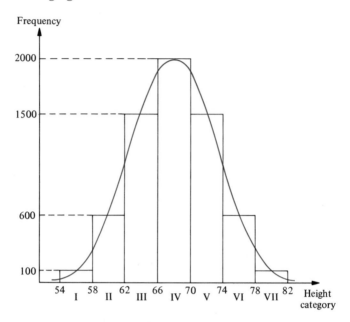

If we now draw a "smooth" (aesthetically appealing) curve passing through the midpoints of the upper edges of the rectangles in the histogram, we obtain a bell-shaped curve like that indicated in the preceding figure, and this curve is an approximation to the normal curve. The *normal curve* represents the distribution of the population (or theoretical universe) from which the sample is imagined to be drawn, and we use the symbols μ and σ (read "mu" and "sigma") to represent the mean and standard deviation, respectively, of this theoretical distribution.

We will assume that the boundary points of the seven categories are as indicated in the preceding figure and that measurements were made to the nearest inch. The following information can now be obtained from the histogram.

(H_1) The mean, median, and mode are all equal to 68 (if it is assumed that all heights are concentrated at the midpoints of the intervals).

(H_2) The histogram is symmetric about a vertical line through 68.

(H_3) If we again assume that all heights are concentrated at the midpoints of the intervals, the SD can be found by grouping like scores as follows:

$$(SD)^2 = \frac{1}{6,400} [200(68 - 56)^2 + 1,200(68 - 60)^2$$

$$+ 3,000(68-64)^2] \doteq 25.$$

Hence, SD = 5 (approximately).

(H_4) Suppose each college man in the survey writes the number of his height category on a ticket and places it in a large container, and that a ticket is chosen at random from this container after it has been thoroughly mixed. It should then be clear that the probabilities for categories I through VII are

$$\frac{1}{64}, \frac{6}{64}, \frac{15}{64}, \frac{20}{64}, \frac{15}{64}, \frac{6}{64}, \frac{1}{64},$$

respectively.

(H_5) Each probability found in (H_4) represents the ratio of the area of a rectangle to the total area of the histogram, e.g., the probability for category II is

$$\frac{600 \cdot 4}{6,400 \cdot 4} = \frac{6}{64}.$$

(H_6) If the base of each rectangle of the histogram were k, instead of 4, the areas of the rectangles would be $100k$, $600k$, etc., and the area of the histogram would be $6,400k$. Hence the probabilities could still be found by dividing the areas of the rectangles by the area of the histogram, e.g., the probability for category II would be

$$\frac{600k}{6,400k} = \frac{6}{64}.$$

Since the normal curve was obtained by assuming a "smooth" (aesthetically appealing) distribution for the heights, we can now make the following observations with regard to the normal curve.

(N_1) The curve is bell-shaped.

(N_2) The *center point*, 68, represents the mean, median, and mode (i.e., $\mu = 68$).

(N_3) The curve is symmetric about a vertical line through the center point.

(N_4) When going further and further away from the center point, the curve gets closer and closer to the horizontal axis, without ever reaching it.

(N_5) A computer can be used to determine the SD from the actual heights in the sample. If this SD = 5, we shall let $\sigma = 5$.

(N_6) The probability that a height chosen at random will be between two given heights of a and b is: the area under the curve from a to b divided by the total area under the curve—and hence it would be convenient if this latter area were unity. **NOTE:** This property follows from (H_6) and the calculus.

From a variety of well-chosen assumptions mathematicians have shown that the equation of the normal curve in the preceding figure is

(1)
$$y = \frac{25,600}{5\sqrt{2\pi}} e^{-\frac{1}{2}z^2}$$

where $z = (x - 68)/5$ is called the *standard score* and indicates the number of standard deviations of height x from the mean (since SD $= 5$), $\pi = 3.14159 \ldots$, and $e = 2.71828 \ldots$ [i.e., $l(e) = 1$ where $l(x)$ is defined in Section 10.9]. The reader should also note that $e^0 = 1$ and $e^{-w} = 1/e^w$.

With the aid of Equation (1), we will now continue to make observations concerning the normal curve. This equation and the calculus can be used to show

(N_7) Approximately 68 per cent of the scores are within one standard deviation of the mean (i.e., between 63 and 73), approximately 95 per cent of the scores are within two standard deviations of the mean (i.e., between 58 and 78), approximately 99.7 per cent of the scores are within three standard deviations of the mean (i.e., between 53 and 83), and approximately 99.98 per cent of the scores are within four standard deviations of the mean (i.e., between 48 and 88).

It should be clear that the normal curve may be applied to a variety of situations, and that each of these situations will have its own mean and its own SD. In order to accommodate all these cases at once, statisticians have developed the *standard form* of the normal curve—which has $\mu = 0$, $\sigma = 1$; and the area under this curve is unity. The equation of the standard form of the normal curve is

$$(2) \qquad\qquad y = \frac{1}{\sqrt{2\pi}} e^{-\frac{1}{2}z^2}$$

where $z = (x - \bar{x})/\text{SD}$ is the "standard score" which indicates the number of standard deviations of x from the mean.

We will now see what happens when the observations for the normal curve are applied to the standard form.

(S_1) The curve is bell-shaped.

(S_2) The *center point*, 0, represents the mean, median, and mode (i.e., $\mu = 0$).

(S_3) The curve is symmetric about a vertical line through the center point.

(S_4) When going further and further away from the center point, the curve gets closer and closer to the horizontal axis, without ever reaching it.

(S_5) $\sigma = 1$.

(S_6) The probability that a score chosen at random will lie between two given scores of z_1 and z_2 is the area under the curve from z_1 to z_2 (since the area under the curve is unity). Hence, it is reasonable to call this curve the *normal probability curve.*

(S_7) Approximately 68 per cent of the scores are within one standard deviation of the mean (i.e., between $z = -1$ and $z = 1$), approximately 95 per cent of the scores are within two standard deviations of the mean (i.e., between $z = -2$ and $z = 2$), approximately 99.7 per cent of the scores are within three standard deviations of the mean (i.e., between $z = -3$ and $z = 3$), and approximately 99.98 per cent of the scores are within four standard deviations of the mean (i.e., between $z = -4$ and $z = 4$).

The preceding properties are illustrated in the following rough graph of the standard form of the normal curve (which henceforth will be called the *normal curve*).

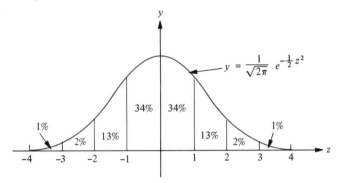

The Normal Curve

The preceding figure helps to illustrate approximate areas under some special portions of the normal curve. In order to obtain more general and detailed results, we will need to have the following table, which was constructed with the aid of the calculus and a computer.

TABLE 7.4.1   Area Under the Normal Curve from 0 to z

z	0	1	2	3	4	5	6	7	8	9
0.	.000	.040	.079	.118	.155	.192	.226	.258	.288	.316
1.	.341	.364	.385	.403	.419	.433	.445	.455	.464	.471
2.	.477	.482	.486	.489	.492	.494	.495	.496	.497	.498
3.	.499	.499	.499	.500	.500	.500	.500	.500	.500	.500

We note that Table 7.4.1 gives more precise results than the preceding graph. For example, it indicates that the area from 0 to 1 is 34.1 per cent, and from 0 to 2 is 47.7 per cent—and hence the area from 1 to 2 is 13.6 per cent.

If we let

(3) $$\phi(z) = \frac{1}{\sqrt{2\pi}} e^{-\frac{1}{2}z^2},$$

then the area under the normal curve from z_1 to z_2 can be represented by the definite integral

(4) $$\int_{z_1}^{z_2} \phi(z)\, dz.$$

This symbol, which is fundamental in the calculus, is read "the integral of fee of z dz from z_1 to z_2." Property (S_6) together with Table 7.4.1 can now be used to answer questions such as the following: Find the probability that a score is

(a) Less than 2 standard deviations from the mean.
(b) More than 2 standard deviations from the mean.
(c) Between 2 and 3 standard deviations from the mean.
(d) Between .4 standard deviations less than the mean and 1.4 standard deviations more than the mean.

The answers to these questions are, respectively:

(a) .477 + .477 = .954 [since symmetry provides that the area from -2 to 0 is the same as the area from 0 to 2; i.e.,

$$\int_{-2}^{2} \phi(z)\,dz = \int_{-2}^{0} \phi(z)\,dz + \int_{0}^{2} \phi(z)\,dz$$

$$= \int_{0}^{2} \phi(z)\,dz + \int_{0}^{2} \phi(z)\,dz].$$

(b) 1 − .954 = .046 (since the total area under the normal curve is 1).
(c) .499 − .477 = .022 [since

$$\int_{2}^{3} \phi(z)\,dz = \int_{0}^{3} \phi(z)\,dz - \int_{0}^{2} \phi(z)\,dz].$$

(d) .155 + .419 = .574 [since

$$\int_{-.4}^{1.4} \phi(z)\,dz = \int_{-.4}^{0} \phi(z)\,dz + \int_{0}^{1.4} \phi(z)\,dz$$

$$= \int_{0}^{.4} \phi(z)\,dz + \int_{0}^{1.4} \phi(z)\,dz].$$

It turns out that 50 per cent of the scores are less than .6745 standard deviations from the mean. On this basis some people label those who are more than .6745 standard deviations from the mean to be "at least slightly abnormal."

We shall now clarify the preceding discussion by means of some practical examples.

EXAMPLE 1
If we are given any distribution that is reasonably symmetrical about its mean and has a single hump in the center, then we often find that we make very little error by assuming that two thirds of the distribution lies less than 1 SD away from the mean, that 95 per cent of the distribution lies less than 2 SD away from the mean, and that less than 1 per cent

of the distribution lies more than 3 SD away from the mean. This is a rough rule, but one which usually works well in practical situations. For example, if the distribution in question is the intelligence of eight-year-olds, as measured by IQ, and we are told only that $\bar{x} = 100$, SD $= 15$, then we might easily picture the distribution as something like the following sketch.

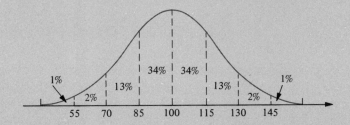

This sketch reflects that eight-year-olds with "average" intelligence are much more prevalent than those who are either geniuses or morons.

The foregoing illustration is typical of the use of the normal curve in helping us to picture a whole distribution (provided it is reasonably symmetrical and contains one hump in the center) from the values of $\bar{x}$ and SD. It should be easy to see that such measures represent the distribution for which they were calculated, when the distribution is "normal."

EXAMPLE 2
If an eight-year-old has an IQ of 130 and we assume a normal distribution, with $\bar{x} = 100$, SD $= 15$ (as in the preceding example), then

$$z = \frac{130 - 100}{15} = 2,$$

which means that the 130 score is 2 standard deviations away from the mean value of the distribution. From the preceding figure, we can conclude that approximately 3 per cent of all eight-year-olds will have an IQ greater than 130; and Table 7.4.1 discloses that 2.3 per cent of all eight-year-olds will have an IQ greater than 130.

EXAMPLE 3
Problem:
For a set of normally distributed scores whose mean is 62 and standard deviation is 7, estimate the number of scores between 55 and 76 if there is a total of 1,000 scores.

Solution:

If z_1, z_2 are the standard scores corresponding to 55, 76, respectively, then

$$z_1 = \frac{55 - 62}{7} = -1 \quad \text{and} \quad z_2 = \frac{76 - 62}{7} = 2.$$

Since

$$\int_{-1}^{2} \phi(z)\, dz = .341 + .477 = .818$$

(by use of Table 7.4.1), it follows that approximately 818 scores will fall in the 55 to 76 range.

EXAMPLE 4

Problem:

If 100 students are to have grades of A, B, C, D, F normally distributed between -4 and $+4$ standard deviations from the mean, how many of each grade will be received?

Solution:

Since 5 grades are to be distributed among 8 standard deviations, each grade interval will be 1.6 standard deviations (as indicated in the figure).

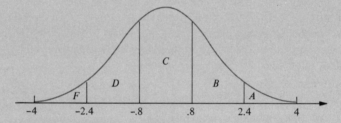

Hence Table 7.4.1 can be used to obtain:

No. of A's = 100 (.500 − .492) = .8.

No. of B's = 100 (.492 − .288) = 20.4.

No. of C's = 100 (.288)(2) = 57.6.

No. of D's = No. of B's = 20.4.

No. of F's = No. of A's = .8.

Some teachers and administrators are normal curve fanatics. That is, they believe that each class should be graded "on the normal curve" and deceive themselves into thinking they are being righteous and scientific. It is silly to attempt to force any set of frequencies to fit the normal curve if they do not do so naturally. For example, to arrange the marks of a class of 30 students so as to conform with the relative frequencies of the normal curve is sheer nonsense. It is not correct to say that this procedure is logically justified by the mathematical theory of statistics, unless one is sure that the concrete situation dealt with actually satisfies all the assumptions on which this part of the theory of statistics is based. Although it is true that the distribution of grades for a "large number" of randomly selected students will probably compare very favorably with the normal distribution (i.e., most of the grades will be C, a smaller number will be B, etc.), it rarely happens that any particular class is truly "normal."

Problem Set 7.4

1. If six coins are tossed, find the probability that there will be h heads when $h =$ (a) 0, (b) 1, (c) 2, (d) 3, (e) 4, (f) 5, (g) 6.

2. If six coins are tossed 6,400 times, find the total (theoretical) number of heads h, when $h =$ (a) 0, (b) 1, (c) 2, (d) 3, (e) 4, (f) 5, (g) 6. [Compare the results of this problem with the "ideal" distribution for the heights of the 6,400 male college students given at the beginning of this section. More than two centuries ago De Moivre (1667–1754), a French refugee mathematician living in London, observed that when n coins are tossed, the frequency distribution of the number of heads appearing approaches a definite form as n becomes larger. In this way he was led to the concept of the normal curve.]

3. If IQ scores are normally distributed, find the probability that the first child born in New York City in the year 2000 will have an IQ more than 1 standard deviation above the mean.

4. In the Exceptional School, the mean IQ over a period of years has been found to be 80 with standard deviation of 20. If these scores are normally distributed and there are 400 children in this school, how many of these children have an IQ of (a) more than 100, (b) less than 50, (c) between 50 and 100?

5. The mean score for a certain test is 72 with a standard deviation of 6. If there is a normal distribution, what per cent of the scores are (a) less than 60, (b) more than 90, (c) between 60 and 90?

*6. A large group of children are randomly selected and their IQ's are normally distributed with $x = 100$ and SD $= 20$. If the upper .5 per cent are regarded as geniuses, find the lower IQ limit for this group.

7. If 100 students are to have grades of A, B, C, D, F normally distributed between -3 and $+3$ standard deviations from the mean, how many of each grade will be received?

*8. Find the maximum value of $\phi(z)$.

9. If there are 400 freshmen, 300 sophomores, 200 juniors, and 100 seniors at Sleepy Eye College, do you believe that the ages of all students at this college are normally distributed? Explain.

10. True–False
   (a) A standard score of zero represents an original score equal to the mean (i.e., if $z = 0$, then $x = \bar{x}$).
   (b) For all practical purposes, the area under the normal curve beyond three standard deviations (in both directions) is negligible.
   (c) If a person has a score within .6745 standard deviations of the mean, then he is "normal."
   (d) If Jane has a standard score of 2.5 on a test, in which the scores are normally distributed, then 99.4 per cent of those who took the test will have a score less than Jane's.
   (e) Every sufficiently large sample of items in a population has a normal frequency distribution.
   (f) Statistics can be used to prove that some people are abnormal.

CHAPTER 8

Linear Algebra

8.1 Equations

In algebra as well as in the "practical world" one often wants to find values that will convert an equation into a true statement. Although the word *equation* occurs in various ways, it can always be interpreted to mean "a statement of equality." The expressions on either side of the equals sign are called *members* of the equation. Some examples now follow.

$$\text{(1)} \qquad x + 2x = 3x.$$
$$\text{(2)} \qquad x + 3 = 5.$$
$$\text{(3)} \qquad x^2 - 7x + 10 = 0.$$
$$\text{(4)} \qquad x = x + 1.$$
$$\text{(5)} \qquad x = \text{day of the week.}$$
$$\text{(6)} \qquad x = \text{capital of New Zealand.}$$
$$\text{(7)} \qquad x = \text{month that her son was born.}$$

If we are given an equation in x (where x represents an element in some given universal set), we ordinarily try to find a particular value of x that will satisfy the equation. If we are successful in finding such an x, it is called a *solution;* and we may then ask, "Is this the only solution?"

Before we can discuss solutions to the preceding equations, we need to specify the universal sets involved. We shall let the universal set be the set of real numbers in examples (1) through (4), the set of days of the week in example (5), the set of cities of the world in example (6), and the set of months in example (7).

In example (1), $x = 5$ is a solution, but so is every other number! An equation in x that is satisfied by every value of x that makes each member meaningful is called an *identity.* An equation that is not an identity is called a *conditional equation.* Since Equation (2) is not satisfied by $x = 1$, it is a conditional equation. We further observe that $x = 2$ is a solution to Equation (2) and that it is the only solution. We note that Equation (3) is a conditional equation with both $x = 2$ and $x = 5$ as solutions. We also observe that Equation (4) is a conditional equation. However, Equation (4) is not satisfied by any value of x, since we cannot find a number that is one more than itself! Equations in x that have no solutions (i.e., they are false for all x in the universal set) are called *pathological equations*.

We now observe that Equation (5) is an identity, and Equation (6) is a conditional equation whose only solution is $x = $ Wellington. Equation (7) is somewhat more complicated since in order to solve this equation we must know: who "her" is and the months in which her sons (if any) were born. At this point we can only conclude that Equation (7) is either (a) an identity (in case "her" had a son born in each month of the year), (b) a conditional equation with less than 12 solutions, or (c) a pathological equation (in case "her" had no sons).

Problem Set 8.1

1. Make up your own examples of an (a) identity, (b) conditional equation, (c) pathological equation. *Clearly indicate the universal sets* involved.

2. If the universal set is the set of real numbers, indicate whether each of the following is (i) an identity, (ii) a conditional equation, or (iii) a pathological equation. Find all solutions of the conditional equations.

(a) $2(x + 3) = 6 + 2x$.

(j) $\frac{x}{2} = 3$.

(b) $2x + 7 = x + 11$.

(k) $x^2 + 1 = 0$.

(c) $x = x + 2$.

(l) $x^2 - x - 6 = 0$.

(d) $\frac{1}{x} = 0$.

(m) $3x + 2x = 5x$.

(e) $\frac{1}{x} = \frac{1}{x}$.

(n) $\frac{x}{3} = 0$.

(f) $x^2 - 1 = 8$.

(o) $\frac{3}{x} = 0$.

(g) $2x = 8$.

(p) $x - x = 0$.

(h) $x - 5 = 2$.

(q) $x + x = 0$.

(i) $x + 5 = 8$.

(r) $x + x = x$.

8.2 Linear Equations

In order to find methods for solving equations, when the universal set is the set of real numbers, we will consider the following examples.

(1)	$x + 2 = 8.$
(2)	$x - 2 = 4.$
(3)	$2x = 12.$
(4)	$\dfrac{x}{2} = 3.$

The solution to each of these equations is easily seen to be $x = 6$, and no other value of x will satisfy any of them. We can formally obtain this answer in Equation (1) by subtracting 2 from each member, in Equation (2) by adding 2 to each member, in Equation (3) by dividing each member by 2 (or by multiplying each member by $\frac{1}{2}$), and in Equation (4) by multiplying each member by 2.

These procedures will now be validated by means of the following principle.

FUNDAMENTAL PRINCIPLE FOR SOLVING EQUATIONS

It is permissible to do the same (legal) thing to each member of an equation, as indicated below. It is not legal to violate the 11th Commandment: "Thou shalt not divide by zero."

Law 1 $(x + a = b) \rightarrow [(x + a) - a = b - a] \rightarrow (x = b - a).$

Law 2 $(x - a = b) \rightarrow [(x - a) + a = b + a] \rightarrow (x = b + a).$

Law 3   If $a \neq 0$, $(ax = b) \rightarrow \left[\dfrac{1}{a}(ax) = \dfrac{1}{a}b\right] \rightarrow \left(x = \dfrac{b}{a}\right).$

Law 4   If $a \neq 0$, $\left(\dfrac{x}{a} = b\right) \rightarrow \left[a\left(\dfrac{x}{a}\right) = ab\right] \rightarrow (x = ab).$

We note that the Fundamental Principle for Solving Equations can be simply stated as, "We can add, subtract, multiply, or divide each member of an equation by the same number, provided that we do not divide by zero."

If we let $1/a = a^{-1}$ when $a \neq 0$, Law 3 becomes

$$(ax = b) \rightarrow (x = a^{-1}b).$$

We shall call a^{-1} the *inverse* of a.

All of the preceding equations are called *linear equations* in x because each member can be reduced to an expression of the form $ax + b$, and the graph of $y = ax + b$ is a straight line.

Problem Set 8.2

1. Use the Fundamental Principle to solve each of the following equations for x.
   (a) $3x = 6$.
   (b) $5x = 4$.
   (c) $x + 1 = 3$.
   (d) $7x + 2 = 5x + 8$.
   (e) $5x + 2 = 7x + 8$.
   (f) $ax + b = cx + d$.
   (g) $2(x - 1) = 4(x - 1)$.
   (h) $2x = 3x$.
   (i) $2(x + 3) = 3x + 4$.
   (j) $\dfrac{x - 1}{3} = 7$.

*2. If $bx = a$, $dy = c$, and $kbd \neq 0$, prove
   (a) $\left(\dfrac{a}{b} = \dfrac{c}{d}\right)$ iff $(ad = bc)$.

   (b) $\dfrac{ak}{bk} = \dfrac{a}{b}$.

*3. If $5x = 2$ and $7y = 11$, find
   (a) $x \cdot y$.
   (c) $x + y$.
   (b) $\dfrac{x}{y}$.
   (d) $x - y$.

*4. If $bx = a$, $dy = c$ and $bd \neq 0$, find
   (a) $x \cdot y$.
   (c) $x + y$.
   (b) $\dfrac{x}{y}$.
   (d) $x - y$.

*5. If $bd \neq 0$, use Problem 4 to find
   (a) $\dfrac{a}{b} \cdot \dfrac{c}{d}$.
   (c) $\dfrac{a}{b} + \dfrac{c}{d}$.

   (b) $\dfrac{a}{b} \div \dfrac{c}{d}$.
   (d) $\dfrac{a}{b} - \dfrac{c}{d}$.

   HINT: $(a/b = x)$ means $(bx = a)$.

6. Use your results in Problem 5 to find:
   (a) $\dfrac{2}{3} \cdot \dfrac{5}{7}$.
   (e) $\dfrac{1}{3} \cdot 6$.
   (i) $\dfrac{1}{7} + \dfrac{3}{7}$.
   (m) $\dfrac{7}{6} - \dfrac{2}{9}$.

   (b) $\dfrac{2}{3} \div \dfrac{5}{7}$.
   (f) $\dfrac{1}{6} \div 6$.
   (j) $\dfrac{2}{3} + \dfrac{5}{6}$.
   (n) $\dfrac{3}{7} - \dfrac{3}{7}$.

   (c) $\dfrac{2}{3} + \dfrac{5}{7}$.
   (g) $6 \div \dfrac{1}{3}$.
   (k) $\dfrac{1}{3} - 5$.
   (o) $\dfrac{3}{7} \div \dfrac{3}{7}$.

   (d) $\dfrac{2}{3} - \dfrac{5}{7}$.
   (h) $\dfrac{1}{3} + 5$.
   (l) $\dfrac{3}{7} - \dfrac{1}{7}$.
   (p) $\dfrac{3}{7} \cdot 1$.

7. Use the Fundamental Principle to solve each of the following equations for y in terms of x.

(a) $x = 7y.$

(c) $\dfrac{x}{2} + \dfrac{y}{3} = 1.$

(b) $3x + 4y + 5 = 0.$

(d) $x = \dfrac{9}{5}y + 32.$

8.3 What Is a Matrix?

NOTE: In the remainder of this chapter we shall assume that all numbers are real numbers, unless otherwise indicated.

Suppose we are given numbers symbolized by a_{11}, a_{12}, a_{21}, a_{22}, y_1, and y_2; and we want to know whether we can find numbers x_1, x_2 such that

(1)
$$\begin{cases} a_{11}x_1 + a_{12}x_2 = y_1 \\ a_{21}x_1 + a_{22}x_2 = y_2 \end{cases}.$$

It is clear that the array of numbers

$$\begin{bmatrix} a_{11} & a_{12} \\ a_{21} & a_{22} \end{bmatrix}$$

is strategic in determining whether there is an x_1 and x_2 that satisfies the linear equations in (1). If there is an x_1 and x_2 that satisfies both equations of (1), then x_1, x_2 is called a *solution* of these equations. If there is only one solution, then x_1, x_2 is called the *unique solution* or *the solution*.

If we now arrange (1) in the form

(2)
$$\begin{bmatrix} a_{11} & a_{12} \\ a_{21} & a_{22} \end{bmatrix}\begin{bmatrix} x_1 \\ x_2 \end{bmatrix} = \begin{bmatrix} y_1 \\ y_2 \end{bmatrix},$$

then (1) is said to be in *matrix form*. If we let

$$\begin{bmatrix} a_{11} & a_{12} \\ a_{21} & a_{22} \end{bmatrix} = A, \qquad \begin{bmatrix} x_1 \\ x_2 \end{bmatrix} = X, \qquad \text{and} \quad \begin{bmatrix} y_1 \\ y_2 \end{bmatrix} = Y,$$

then (2) becomes converted to

(3)
$$AX = Y.$$

The symbols A, X, and Y introduced above are called *matrices*. In general, a *matrix* is a rectangular array of numbers or *elements*. If the matrix has m rows and n columns, it is called an $m \times n$ *matrix* (read "m by n matrix"). If matrix A has the element a_{ij} in its ith row, jth column, we shall write $A = [a_{ij}]$.

In this chapter we shall be primarily interested in 2×2 and 2×1 matrices. If a matrix has only one column, such as X above, it is called a (*column*) *vector*. Similarly, a matrix with only one row is called a (*row*) *vector*.

DEF 8.3.1

If $A = [a_{ij}]$ and $B = [b_{ij}]$, then we shall say $A = B$ iff $a_{ij} = b_{ij}$ for all i, j.

NOTE: The preceding definition can be used whenever A and B are both $m \times n$ matrices.

EXAMPLE 1
If

$$\begin{bmatrix} x & y \\ z & w \end{bmatrix} = \begin{bmatrix} 2 & -3 \\ 0 & 4 \end{bmatrix},$$

then $x = 2$, $y = -3$, $z = 0$, $w = 4$.

EXAMPLE 2
The pair of linear equations

(4) $2x_1 + 3x_2 = 1$
(5) $7x_1 + 5x_2 = 9$

can be solved as follows. Multiply each member of Equation (4) by 5 and each member of Equation (5) by 3 to obtain

(4') $10x_1 + 15x_2 = 5$
(5') $21x_1 + 15x_2 = 27.$

Now subtract Equation (4') from Equation (5') so that we have

(6) $11x_1 = 22.$

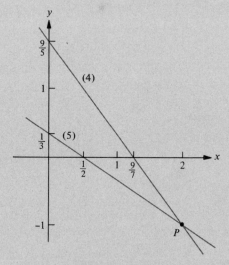

FIGURE 8.1.

Dividing each member of Equation (6) by 11 (or multiplying each member by 11^{-1}) yields the answer

(7) $$x_1 = 2.$$

A similar process can be used to show that $x_2 = -1$.

If x_1, x_2 are replaced, respectively, by 2, -1 in Equations (4) and (5), we find that these equations are converted into true statements. Hence, $x_1 = 2$, $x_2 = -1$ is a solution of Equations (4) and (5).

If we now let $x_1 = x$ and $x_2 = y$, and graph Equations (4) and (5), we obtain Fig. 8.1. Since point P is on both (4) and (5), its coordinates must satisfy both equations. Therefore P has coordinates $(2, -1)$, and is called the *geometric solution* of (4) and (5). Clearly, this solution is unique.

EXAMPLE 3

In order to solve the pair of linear equations

(8) $$2x_1 + 3x_2 = y_1$$
(9) $$4x_1 + 6x_2 = y_2$$

for x_1 and x_2, we will consider two cases.

Case 1

$$y_2 = 2y_1 \qquad (\text{e.g., } y_1 = 3, \ y_2 = 6).$$

If we graph Equations (8) and (9) we find that the graphs are identical. Therefore the coordinates of each point (x_1, x_2) on (8) satisfies both (8) and (9), and we conclude that there are infinitely many values of x_1 and x_2 that will satisfy both (8) and (9).

Case 2

$$y_2 \neq 2y_1 \qquad (\text{e.g., } y_1 = 0, \ y_2 = 8).$$

If we now graph Equations (8) and (9), we obtain parallel lines—and therefore these equations cannot have a point in common—which means that there can be no common solution. If we attempt an algebraic solution by multiplying Equation (8) by 2 and then subtracting, we obtain $0 = y_2 - 2y_1$, which is clearly impossible when $y_2 \neq 2y_1$.

EXAMPLE 4

We now return to Equations (1) and will transcribe them as

(10) $$a_{11}x_1 + a_{12}x_2 = y_1$$
(11) $$a_{21}x_1 + a_{22}x_2 = y_2.$$

If we proceed to solve them by using the method illustrated in Example 2, we find

(12) $$(a_{11}a_{22} - a_{12}a_{21})x_1 = a_{22}y_1 - a_{12}y_2$$
(13) $$(a_{11}a_{22} - a_{21}a_{12})x_2 = a_{11}y_2 - a_{21}y_1.$$

We now find it convenient to have the following definition available.

DEF 8.3.2

$$|A| \equiv \begin{vmatrix} a_{11} & a_{12} \\ a_{21} & a_{22} \end{vmatrix} \equiv a_{11}a_{22} - a_{12}a_{21},$$

and $|A|$ is called the *determinant* of A.

By virtue of the preceding definition, Equations (12) and (13) can be written as

(12′) $$|A|x_1 = a_{22}y_1 - a_{12}y_2$$
(13′) $$|A|x_2 = a_{11}y_2 - a_{21}y_1.$$

If $|A| \neq 0$, then Equations (12′) and (13′) can be solved for x_1 and x_2, and this solution is unique (e.g., see Example 2). If $|A| = 0$ and $a_{22}y_1 - a_{12}y_2 \neq 0$ or $a_{11}y_2 - a_{21}y_1 \neq 0$, then there is no solution for x_1, x_2 (e.g., see Example 3, Case 2). However, if $|A| = 0$ and

$$a_{22}y_1 - a_{12}y_2 = a_{11}y_2 - a_{21}y_1 = 0,$$

then there will be infinitely many values of x_1 and x_2 that satisfy Equations (12) and (13) (e.g., see Example 3, Case 1), and hence infinitely many solutions.

Problem Set 8.3

1. Solve Equations (4) and (5) for x_2.

2. Write Equations (4) and (5) in matrix form.

3. Graph Equations (8) and (9) when
   (a) $y_2 = 2y_1 = 6$.   (b) $y_2 = 8$, $y_1 = 0$.

4. If $|A| \neq 0$, show that Equations (10) and (11) have the following solution.

$$x_1 = \frac{\begin{vmatrix} y_1 & a_{12} \\ y_2 & a_{22} \end{vmatrix}}{|A|}, \qquad x_2 = \frac{\begin{vmatrix} a_{11} & y_1 \\ a_{21} & y_2 \end{vmatrix}}{|A|}$$

This rule for finding x_1 and x_2 is called *Cramer's Rule* (for two equations and two unknowns).

5. Use Cramer's Rule to solve for x_1 and x_2 when

(a) $\begin{cases} 2x_1 + 3x_2 = 5 \\ 7x_1 + 4x_2 = 6 \end{cases}$.

(b) $\begin{cases} 2x_1 + 3x_2 = 5 \\ 4x_1 + 6x_2 = 7 \end{cases}$.

*6. If $|A| = 0$ in Example 4, prove that $(a_{22}y_1 - a_{12}y_2 = 0)$ iff $(a_{11}y_2 - a_{21}y_1 = 0)$.

7. If

$$\begin{cases} a_{11}x_1 + a_{12}x_2 + a_{13}x_3 = y_1 \\ a_{21}x_1 + a_{22}x_2 + a_{23}x_3 = y_2 \\ a_{31}x_1 + a_{32}x_2 + a_{33}x_3 = y_3 \end{cases},$$

convert this system of linear equations to the matrix form $AX = Y$, and clearly indicate the meaning of A, X, and Y.

8. In Problem 7 use words to describe the method for obtaining the product AX.

8.4 Addition of Matrices

If A and B are 2×2 matrices, the reader may ask whether there is a reasonable definition for the "sum" $A + B$. In order to obtain an affirmative answer to this question we will interpret the equation

(1) $$AX = Y$$

(where A, X, and Y are defined as in the previous section) to mean that the matrix A is transforming the vector X into the vector Y. If we now let matrix B transform vector X into vector Z so that

(2) $$BX = Z$$

where

(3) $$B = \begin{bmatrix} b_{11} & b_{12} \\ b_{21} & b_{22} \end{bmatrix}, \qquad X = \begin{bmatrix} x_1 \\ x_2 \end{bmatrix}, \qquad Z = \begin{bmatrix} z_1 \\ z_2 \end{bmatrix},$$

then it is reasonable to let

(4) $$(A + B)X \equiv AX + BX$$

and

(5) $$Y + Z \equiv \begin{bmatrix} y_1 \\ y_2 \end{bmatrix} + \begin{bmatrix} z_1 \\ z_2 \end{bmatrix} \equiv \begin{bmatrix} y_1 + z_1 \\ y_2 + z_2 \end{bmatrix},$$

so that

(6) $$(A + B)X = Y + Z;$$

and hence $A + B$ can be regarded as a 2×2 matrix which transforms vector X into vector $Y + Z$. If we combine the last two equations with both (1) and (2), we obtain

$$(7) \quad Y + Z = \begin{bmatrix} y_1 + z_1 \\ y_2 + z_2 \end{bmatrix} = \begin{bmatrix} (a_{11} + b_{11})x_1 + (a_{12} + b_{12})x_2 \\ (a_{21} + b_{21})x_1 + (a_{22} + b_{22})x_2 \end{bmatrix} = (A + B)X,$$

with the aid of the distributive law. Therefore

$$(8) \qquad A + B = \begin{bmatrix} a_{11} + b_{11} & a_{12} + b_{12} \\ a_{21} + b_{21} & a_{22} + b_{22} \end{bmatrix},$$

which is the desired result. We thus see that it is reasonable to define the sum of matrices A and B as follows.

DEF 8.4.1

$$A + B \equiv [a_{ij}] + [b_{ij}] \equiv [a_{ij} + b_{ij}].$$

NOTE: The preceding definition for the sum of matrices can be used whenever A and B are both $m \times n$ matrices.

EXAMPLE 1
If

$$A = \begin{bmatrix} 2 & 3 \\ 4 & 7 \end{bmatrix} \quad \text{and} \quad B = \begin{bmatrix} 0 & 6 \\ -4 & -3 \end{bmatrix},$$

then

$$A + B = \begin{bmatrix} 2 & 9 \\ 0 & 4 \end{bmatrix}.$$

Since $A + B$ is defined in such a simple-minded way, one would expect matrices to behave like ordinary numbers. For example, we would expect to have the following rules for matrices.

(M_1) $A + B = B + A$ (Commutative $+$).
(M_2) $A + (B + C) = (A + B) + C$ (Associative $+$).
(M_3) $A + [0] = A$ (Identity $+$).

NOTE: $[0]$ represents a matrix with 0 in every position, and is called the *zero matrix*.

(M_4) $A + B = [0]$ when $B = -A = [-a_{ij}]$ (Inverse $+$).

EXAMPLE

If $A = \begin{bmatrix} 2 & -3 \\ 5 & 0 \end{bmatrix}$, then $-A = \begin{bmatrix} -2 & 3 \\ -5 & 0 \end{bmatrix}$.

It would be a pity if the proofs of the preceding four properties were worked out here, for then the reader might not work them out for himself. Since proving these properties provides good practice, they are included as problems.

If we let $A + A = 2A$, $2A + A = 3A$, etc., it follows that

$$A + A = 2A = \begin{bmatrix} 2a_{11} & 2a_{12} \\ 2a_{21} & 2a_{22} \end{bmatrix},$$

$$2A + A = 3A = \begin{bmatrix} 3a_{11} & 3a_{12} \\ 3a_{21} & 3a_{22} \end{bmatrix},$$

etc., and hence it is reasonable to have the following definition.

DEF 8.4.2

If k represents any real number, then

$$kA \equiv k[a_{ij}] \equiv [ka_{ij}].$$

Thus if a matrix is multiplied by a real number, each element of the matrix is multiplied by that number.

NOTE: The preceding definition can be used whenever A is an $m \times n$ matrix.

EXAMPLE

If $A = \begin{bmatrix} 3 & -4 \\ 1 & 0 \end{bmatrix}$,   then $-2A = \begin{bmatrix} -6 & 8 \\ -2 & 0 \end{bmatrix}$.

It may be of interest to note that the set of all $m \times n$ matrices can serve as concrete interpretations for some important abstract mathematical structures. For example, the set of all $m \times n$ matrices with real elements forms a *commutative group with respect to addition* and also a *linear (vector) space over the real number field*.

Problem Set 8.4

1. Show how the distributive law, as defined in Section A.3, can be used to obtain Equation (7).

2. Give a reasonable definition for $A - B$.

3. If $A = \begin{bmatrix} 2 & -3 \\ 4 & 5 \end{bmatrix}$ and $B = \begin{bmatrix} 4 & 3 \\ -2 & 1 \end{bmatrix}$, find (a) $A + B$, (b) $2A$, (c) kA, (d) $A - B$, (e) $-A$.

4. If

$$A = \begin{bmatrix} a_{11} & a_{12} \\ a_{21} & a_{22} \end{bmatrix}, \qquad B = \begin{bmatrix} b_{11} & b_{12} \\ b_{21} & b_{22} \end{bmatrix}, \qquad C = \begin{bmatrix} c_{11} & c_{12} \\ c_{21} & c_{22} \end{bmatrix},$$

prove (a) (M_1), (b) (M_2), (c) (M_3), (d) (M_4).

5. Do the $m \times n$ matrices satisfy Properties (M_1), (M_2), (M_3), and (M_4)?

*6. Consult a book on modern algebra or abstract algebra to find definitions for the following mathematical structures: (a) group, (b) commutative or Abelian group, (c) field, (d) linear (vector) space over a field.

*7. Find all numbers k and all vectors X that satisfy the equation $AX = kX$ when $A =$

(a) $\begin{bmatrix} 2 & 3 \\ 4 & 6 \end{bmatrix}$. (c) $\begin{bmatrix} 1 & -1 \\ 1 & 3 \end{bmatrix}$. (e) $\begin{bmatrix} 2 & 0 \\ 0 & 2 \end{bmatrix}$.

(b) $\begin{bmatrix} 2 & 1 \\ 0 & 5 \end{bmatrix}$. (d) $\begin{bmatrix} 0 & 0 \\ 0 & 0 \end{bmatrix}$.

   NOTE: If there exists

$$X \neq \begin{bmatrix} 0 \\ 0 \end{bmatrix} \quad \text{such that } AX = kX,$$

then k is called an *eigenvalue* of A and X is called an *eigenvector* of A with *eigenvalue* k.

8. True–False
   (a) If $C = A + B$, then $c_{ij} = a_{ij} + b_{ij}$.
   (b) If $C = kA$, then $c_{ij} = ka_{ij}$.
   (c) If $C = -A$, then $c_{ij} = -a_{ij}$.
   (d) If $C = [0]$, then $c_{ij} = 0$.
   (e) If $C = A - B$, then $c_{ij} = a_{ij} - b_{ij}$.

8.5 Multiplication of Matrices

Our next objective is to develop a reasonable definition for the "product" BA, when B and A are 2×2 matrices. We shall do so by letting matrix A transform vector X into vector Y and matrix B transform vector Y into vector Z, so that

(1) $AX = Y$ and $BY = Z$,

where A, B, X, Y, Z are defined as in the previous section. If we now let

(2) $(BA)X \equiv B(AX),$

then (1) yields

(3) $Z = BY = B(AX) = (BA)X,$

and hence BA can be regarded as a 2×2 matrix which transforms vector X into vector Z. If we combine (3) with both (1) and (2) we obtain

$$Z = BY = \begin{bmatrix} b_{11}y_1 + b_{12}y_2 \\ b_{21}y_1 + b_{22}y_2 \end{bmatrix}$$

$$= \begin{bmatrix} b_{11}(a_{11}x_1 + a_{12}x_2) + b_{12}(a_{21}x_1 + a_{22}x_2) \\ b_{21}(a_{11}x_1 + a_{12}x_2) + b_{22}(a_{21}x_1 + a_{22}x_2) \end{bmatrix}$$

$$= \begin{bmatrix} (b_{11}a_{11} + b_{12}a_{21})x_1 + (b_{11}a_{12} + b_{12}a_{22})x_2 \\ (b_{21}a_{11} + b_{22}a_{21})x_1 + (b_{21}a_{12} + b_{22}a_{22})x_2 \end{bmatrix} = (BA)X$$

with the aid of the distributive law. Therefore, it is reasonable to define the product BA as follows.

DEF 8.5.1

$$BA = \begin{bmatrix} b_{11} & b_{12} \\ b_{21} & b_{22} \end{bmatrix} \begin{bmatrix} a_{11} & a_{12} \\ a_{21} & a_{22} \end{bmatrix} \equiv \begin{bmatrix} b_{11}a_{11} + b_{12}a_{21} & b_{11}a_{12} + b_{12}a_{22} \\ b_{21}a_{11} + b_{22}a_{21} & b_{21}a_{12} + b_{22}a_{22} \end{bmatrix}.$$

We can describe the rule for multiplying two matrices by saying, "The term in the ij position (i.e., ith row, jth column) in the product of two matrices is obtained by multiplying the elements in the ith row of the left matrix by the corresponding elements in the jth column of the right matrix, and then adding." Using symbols, if $C = BA$, then

(5) $c_{ij} = b_{i1}a_{1j} + b_{i2}a_{2j}$

The method for multiplying two matrices is sometimes called *row by column multiplication*.

By virtue of the preceding definition, the product AA is meaningful, and as expected we will let

(6) $A^2 \equiv AA, \qquad A^3 \equiv A^2A, \qquad A^4 \equiv A^3A, \qquad$ etc.

EXAMPLE
If

$$B = \begin{bmatrix} 2 & 3 \\ 4 & 5 \end{bmatrix} \quad \text{and} \quad A = \begin{bmatrix} 6 & 7 \\ 0 & 1 \end{bmatrix},$$

then

$$BA = \begin{bmatrix} 2 & 3 \\ 4 & 5 \end{bmatrix} \begin{bmatrix} 6 & 7 \\ 0 & 1 \end{bmatrix} = \begin{bmatrix} 2 \cdot 6 + 3 \cdot 0 & 2 \cdot 7 + 3 \cdot 1 \\ 4 \cdot 6 + 5 \cdot 0 & 4 \cdot 7 + 5 \cdot 1 \end{bmatrix} = \begin{bmatrix} 12 & 17 \\ 24 & 33 \end{bmatrix}.$$

In the previous section we found that the sum for matrices behaves very much like the sum for ordinary numbers. We will now investigate the following five questions for the product of 2×2 matrices.

(Q_1) Does $AB = BA$ for all A, B (i.e., is matrix multiplication commutative)?

(Q_2) Does $A(BC) = (AB)C$ for all A, B, C (i.e., is matrix multiplication associative)?

(Q_3) Is there a matrix I such that $AI = IA = A$ for all A (i.e., do matrices have a multiplicative identity)?

(Q_4) If the answer to (Q_3) is yes and A is any given matrix, can we always find a matrix B such that $AB = BA = I$ (i.e., does every matrix have a multiplicative inverse)?

(Q_5) Does $A(B + C) = AB + AC$ for all A, B, C (i.e., is matrix multiplication distributive over addition)?

NOTE: Before reading further, the reader should attempt to find answers to all of the preceding questions.

Question Q_1

If $A = \begin{bmatrix} 1 & 0 \\ 0 & 0 \end{bmatrix}$ and $B = \begin{bmatrix} 0 & 1 \\ 0 & 0 \end{bmatrix}$, then $AB = B$ and $BA = [0]$. Thus we have an example in which $AB \neq BA$, and therefore the answer to Question Q_1 is no.

Question Q_2

The answer is yes—and the proof will be left to the reader.

Question Q_3

Since $I = \begin{bmatrix} 1 & 0 \\ 0 & 1 \end{bmatrix}$ plays the required role, the answer to this question is also yes—and it should be verified by the reader. It should be noted that this property permits us to call I an *identity matrix*.

Question Q_4

If $A = I$, then $AB = I$ when $B = I$. However, if

$$A = \begin{bmatrix} 1 & 0 \\ 0 & 0 \end{bmatrix},$$

it can be easily shown that $AB \neq I$ for all B. From this latter example we conclude that the answer to Question Q_4 is no. However the class of matrices for which the answer is yes is important. One reason for this importance is given in the following example.

EXAMPLE 1

If $AX = Y$ and there exists B such that $BA = I$, then

$$(AX = Y) \rightarrow (X = BY),$$

since $BY = B(AX) = (BA)X = IX = X$. Thus, we would have a ready-made solution for X.

In order to determine those matrices A for which the answer is yes, we proceed as follows. Assume $AB = I$. Then by DEF 8.5.1 we have

(7)
$$\begin{bmatrix} a_{11}b_{11} + a_{12}b_{21} & a_{11}b_{12} + a_{12}b_{22} \\ a_{21}b_{11} + a_{22}b_{21} & a_{21}b_{12} + a_{22}b_{22} \end{bmatrix} = \begin{bmatrix} 1 & 0 \\ 0 & 1 \end{bmatrix}.$$

Therefore by DEF 8.3.1 we obtain

(8)
$$\begin{cases} a_{11}b_{11} + a_{12}b_{21} = 1 & a_{11}b_{12} + a_{12}b_{22} = 0 \\ a_{21}b_{11} + a_{22}b_{21} = 0 & a_{21}b_{12} + a_{22}b_{22} = 1 \end{cases}.$$

If we solve each pair of these equations for the b_{ij} we find

(9)
$$\begin{cases} |A|\, b_{11} = a_{22} & |A|\, b_{12} = -a_{12} \\ |A|\, b_{21} = -a_{21} & |A|\, b_{22} = a_{11} \end{cases},$$

where $|A|$ represents the determinant of A (i.e., $|A| = a_{11}a_{22} - a_{12}a_{21}$). If $|A| = 0$, then (9) reveals that $a_{22} = a_{21} = a_{12} = a_{11} = 0$ [which conflicts with the first equation in (8)], and therefore there can be no solution to (8). If $|A| \neq 0$, then clearly all b_{ij} can be found by use of (9). Thus we have proved the following.

THEOREM 8.5.1 *If A is any given 2×2 matrix, then there exists a 2×2 matrix B such that $AB = BA = I$ iff $|A| \neq 0$.*

DEF 8.5.2

If there exists a matrix B such that $AB = BA = I$, then A is called *non-singular* or *invertible*, B is called an *inverse of A*, and we write $B = A^{-1}$.

We will now use the preceding theory and symbolism to solve the equations of Example 2 in Section 8.3.

EXAMPLE 2

If $A = \begin{bmatrix} 2 & 3 \\ 7 & 5 \end{bmatrix}$, $X = \begin{bmatrix} x_1 \\ x_2 \end{bmatrix}$, and $Y = \begin{bmatrix} 1 \\ 9 \end{bmatrix}$, then the equations to be solved can be written as $AX = Y$. Since $BA = I$ when

$$B = -\frac{1}{11}\begin{bmatrix} 5 & -3 \\ -7 & 2 \end{bmatrix},$$

we have

$$X = BY - \frac{1}{11}\begin{bmatrix} -22 \\ 11 \end{bmatrix} = \begin{bmatrix} 2 \\ -1 \end{bmatrix}$$

by virtue of Example 1 and Def. 8.4.2. Therefore $x_1 = 2$, $x_2 = -1$ is the solution.

Question Q_5

The answer is yes—and the proof will be left to the reader.

In the previous section we noted that the set of all $m \times n$ matrices with real elements forms a *commutative group* as well as a *vector space*. We can now use those results together with the affirmative answers to the preceding questions to establish that the set of all 2×2 matrices with real elements forms an *associative linear algebra over the real number field.* If Def. 8.5.1 is extended in the expected way (see Problem 2 below), then all $n \times n$ matrices with real elements can also be shown to form an associative linear algebra over the real number field.

Problem Set 8.5

1. If $A = \begin{bmatrix} a_{11} & a_{12} \\ a_{21} & a_{22} \end{bmatrix}$, find BA when $B =$

(a) $\begin{bmatrix} 0 & 1 \\ 1 & 0 \end{bmatrix}$.   (d) $\begin{bmatrix} 1 & 0 \\ 0 & 1 \end{bmatrix}$.

(b) $\begin{bmatrix} 1 & 0 \\ 0 & 3 \end{bmatrix}$.   (e) $\begin{bmatrix} 0 & 0 \\ 0 & 0 \end{bmatrix}$.

(c) $\begin{bmatrix} 1 & 0 \\ 4 & 1 \end{bmatrix}$.   (f) $\begin{bmatrix} 2 & 0 \\ 0 & 2 \end{bmatrix}$.

2. If B is an $m \times n$ matrix and A is an $n \times p$ matrix, give a reasonable definition for BA.

3. Find 2×2 matrices A and B such that $AB = BA$.

4. Prove that the answer to each of the following questions is yes.
   °(a) Question Q_2. (b) Question Q_3. °(c) Question Q_5.

°5. If A, B, C are 2×2 matrices, prove that

$$(A + B)C = AC + BC.$$

6. If $A = \begin{bmatrix} 1 & 0 \\ 0 & 0 \end{bmatrix}$, prove that it is impossible to find a matrix B such that $AB = I$.

7. If $A = \begin{bmatrix} 2 & -1 \\ -3 & 4 \end{bmatrix}$, find A^{-1} by using (a) equations of (9),

   (b) Def. 8.5.2 *directly.*

°8. If A and B are 2×2 matrices such that $AB = I$, prove that $BA = I$.

9. If $AX = Y$ and $BA = I$, prove that $X = BY = A^{-1}Y$.

°10. If matrix A has an inverse, prove that this inverse is unique.

11. Establish all the results indicated in Example 2. Why can't the same method be used to solve the equations of Example 3 in Section 8.3?

°12. If A is a 3×3 matrix and A^{-1} exists, what other property must A have?

13. True-False
   Let A, B, and C be any 2×2 matrices.
   (a) If $AB = [0]$, then $A = [0]$ or $B = [0]$.
   (b) If $AB = AC$, then $B = C$.
   (c) $AB = BA$.
   (d) $BI = IB$.
   (e) If $A^2 = B^2$, then $A = \pm B$.
   (f) If $A^2 = A$, then $A = I$ or $A = [0]$.
   (g) If $A = I$ or $A = [0]$, then $A^2 = A$.

°14. Consult a book on modern algebra or abstract algebra to find a definition for the following mathematical structures: (a) linear algebra, (b) associative linear algebra.

8.6 Applications of Matrices

Matrices have important applications in mathematics as well as in the various areas of science. One of the applications to mathematics was illustrated in the previous section when we showed how matrices can be used to solve a system of linear equations. Modern physics uses matrices in quantum mechanics as well as in the study of atomic and crystal structure. Most branches of engineering (especially electrical and aeronautical) use matrices to solve basic problems. For example, matrices are used to solve certain types of differential equations (originating in the calculus) that are important to the engineer. Matrices are also used in psychology, sociology, economics, political science, and the biological sciences (especially in the study of heredity). The following examples indicate how matrices can be used.

EXAMPLE 1 Complex Numbers

In the Appendix we note that x^2 cannot be negative when x is a real number. Thus, there cannot exist a real number x such that

$$(1) \qquad\qquad x^2 = -1.$$

We observe that (1) will have a solution if we invent a new number, called i or the *imaginary unit*, which has the property

$$i^2 = -1.$$

Numbers of the form $a + bi$, where a and b represent real numbers and i is the imaginary unit, are of fundamental importance in both mathematics and physics, and are given special names.

DEF 8.6.1

A *complex number* is any number that can be written in the form $a + bi$, where a and b are real and $i^2 = -1$. We shall call a the *real part* and b the *imaginary part* of $a + bi$. If $b = 0$, then

$$a + bi = a + 0i = a$$

is called *real*. If $b \neq 0$, then $a + bi$ is called *imaginary*. If $a = 0, b \neq 0$, then

$$a + bi = 0 + bi = bi$$

is called *pure imaginary*.

We will say that two complex numbers are equal iff their real parts and their imaginary parts are equal, as indicated in the following definition.

DEF 8.6.2

$$a + bi = c + di \text{ iff } [(a = c) \text{ and } (b = d)].$$

To add two complex numbers we would naturally expect to add their real and imaginary parts, as in the following.

DEF 8.6.3
$$(a + bi) + (c + di) \equiv (a + c) + (b + d)i.$$

If we use the distributive laws to multiply two complex numbers, we find

$$(a + bi)(c + di) = ac + (ad + bc)i + (bd)i^2$$
$$= (ac - bd) + (ad + bc)i,$$

since $i^2 = -1$. This procedure reveals the motivation for the following definition.

DEF 8.6.4
$$(a + bi)(c + di) \equiv (ac - bd) + (ad + bc)i.$$

If we now let the matrix $\begin{bmatrix} a & b \\ -b & a \end{bmatrix}$ correspond to the complex number $a + bi$ and the matrix $\begin{bmatrix} c & d \\ -d & c \end{bmatrix}$ correspond to the complex number $c + di$, we find that these matrices behave like their corresponding complex numbers with regard to equality, addition, and multiplication. For example, in the case of multiplication we find

$$\begin{bmatrix} a & b \\ -b & a \end{bmatrix}\begin{bmatrix} c & d \\ -d & c \end{bmatrix} = \begin{bmatrix} ac - bd & ad + bc \\ -(ad + bc) & ac - bd \end{bmatrix},$$

which corresponds to the equation of Def. 8.6.4. Thus, complex numbers can be interpreted as matrices.

EXAMPLE 2 Markov Chain
Let us assume that $\frac{1}{20}$ of the city population moves into the suburbs or country (which for the sake of brevity will be called *suburbs*) and $\frac{1}{40}$ of the suburban population moves into the city each year. Then this situation can be represented by means of the following matrix.

	Portion to City	Portion to Suburbs
City	$\dfrac{19}{20}$	$\dfrac{1}{20}$
Suburbs	$\dfrac{1}{40}$	$\dfrac{39}{40}$

At first glance you may feel that eventually the entire population will be in the suburbs. But this is not the case!

Let C_0 be the proportion of the population originally in the city and S_0 the proportion originally in the suburbs. This can be represented by the matrix $[C_0 \quad S_0]$. In a similar fashion let $[C_k \quad S_k]$ represent the proportions in the city and suburbs at the end of the kth year.

Since $C_1 = \frac{19}{20} C_0 + \frac{1}{40} S_0$ and $S_1 = \frac{1}{20} C_0 + \frac{39}{40} S_0$ are the proportions of the population in the city and suburbs, respectively, at the end of the first year, we have

$$[C_1 \quad S_1] = [C_0 \quad S_0] \begin{bmatrix} \dfrac{19}{20} & \dfrac{1}{20} \\ \dfrac{1}{40} & \dfrac{39}{40} \end{bmatrix}$$

at the end of the first year. Similarly, we have

$$[C_2 \quad S_2] = [C_1 \quad S_1] \begin{bmatrix} \dfrac{19}{20} & \dfrac{1}{20} \\ \dfrac{1}{40} & \dfrac{39}{40} \end{bmatrix}$$

$$= [C_0 \quad S_0] \begin{bmatrix} \dfrac{19}{20} & \dfrac{1}{20} \\ \dfrac{1}{40} & \dfrac{39}{40} \end{bmatrix} \begin{bmatrix} \dfrac{19}{20} & \dfrac{1}{20} \\ \dfrac{1}{40} & \dfrac{39}{40} \end{bmatrix}$$

$$= [C_0 \quad S_0] \begin{bmatrix} \dfrac{19}{20} & \dfrac{1}{20} \\ \dfrac{1}{40} & \dfrac{39}{40} \end{bmatrix}^2$$

at the end of the second year,

$$[C_3 \quad S_3] = [C_2 \quad S_2] \begin{bmatrix} \dfrac{19}{20} & \dfrac{1}{20} \\ \dfrac{1}{40} & \dfrac{39}{40} \end{bmatrix} = [C_0 \quad S_0] \begin{bmatrix} \dfrac{19}{20} & \dfrac{1}{20} \\ \dfrac{1}{40} & \dfrac{39}{40} \end{bmatrix}^3$$

at the end of the third year, and

$$[C_k \quad S_k] = [C_0 \quad S_0] \begin{bmatrix} \dfrac{19}{20} & \dfrac{1}{20} \\ \dfrac{1}{40} & \dfrac{39}{40} \end{bmatrix}^k$$

at the end of the kth year. As k becomes larger and larger, the matrix

$$\begin{bmatrix} \dfrac{19}{20} & \dfrac{1}{20} \\ \dfrac{1}{40} & \dfrac{39}{40} \end{bmatrix}^{k}$$

can be shown to become closer and closer to

$$\begin{bmatrix} \dfrac{1}{3} & \dfrac{2}{3} \\ \dfrac{1}{3} & \dfrac{2}{3} \end{bmatrix},$$

and therefore $[C_k \quad S_k]$ becomes closer and closer to $[\frac{1}{3} \quad \frac{2}{3}]$, since $C_0 + S_0 = 1$. Thus, eventually the suburbs will have twice the population of the city, no matter what the original proportions C_0 and S_0.

The preceding example is a simplification of a Markov chain, named in honor of the Russian mathematician A. A. Markov, who pioneered the subject in 1907. In Markov chains, the probability at a given time depends on the outcome of the experiment that immediately precedes it. Arguments of this type are of real importance in the social and biological sciences, as well in diffusion studies in physics, chemistry, and geology.

One may feel that Example 2 is unrealistic, since it is highly improbable that the percentage moving to and from the city is a constant. This idealized situation can be made more realistic by introducing matrices with variable elements in place of the constant elements used above. In recent years electronic computers have been employed to perform these more complicated computations.

EXAMPLE 3   Cryptography

Ever since language was invented, some people (including children) have wanted to send messages that could be understood only by those who were privileged to know the secret code. In times of world crisis, knowing the right code at the right time can provide the power to make or break a nation. Thus the development of "unbreakable" codes has been a major concern of world leaders. We shall now illustrate how matrices can be used to obtain a code that is relatively difficult to break.

Step 1: Let 1 represent a, 2 represent b, . . . , 26 represent z, and 27 represent a blank space. (All punctuation marks will be disregarded.)

Step 2: Break the message into groups of two letters each. Thus

DON'T GIVE UP THE SHIP

becomes

4 15|14 20|27 7|9 22|5 27|21 16|27 20|8 5|27 19|8 9|16 27

Step 3: Arrange each group of two symbols as a column vector, so that our message now reads

$$\begin{bmatrix}4\\15\end{bmatrix}\begin{bmatrix}14\\20\end{bmatrix}\begin{bmatrix}27\\7\end{bmatrix}\begin{bmatrix}9\\22\end{bmatrix}\begin{bmatrix}5\\27\end{bmatrix}\begin{bmatrix}21\\16\end{bmatrix}\begin{bmatrix}27\\20\end{bmatrix}\begin{bmatrix}8\\5\end{bmatrix}\begin{bmatrix}27\\19\end{bmatrix}\begin{bmatrix}8\\9\end{bmatrix}\begin{bmatrix}16\\27\end{bmatrix}$$

Step 4: Choose *any* 2 × 2 matrix that has a multiplicative inverse and proceed to multiply each of the preceding column vectors by this matrix. If we choose the matrix

$$A = \begin{bmatrix}2 & 3\\5 & 8\end{bmatrix},$$

then multiplying each of the preceding column vectors by A yields

$$\begin{bmatrix}53\\140\end{bmatrix}\begin{bmatrix}88\\230\end{bmatrix}\begin{bmatrix}75\\191\end{bmatrix}\cdots$$

Step 5: Transmit the coded message horizontally, so that the preceding appears as

53   140   88   230   75   191   ...

When the secret agent receives the message, he divides it into groups of two and converts each group of two into a column vector. After multiplying each column vector by the inverse matrix A^{-1}, the message can be made intelligible by converting 1 to *a*, 2 to *b*, etc. . . . The reader should try it and see! This code can be modified in various ways. For example, long messages could be arranged in groups of 10, thus requiring a 10 × 10 matrix (and a computer?) for coding and decoding.

Problem Set 8.6

1. Use the matrix method and matrix A of Example 3 to encode the message:

ARE YOU AN UNGUIDED MISSILE?

2. As a supersecret agent your code book contains the following instruction: "Today's secret matrix is

$$\begin{bmatrix}1 & 1\\2 & 3\end{bmatrix}.$$

Eat this page." With these instructions, use the method of Example
3 to decode the following message: 19 53 34 88 29 60 32 91
33 80 38 99 9 22 29 60 52 131 28 64 32 91 21 57 34 95.

*3. Try to find an application of matrices in your own field of interest
by examining books and periodicals in your school library.

*4. Read and write a report on the article "What Is a Matrix," by
C. C. Mac Duffee in *American Mathematical Monthly*, Vol 50
(1943), p. 360.

8.7 Linear Programming

The search for the maximum, the minimum, or in general the most favorable
or optimum solution to a problem has intrigued man throughout the ages.
For example, in about 300 B.C. Euclid described how to find the maximum
area of a parallelogram whose perimeter was given. However, the rigorous
approach to this and more sophisticated problems had to wait until the great
mathematicians of the seventeenth, eighteenth, and nineteenth centuries (e.g.,
Leibniz, Newton, the Bernoullis, Euler, Cauchy, and Weierstrass) developed
the powerful methods of the calculus and the calculus of variations. These
techniques can be used to obtain systematic solutions to a wide range of
optimization problems in both geometry and the physical sciences. Problems
such as finding the shortest distance between two points on some surface (i.e.,
the geodesic problem) and the path of quickest descent of a weighted particle
moving between two given points in a gravitational field (i.e., the brachy-
stochrone problem) are resolved by these classical optimization methods.

Since about 1940 a new class of optimization problems has developed from
the complex organizational structures that permeate modern society. For
example, industrialists wanted to know the most efficient manner in which
to run the various phases of their industries, militarists wanted to know the
optimum deployment of aircraft that would maximize their country's chances
of winning a war, and dieticians wanted to know the diet that satisfies the
minimum daily requirement at a minimum cost. Research on how to formulate
and solve such problems has led to the development of new and important
optimization techniques—and the subject of linear programming.

Historically, the general problem of linear programming was first developed
and applied in 1947 by George B. Dantzig (1914–   ) and his associates who
were working on a U.S. Air Force project involving the feasibility of applying
mathematical techniques to military supply problems. The early applications
of linear programming methods fell into three major categories: (1) military,
(2) industry, and (3) game theory (which deals with "games" in which the
players have the opportunity to make choices and use rational strategies such
as in chess, where no chance is involved, or in poker, where a mixture of

chance and strategy occurs. Since business, politics, and war are "games," the theory can be applied to these subjects. John von Neumann (1903–1957) was the first to show that certain types of problems in game theory can be solved by reducing them to problems in linear programming). In recent years these areas of applications have been extended and developed, but the main emphasis has shifted to the general industrial area.

In 1947, Dantzig made the initial mathematical statement of the general problem of linear programming together with a systematic procedure for solving the problem. Because the solutions to many linear programming problems involve complicated computations, the advent of high-speed computing systems has helped to kindle the great interest in this subject. The first successful solution of a linear programming problem on a high-speed electronic computer occurred in 1952 at the U.S. National Bureau of Standards. Linear programming has now become an important part of both theoretical and applied mathematics, and is closely involved with matrix theory.

Linear programming problems that involve only two variables can be solved graphically, and we shall consider only this type. An examination of things that occur in the simple cases involving only two variables provides a great deal of insight into what can happen in the more general case with any number of variables.

We shall now use problems to help illustrate the meaning of linear programming.

PROBLEM 1

The Zingo Company manufactures two products: Jingos and Ringos. Each Jingo yields a profit of $3 and each Ringo earns $7. Because of various commitments and limited facilities, the company must manufacture at least 1 Jingo per day, but no more than 4; and at most 6 Ringos per day. Also, the number of Jingos cannot exceed the number of Ringos. How many of each should the company manufacture in order to obtain a maximum profit?

Solution:

First, let x = number of Jingos to be produced each day, y = number of Ringos to be produced each day, z = profit per day.

Now we can translate the problem into symbols as follows:

(1) $x \geq 1$ (at least 1 Jingo).
(2) $x \leq 4$ (at most 4 Jingos).
(3) $y \leq 6$ (at most 6 Ringos).
(4) $x \leq y$ (Jingos may not exceed Ringos).
(5) $x \geq 0, y \geq 0$ (not possible to produce a negative number of either product).

The preceding restrictions on x and y are called *constraints*, and the values of x and y that satisfy all of the constraints are called *feasible values*. Since each Jingo yields a profit of $3, the profit for Jingos will be $3x$ dollars per day. Similarly the profit from Ringos will be $7y$ dollars per day. Therefore we have

(6) $z = 3x + 7y$

and the problem can now be stated, "Find the feasible values of x and y that will yield the maximum value for z." We shall proceed to solve this problem with the aid of graphs. We shall first sketch the graph of each constraint by use of shading.

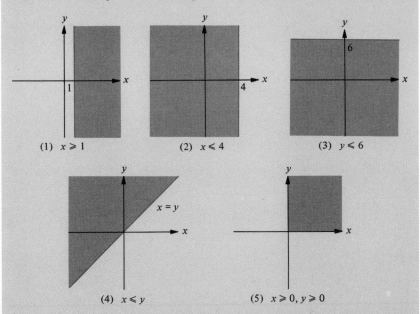

(1) $x \geqslant 1$ (2) $x \leqslant 4$ (3) $y \leqslant 6$

(4) $x \leqslant y$ (5) $x \geqslant 0, y \geqslant 0$

Since all five constraints must be satisfied by x and y, the graph of the set of feasible values (i.e., the *feasible region*) will be the intersection of all five graphs, which is the shaded region of Fig. 8.2.

The problem may now be stated geometrically as follows: "Find x and y from the shaded region of Fig. 8.2 that will produce a maximum value for $3x + 7y$." One way of proceeding is to select values of x and y from the feasible region and hope that the list contains the right one. For example, we may list the following:

x	1	1	1	1	2	4	4	3	2
y	1	2	4	6	6	6	4	4	5
$3x + 7y = z$	10	17	31	45	48	54	40	37	41

and can conclude that if judicious choices were made, then the right one is included—and hence the answer would be $x = 4$, $y = 6$. This method is not satisfactory (even though it may have yielded the correct answer),

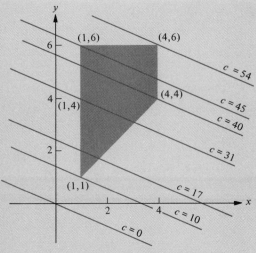

FIGURE 8.2.

and therefore we must use another device. Since our investigation is closely tied up with the graph of Fig. 8.2, we shall now try to learn more from it.

If $3x + 7y$ is to have a maximum value, then the largest value of c for which the line $3x + 7y = c$ intersects the feasible region will be the desired maximum value of z. In order to find this largest value of c, we shall superimpose lines of the form $3x + 7y = c$ (all of which will be parallel to one another) onto Fig. 8.2 with $c = 0, 10, 17, 31, 40, 45, 54$. We observe that e is larger when the line is further away from the origin. Since the line that is furthest from the origin and also intersects the feasible region is the one passing through the point $(4, 6)$ (i.e., when $c = 54$), we find that our earlier answer, which was obtained by selecting random values of x and y within the feasible region, was correct—but just by chance? We can now conclude that the Zingo Company will obtain a maximum profit if it produces 4 Jingos and 6 Ringos every day.

The solution to the preceding problem now leads us to the following reasonable conjecture.

CONJECTURE

The optimum value of z occurs at a corner point on the boundary of the feasible region.

If we had known that this conjecture was a theorem (for our problem at least), we could have solved the problem by merely computing $z = 3x + 7y$ at the corner points, and then concluding that the largest of these z values yields the solution.

The reader should test this conjecture in each problem.

PROBLEM 2

Suppose that a university wants to charter a sufficient number of aircraft to transport 500 students to an athletic event. Two types of aircraft are available. Type *A* carries 50 passengers, has a crew of 6 including 3 hostesses, and costs $1,000 for the trip. Type *B* carries 100 passengers, has a crew of 8, with 4 hostesses, and costs $3,000 for the trip. On the day of the trip 24 hostesses are available. How many of each type of aircraft should be chartered in order to perform this airlift at minimum cost?

Solution:

We shall let x denote the number of aircraft of type A, and y denote the number of aircraft of type B to be chartered. The data can then be tabulated as follows:

	Totals	Type *A*	Type *B*
Aircraft	$x + y$	x	y
Cost	$1,000x + 3,000y$	1,000	3,000
Passengers	500	50	100
Hostesses	24	3	4

We can now use the preceding table to obtain the following algebraic formulation of the problem:

Find x, y such that
  (1) $50x + 100y \geq 500$ (aircraft must be able to carry at least 500)
  (2) $3x + 4y \leq 24$ (24 hostesses available)
  (3) $x \geq 0$, $y \geq 0$ (cannot have negative number of aircraft)
  (4) $z = 1,000x + 3,000y$ to be minimized
We shall now proceed to graph the first two constraints [assuming constraint (3)]

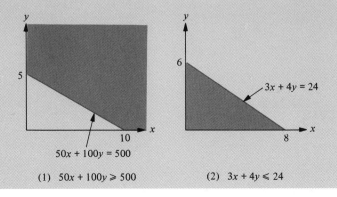

  (1) $50x + 100y \geqslant 500$ (2) $3x + 4y \leqslant 24$

The feasible region can now be represented as the intersection of the preceding two regions, as indicated in Fig. 8.3.

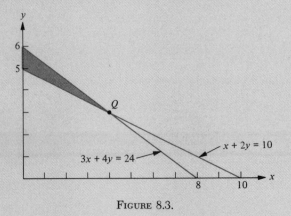

FIGURE 8.3.

To solve this linear programming problem, we must find the point or points in the feasible region that give the smallest value to z. We now proceed as before and consider lines of the form

$$1,000x + 3,000y = c.$$

By letting $c = 0, 1,000, 13,000, 15,000, 18,000, \ldots$ we find that the lines closer to the origin have smaller values of c. Of all these lines that intersect the feasible region, the one with the smallest value of c passes through point Q—a corner point! Thus our problem will be solved once we find the coordinates of Q. Since Q is at the intersection of the two lines

$$x + 2y = 10$$
$$3x + 4y = 24$$

we only need to find their common solution. Using methods developed in this chapter, we find that the solution is $x = 4$, $y = 3$. Hence, the university should charter four aircraft of type A and three aircraft of type B, if it wishes to minimize the cost.

Problem Set 8.7

1. Solve Problem 2 above when the cost of type A is \$2,000 but everything else remains the same.

2. Solve the following linear programming problems graphically and shade in the region representing the feasible solutions (i.e., the feasible region).

(a) $2x + y \leq 6$, $x + y \leq 4$, $x \geq 0$, $y \geq 0$.
$z = 5x + 3y$ is a maximum.

(b) $5x + 10y \leq 50$, $x + y \geq 1$, $y \leq 4$, $x \geq 0$ $y \geq 0$.
$z = x + y$ is a maximum.

(c) $x + 3y \geq 3$, $x + y \geq 2$, $x \geq 0$, $y \geq 0$.
$z = 3x + 5y$ is a minimum.

(d) $2x + y \geq 10$, $3x + 4y \leq 12$, $x \geq 0$, $y \geq 0$.
$z = x + y$ is a minimum.

3. A dining hall dietician wants to provide at least 16 units of Vitamin A, 5 units of Vitamin B, and 20 units of Vitamin C per serving. What is the minimum cost per serving (which satisfies the minimum vitamin requirement) if she has two choices of food (X and Y) available with the costs and contents of 1 ounce shown in the following table?

Food	Cost	Units of A	Units of B	Units of C
X	5¢	8	1	2
Y	10¢	2	1	7

4. A baker makes both bread and biscuits. Bread requires 1 hour mixing time, 6 hours rising time, and 2 hours baking time with a profit of $3 per batch. Biscuits require 1, 3, and 4 hours, respectively, for a $2 profit per batch. With a total of 20, 150, and 60 hours available for each process, respectively, how many batches of each should he bake for a maximum profit?

5. A manufacturer produces two different models, called X and Y. Each model must be processed by two machines, called I and II. To complete one unit of each model, the two machines must work the number of hours indicated in the following table. Neither machine may operate more than 12 hours a day. If the profit is $3 on each unit of model X and $6 on each unit of model Y, how many of each model should be produced each day in order to have a maximum profit?

	X	Y
I	3	1
II	1	3

CHAPTER 9

Game Theory

9.1 What Is Game Theory?

The word *game* is commonly used by both children and adults, and usually means competition between two or more persons—where a "person" might be a team, political party, business, army, country, or just plain person. In a competition, the *players* use *strategies* to win and the *prize* may be self-satisfaction, money, trophy, control, etc. Some people consider mathematics to be a game between human beings and Nature—since if a human plays according to the rules, nothing strange happens, but if he violates the rules, mathematical disasters may occur (e.g., see what happens when the 11th Commandment is violated in Example 4 of Section 1.1).

The great impetus to the theory of games was provided in 1944 by the appearance of the notable book *The Theory of Games and Economic Behavior*, written jointly by the mathematician John von Neumann and the economist Oskar Morgenstern, which resulted in part from a need to develop game theory techniques during World War II. The theory of games involves *games of strategy*, where it is assumed that players can influence the final outcome, and therefore that the outcome is not exclusively dependent upon chance. In this sense the parlor games of tick-tack-toe and chess (where no chance is involved) as well as bridge and poker (where a mixture of chance and strategy occur) are games of strategy. The theory of games is also applicable to serious "games," such as economic competition, politics, and war. In fact, the preceding description of games of strategy permits us to call *life* and *mathematics* games, but these are too complicated to be pursued here. However, since dice and Russian roulette (as usually formulated) are based exclusively on chance, they are studied in probability rather than in game theory.

The central features common to all games considered in the theory of games are:

(1) There is a set of rules for the players.
(2) There are at least two players with conflicting interests who choose their own actions (or strategies) within the rules of the game.

(3) All players will always make "intelligent" choices based on the available information, where "intelligent" choice is interpreted to mean "best" of the "worst." (Some readers may disagree with this psychological motivation for playing games, for they insist that some people play for the pleasure of winning long shots or for other reasons. Thus there is a legitimate basis for questioning the motivation attributed to the players, but not the mathematics resulting from our assumptions.)

The fundamental questions in the theory of games are:

(1) Are there "best" strategies for the players to adopt?

(2) If so, how can they be determined?

When we say, "A game has a solution," we shall mean "The 'best' strategy for each player can be found—after the meaning of 'best' is known."

In order to make the preceding discussion more meaningful, we shall now give some examples of games but will defer the development of their solutions to later sections.

EXAMPLE 1A   Matching Pennies

Two players, named R and C, each have a penny; and each one chooses either the pure strategy head (H) or the pure strategy tail (T) in ignorance of the other player's choice. Suppose R wins 1 unit if they both make the same choice and loses 1 unit if they make opposite choices. This game can be summarized by means of the following table.

R \ C	H	T
H	1	-1
T	-1	1

Here, the entries represent the payments from C to R. Thus if both R and C choose heads, R matches C and receives a payoff of 1 unit from him; but if R chooses heads and C tails, then R receives -1 from C (i.e., R pays 1 unit to C). The other two entries are determined similarly.

This game is an example of a *zero-sum* game since at the end of each play one person gains what the other loses, so that the sum of the amounts won by the players is always zero (where a loss is considered a negative win or negative payoff).

This game can be completely described with the aid of a matrix, and therefore it is called a *matrix game*. In particular, the following matrix is called the *payoff matrix to* R or the R-*payoff matrix* because the positive entries mean gains for R and the negative entries mean losses for R.

$$\begin{array}{cc} & \begin{array}{cc} H & T \end{array} \\ \begin{array}{c} H \\ T \end{array} & \begin{bmatrix} 1 & -1 \\ -1 & 1 \end{bmatrix} \end{array}$$

At this point, the reader should try to answer the following questions:
  (1) What is the "best" strategy for R?
  (2) What is the "best" strategy for C?
Before answering these questions, one naturally needs to know what is meant by "best" strategy?

EXAMPLE 2   Another Matrix Game
The reader may have observed that the Matching Pennies game, just described, can be played even if R and C have no pennies—for only the selections of "pure strategy H" and "pure strategy T" were involved. With this observation we can easily generalize that game by letting any matrix (whose elements are integers) serve as an R-payoff matrix.
We will now consider the matrix game which is determined by the following R-payoff matrix.

$$\begin{bmatrix} -2 & 7 & 1 & 9 \\ 6 & 5 & 4 & 5 \\ -8 & -6 & 0 & 3 \end{bmatrix}$$

This means that R selects a row (i.e., pure strategy 1, 2, or 3) and C, in ignorance of R's selection, chooses a column (i.e., pure strategy 1, 2, 3, or 4). (The reader should now be aware of the reason why we named our players R and C.) As soon as R selects a row and C selects a column, the game "has been played," and the element at the intersection of the selected row and column indicates the number of units paid to R. For example, if R has chosen strategy 1 and C has chosen strategy 4, then R is paid the amount in the first row and fourth column, namely, 9 units. If R and C both chose strategy 1, then R is paid -2 by C (i.e., R pays 2 units to C). The choice of a row is called a *pure strategy* for R, and the choice of a column is called a *pure strategy* for C.
At this point the reader should try to answer the following questions:
  (1) What is the "best" strategy for R?
  (2) What is the "best" strategy for C?
These questions can be combined into the single basic question, "How should R and C play in order to guarantee themselves as much as possible, no matter what selection the other player makes?"
We now leave this example with the following remark, which may come as a surprise: The solution to the game of Example 2 is far more immediate than that of Example 1A!

EXAMPLE 3A   Gasoline War—a Nonzero-sum Game
Players A and B own gasoline stations on opposite sides of the road, and no other stations are nearby. Let us assume the following three rules for the players:

(1) There are only two prices they can charge: high or low.
(2) At the start of each day they must decide which price they will charge, and are not permitted to change prices during the day.
(3) Their daily gross income is indicated in the following table.

A \ B	High	Low
High	(9, 9)	(5, 17)
Low	(17, 5)	(6, 6)

In each ordered pair of numbers enclosed in parentheses, the first number is A's income and the second number is B's income. For example, when A charges the high price and B charges the low price, we obtain the ordered pair (5, 17) which indicates that A will receive 5 and B will receive 17. In this way the table reveals

(1) If both charge the high price, each receives 9.
(2) If both charge the low (gas war) price, their income is cut to 6 for the day.
(3) If one charges the high price and the other the low price, the low-priced player will draw business away not only from his immediate competitor but also from elsewhere; and the increased volume of his business will yield him 17 and his opponent only 5.

This is an example of a *nonzero-sum* game, since one player does not lose what the other gains. The reader should now attempt to answer the following questions:

(1) If we assume that players A and B do not wish to cooperate or form a coalition (i.e., it is a *noncooperative* game), what are the "best" strategies for A and B?
(2) If we assume that players A and B want to cooperate (i.e., it is a *cooperative* game), what are the "best" strategies for A and B?

EXAMPLE 4A Voting Game I
In Corporation I, stockholder A owns 52 per cent of the stock, stockholder B owns 26 per cent, and the rest is distributed among the remaining stockholders. As usual, each stock certificate carries one vote and the policies of the corporation are determined by majority vote. Under these conditions one might expect the number of votes a stockholder has to be a good index of his power in the corporation. But if this were true, then we would have to agree that A has twice as much voting power as B, since 52 equals 2 times 26. However, in reality, A has all the power and B has none; and therefore we can conclude that A is a "dictator" and each of the other stockholders is a "dummy."

EXAMPLE 4B Voting Game II
Corporation II is owned by its three stockholders, A, B, and C, who hold
100, 200, and 300 shares, respectively. The reader should now try to
answer the following questions:
   (1) Are $\frac{1}{6}$, $\frac{1}{3}$ and $\frac{1}{2}$ reasonable measures for the relative voting power
       of A, B, and C, respectively?
   (2) If not, what are the reasonable measures?

The last two examples are called *n-person simple games*. Solutions to these
games provide useful information on the power of political groups to elect
their candidates, pass their bills, etc.

9.2 Matrix Games with Saddle Points

We shall now return to the matrix game of Example 2 in which the R-payoff
matrix is given by

$$\begin{bmatrix} -2 & 7 & 1 & 9 \\ 6 & 5 & 4 & 5 \\ -8 & -6 & 0 & 3 \end{bmatrix}$$

and shall try to find the "best" strategies for both R and C.

We first observe that R would like to win as much as possible (i.e., 9), but
he reasons that if he picks row 1 and C picks column 1, then he loses 2. Player
R now argues as follows: If I pick row 1, the worst that can happen is that
C picks column 1, and I lose 2. If my choice is row 2, the worst that can
happen is when C picks column 3 and I win 4. If my choice is row 3, the
worst that can happen is when C picks column 1 and I lose 8. Therefore,
the safest choice for me is row 2, because then I would win 4 even if C makes
the best possible choice for himself. Briefly, R looks at the minimum payoff
in each row (called the *row minima*) and chooses the maximum of the row
minima (i.e., the "best" of the "worst").

Similarly, C argues as follows: If my choice is column 1, the worst that
can happen is when R picks row 2, for then he wins 6. If my choice is column
2, the worst that can happen is when R picks row 1, for then he wins 7. If
my choice is column 3, the worst that can happen is when R picks row 2,
for then he wins 4. If my choice is column 4, the worst that can happen is
when R picks row 1, for then he wins 9. Therefore, the safest choice for me
is column 3 because it is then guaranteed that R can win no more than 4,
even if he makes the best possible choice for himself. Briefly, C looks at the
maximum payoff in each column (called the *column maxima*) and chooses the
column yielding the minimum of the column maxima (i.e., the "best" of the
"worst").

From the preceding investigation, we conclude that R should choose row
2 and C should choose column 3, so that R assures himself of winning at least
4 and C is sure that R will win no more than 4. The choice of row 2 is called

an *optimal pure strategy* for R, the choice of column 3 is called an *optimal pure strategy* for C, and 4 is called the *value of the game*.

We note that 4 is the smallest number in its row and the largest in its column. Such a number is called a *saddle value* and its position in the matrix (here row 2, column 3) is called a *saddle point* of the matrix. This term is used because of the analogy with the point P on a saddle that is a minimum in one direction and a maximum in another, as indicated in the following figure.

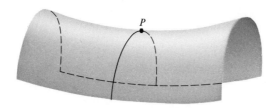

This matrix game was easily solved because there is a number in the matrix (i.e., 4) which is the smallest in its row and the largest in its column (i.e., a saddle value), for it was the existence of this number that gave rise to the concept of "optimal" or "best" strategies for both R and C (i.e., second row for R and third column for C).

The preceding discussion can be summarized as follows.

R \ C	1	2	3	4	Row minima
1	−2	7	1	9	−2
2	6	5	④	5	④
3	−8	−6	0	3	−8
Column maxima	6	7	④	9	

Problem Set 9.2

1. (a) Do you agree with the following remark concerning the preceding matrix game? "If C is really intelligent, his best strategy is to say 'I refuse to play, since this game is not fair to me.'" Why?
   (b) How would you define a "fair" matrix game? Give an example.

2. Determine which of the following R-payoff matrices have saddle points.

   (a) $\begin{bmatrix} 2 & 3 \\ 5 & 4 \end{bmatrix}$.   (b) $\begin{bmatrix} 1 & -1 \\ -1 & 1 \end{bmatrix}$.   (c) $\begin{bmatrix} 1 & 1 \\ 1 & 1 \end{bmatrix}$.

(d) $\begin{bmatrix} 0 & 0 \\ 0 & 1 \end{bmatrix}$.   (e) $\begin{bmatrix} 2 & 3 \\ 4 & 1 \end{bmatrix}$.

3. If each of the following represents an *R*-payoff matrix, find (i) optimal pure strategy for *R*, (ii) optimal pure strategy for *C*, and (iii) value of the game.

(a) $\begin{bmatrix} 2 & 0 \\ 7 & -2 \end{bmatrix}$.   (d) $\begin{bmatrix} 100 & -1 \\ 0 & 0 \end{bmatrix}$.

(b) $\begin{bmatrix} 0 & 0 \\ 0 & -1 \end{bmatrix}$.   (e) $\begin{bmatrix} 1 & -1 & 0 \\ 4 & 3 & 2 \end{bmatrix}$.

(c) $\begin{bmatrix} 7 & -7 & 0 & 6 \\ -1 & -3 & 2 & 5 \\ 3 & -2 & 3 & 4 \end{bmatrix}$.   (f) $\begin{bmatrix} -1 & -3 \\ 0 & -5 \end{bmatrix}$.

4. Use your answer to Problem 1b to determine which of the games in the preceding problem are "fair."

5. Let us assume that ping pong players *R* and *C* have two pure strategies: offensive (*O*) and defensive (*D*). If each of the following represents an *R*-payoff matrix, find (i) optimal pure strategy for *R*, (ii) optimal pure strategy for *C*, and (iii) value of the game.

(a) $\begin{array}{c} \\ O \\ D \end{array}\begin{array}{cc} O & D \\ \begin{bmatrix} -1 & -1 \\ 1 & 1 \end{bmatrix} \end{array}$.   (c) $\begin{array}{c} \\ O \\ D \end{array}\begin{array}{cc} O & D \\ \begin{bmatrix} -1 & -1 \\ 1 & 0 \end{bmatrix} \end{array}$.

(b) $\begin{array}{c} \\ O \\ D \end{array}\begin{array}{cc} O & D \\ \begin{bmatrix} 0 & -1 \\ 1 & 1 \end{bmatrix} \end{array}$.   (d) $\begin{array}{c} \\ O \\ D \end{array}\begin{array}{cc} O & D \\ \begin{bmatrix} 0 & -1 \\ 1 & 0 \end{bmatrix} \end{array}$.

6. Suppose town *T* has two wards and is about to have an election for mayor between the *X* and *Y* political parties. We further assume that each party has two representatives who can pass out leaflets favoring their own candidate. According to the rules, each party leader may send both of their representatives to one of the wards *or* one representative to each ward. If the same number of representatives appear at a given ward, the net advantage to each party is zero. Otherwise the party with the greater number of representatives wins the ward. Further, if two representatives of one party

and one representative of the other party show up at the same ward, then the lone representative is forced to distribute the leaflets of the opposing party, thus giving that party an additional advantage.

(a) If the X-payoff matrix is given as below, how should each party leader divide his representatives?

(b) What is the value of this game?

X \ Y	$0:2$	$1:1$
$0:2$	0	1
$1:1$	-1	0

7. Suppose bill collector B can collect 1 unit from customer C iff he arrives at C's house when C is at home, and otherwise can collect nothing.

(a) Write the B-payoff matrix for this game.

(b) Find the optimal pure strategies for both B and C.

(c) What is the value of this game?

8. Suppose student R plays the following game with Destiny (whose strategy is unpredictable). Student R has two pure strategies T and N with possible outcomes P and F, where T indicates he tries (i.e., studies hard), N indicates he does not try, P means he passes, and F means he fails. Let the following be the R-payoff matrix (where the payoffs are in "psychological units").

$$\begin{array}{c c c} & P & F \\ T & \begin{bmatrix} 10 & -20 \\ N & 2 & -1 \end{bmatrix} \end{array}$$

(a) What is the optimal strategy for R?

(b) Do you consider this optimal strategy to be intelligent? Explain.

9. True–False

The matrix $\begin{bmatrix} a & b \\ c & d \end{bmatrix}$

(a) can have two saddle points.

°(b) can have three saddle points.

(c) can have four saddle points.

°(d) can have two saddle points with two different saddle values.

(e) must have a saddle point if $a = b$.

(f) must have a saddle point if $a = c$.

(g) must have a saddle point if $a = d$.

(h) has value 0 if $a = d = 0$ and $b = -c$.

*10. True–False

In any R-payoff matrix

(a) The maximum of the row minima is less than or equal to the minimum of the column maxima.

(b) The maximum of the row minima is equal to the minimum of the column maxima iff the matrix has a saddle point.

9.3 Solution of the Matching Pennies Game

In order to find the "best" strategies for the Matching Pennies game described in Example 1A, we cannot use the technique developed in the previous section because the payoff matrix does not have a saddle point. We will therefore need to develop a new interpretation for "best" strategy.

First, let us review the Matching Pennies game by exhibiting its R-payoff matrix

R \diagdown C	H	T	Row minima
H	1	-1	-1
T	-1	1	-1
Column maxima	1	1	

From this arrangement, we observe that the maximum of the row minima is -1 whereas the minimum of the column maxima is 1, and therefore no saddle value can exist.

The question that now arises is, "How should this game be played?" If it is played a large number of times, it is clear that R should not always play the same pure strategy, say H; for if he did, C would (since he is supposed to be intelligent) always play the opposite, T, and thus win. Therefore, R should play H some fraction, p, of the time and T the rest, or $1 - p$, of the time. In the language of probability, we are saying that R must play H with probability p and T with probability $1 - p$, where $0 \leq p \leq 1$.

If C chooses H, then R's (mathematical) expectation is

(H) $$E_H = p(1) + (1 - p)(-1) = 2p - 1$$

If C chooses T, then R's expectation is

(T) $$E_T = p(-1) + (1 - p)(1) = 1 - 2p$$

It should be clear that R wants to maximize his expectation. Since

$$E_H < 0 \text{ when } p < \tfrac{1}{2},$$
$$E_T < 0 \text{ when } p > \tfrac{1}{2},$$

and

$$E_H = E_T = 0 \text{ when } p = \tfrac{1}{2},$$

we conclude that R should choose $p = \tfrac{1}{2}$, for otherwise he could have a negative expectation.

A similar argument applies to player C and the same result is obtained. Thus, the best strategy for each player is to choose H one half of the time; then there will be an expectation of zero for each.

This problem can also be solved with the aid of graphs. If we draw the graphs for Equations (H) and (T), we find

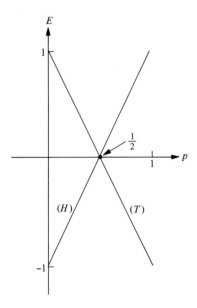

and note that $(\tfrac{1}{2}, 0)$ are the coordinates of the point of intersection. From the graph of (H) we observe that the "worst" expectations for R (i.e., the smallest values of E_H) occur when $p < \tfrac{1}{2}$, for then $E_H < 0$. Similarly, from the graph of (T) we observe that the "worst" expectations for R (i.e., the smallest values of E_T) occur when $p > \tfrac{1}{2}$, for then $E_T < 0$. Thus the "best" of the "worst" (or the maximum of the minima) expectations for R occurs when the "strategy" for R is $p = \tfrac{1}{2}$, $1 - p = \tfrac{1}{2}$. That is, the "optimal" strategy for R is to play H one half of the time and T one half of the time. With this "optimal" or "best" strategy, R's expectation is zero. Similar reasoning can be used to show that the "optimal" strategy for C is also $(\tfrac{1}{2}, \tfrac{1}{2})$—and that the expectation for R, when C uses this "optimal" or "best" strategy, is again zero.

We call the choice of rows for player R and columns for player C the *pure strategies* of R and C, respectively; and a choice of probabilities or relative frequencies, such as $(\frac{1}{2}, \frac{1}{2})$, with which to play these pure strategies is called a *mixed strategy*.

After players R and C have decided upon probabilities $(\frac{1}{2}, \frac{1}{2})$ for H and T, problems can still arise. For if R should decide to play H and T according to some fixed pattern (e.g., alternately), then C (assuming he is intelligent) would soon learn this pattern and play the opposite. Thus randomness of play is needed—and in order to insure this randomness, some chance device with probability $\frac{1}{2}$ should be used to determine the next choice. The reader may be aware that in this particular game, the players usually toss a coin, since it is a chance device with probability $\frac{1}{2}$. In this way the correct frequencies are not only attained, but the player himself does not know what he will play next and thus it cannot be known by the opposing player—even with ESP.

In this example our theory emerges with the same "best" mixed strategies as those that have been arrived at in practice throughout the years.

A mixed strategy of player R which maximizes his minimum expectations (i.e., is the "best" of the "worst" expectations) against C's pure strategies is called *optimal* or *best* for R; and a mixed strategy of player C which minimizes R's maximum expectations (i.e., is the "best" of the "worst" expectations) against R's pure strategies is called *optimal* or *best* for C. It can be proved that with mixed strategies in a matrix game, the maximum of the minimum expectations is always equal to the minimum of the maximum expectations. That is, every game has a saddle-point solution for expectations in mixed strategies. This so-called *minimax principle* was first proved by von Neumann in 1928 and forms the basis for much of the elaborate theory of games which has been developed in recent years.

In the next section we will state the minimax principle in symbolic form.

9.4 Matrix Games Without Saddle Points

If A is an $m \times n$ matrix with the element a_{ij} in the ith row, jth column, then the matrix game corresponding to A (i.e., A is the R-payoff matrix) can be written as

$$A = \begin{bmatrix} a_{11} & a_{12} & \cdots & a_{1n} \\ a_{21} & a_{22} & \cdots & a_{2n} \\ \cdot & \cdot & \cdots & \cdot \\ \cdot & \cdot & \cdots & \cdot \\ a_{m1} & a_{m2} & \cdots & a_{mn} \end{bmatrix}.$$

The choice of a row is a *pure strategy* for player R and the choice of a column is a *pure strategy* for player C. If there are optimal pure strategies (i.e., a saddle point), then these strategies are the solutions to the game. However, if there are no optimal pure strategies (i.e., no saddle point), then we must look for *optimal mixed strategies.*

If the first row is chosen with relative frequency (or probability) p_1, the second row is chosen with relative frequency p_2, etc., then the choice of probabilities

$$P = (p_1, p_2, \ldots, p_m),$$

where

$$p_i \geq 0 \qquad \text{and} \qquad p_1 + p_2 + \cdots + p_m = 1,$$

with which to play the rows is called a *mixed strategy* for R. Similarly, if the first column is chosen with relative frequency (or probability) q_1, the second column is chosen with relative frequency q_2, etc., then the choice of probabilities

$$Q = (q_1, q_2, \ldots, q_n),$$

where

$$q_j \geq 0 \qquad \text{and} \qquad q_1 + q_2 + \cdots + q_n = 1,$$

with which to play the columns is called a *mixed strategy* for C.

If C selects pure strategy j (where $1 \leq j \leq n$), then the expectation of R for the mixed strategy

$$P = (p_1, p_2, \ldots, p_m)$$

is

$$E(P, j) = p_1 a_{1j} + p_2 a_{2j} + \cdots + p_m a_{mj}$$

(since the first row is chosen with relative frequency p_1, the second row with relative frequency p_2, etc.). The "worst" value of $E(P, j)$, as far as R is concerned, is its minimum value as j runs through $1, 2, \ldots, n$. Symbolically we write this as

$$\text{For R: worst } E(P, j) = \min_{(\text{all } j)} E(P, j)$$
$$= \min\{E(P, 1), E(P, 2), \ldots, E(P, n)\}.$$

The "best" of these worst expectations for R is obtained by finding the mixed strategy

$$P = (p_1, p_2, \ldots, p_m)$$

of R that maximizes the quantity

$$\min_{(\text{all } j)} E(P, j).$$

The mixed strategy P which accomplishes this feat is called an *optimal mixed strategy* for R.

If R selects pure strategy i (where $1 \leq i \leq m$), then the expectation of R for the mixed strategy

$$Q = (q_1, q_2, \ldots, q_n)$$

of C is

$$E(i, Q) = q_1 a_{i1} + q_2 a_{i2} + \cdots + q_n a_{in}$$

(since the first column is chosen with relative frequency q_1, the second column with relative frequency q_2, etc.). The "worst" value of $E(i, Q)$, as far as C is concerned, is its maximum value as i runs through $1, 2, \ldots, m$. Symbolically we write this as

$$\text{For } C: \operatorname*{worst}_{(\text{all } i)} E(i, Q) = \operatorname*{max}_{(\text{all } i)} E(i, Q)$$
$$= \max\{E(1, Q), E(2, Q), \ldots, E(m, Q)\}.$$

The "best" of these worst expectations, for C, is obtained by finding the mixed strategy

$$Q = (q_1, q_2 \ldots, q_n)$$

of C which minimizes the quantity

$$\operatorname*{max}_{(\text{all } i)} E(i, Q).$$

The mixed strategy Q which accomplishes this feat is called an *optimal mixed strategy* for C.

Using the preceding symbolism, we can now state the fundamental theorem as follows:

THE MINIMAX THEOREM OF VON NEUMANN   *For any matrix game, there exist optimal mixed strategies P and Q for R and C, respectively, such that*

$$\operatorname*{min}_{(\text{all } Q)} \left[\operatorname*{max}_{(\text{all } i)} E(i, Q) \right] = \operatorname*{max}_{(\text{all } P)} \left[\operatorname*{min}_{(\text{all } j)} E(P, j) \right],$$

and this common value is called v or the value *of the game.*

Thus the Minimax Theorem is a *generalized saddle-point theorem*.

If $v > 0$, then the game is favorable to R; and if $v < 0$, then the game is favorable to C (since v is the expected winning value for R and the expected losing value for C). Therefore a matrix game is called *fair* iff $v = 0$ (e.g., the Matching Pennies game is fair).

EXAMPLE 1B   Modified Matching Pennies Game
Suppose the game is the same as the Matching Pennies game of Example 1A, except that the R-payoff matrix is

$$\begin{array}{cc} & \begin{array}{cc} H & T \end{array} \\ \begin{array}{c} H \\ T \end{array} & \left[\begin{array}{cc} 4 & -3 \\ -3 & 2 \end{array}\right]. \end{array}$$

We first observe that there is no saddle point, and hence no solution in pure strategies. Therefore we proceed to mixed strategies. Let us first assume that $0 \le p \le 1$. Then

$$P = (p,\, 1 - p)$$

is a mixed strategy for R. If player C selects pure strategy 1 (or H), then the expectation for R is

(1) $y_1 = E(P, 1) = p(4) + (1 - p)(-3) = 7p - 3$

If player C selects pure strategy 2 (or T), then the expectation for R is

(2) $y_2 = E(P, 2) = p(-3) + (1 - p)(2) = 2 - 5p$

If we graph Equations (1) and (2) we find

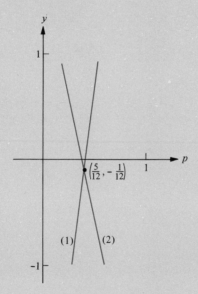

We first note that the coordinates of the point of intersection can be found by solving Equations (1) and (2) for their common solution. We then find that these coordinates are $p = \frac{5}{12}$ and $y = -\frac{1}{12}$, as indicated on the graph. The graph of Equation (1) reveals that the "worst" expectations for R (i.e., the smallest values of y_1) occur when $p < \frac{5}{12}$, for then $y_1 < -\frac{1}{12}$. Similarly, the graph of Equation (2) reveals that the "worst" expectations for R (i.e., the smallest values of y_2) occur when $p > \frac{5}{12}$, for then

$y_2 < -\frac{1}{12}$. Thus the "best" of the "worst" (or the maximum of the minima) expectations for R occurs when the mixed strategy for R is $p = \frac{5}{12}$, $1 - p = \frac{7}{12}$. That is, the optimal mixed strategy for R is to play H five twelfths of the time and T seven twelfths of the time. With this optimal strategy, R's expectation is $-\frac{1}{12}$.

Similar reasoning can be used to show that the optimal mixed strategy for C is also $(\frac{5}{12}, \frac{7}{12})$, and that the expectation for R, when C uses this optimal strategy, is again $-\frac{1}{12}$. Thus the value of the game is $-\frac{1}{12}$—which is clearly not fair to R, for it indicates that the use of optimal mixed strategies by both R and C would cause R to expect to lose one twelfth per play in the long run. This may come as a surprise, since the payoff matrix seems to suggest that R has an even chance of winning six or losing six.

Problem Set 9.4

1. For each of the following R-payoff matrices, find (i) optimal mixed strategy for R, (ii) optimal mixed strategy for C, and (iii) value of the game.

   (a) $\begin{bmatrix} 2 & 0 \\ 0 & 1 \end{bmatrix}$.   (b) $\begin{bmatrix} -1 & 1 \\ 2 & -1 \end{bmatrix}$.   (c) $\begin{bmatrix} 2 & 3 \\ 5 & 4 \end{bmatrix}$.

2. Suppose that a game with pure strategies Integrate (I) and Segregate (S) is played between people of the R and C races. If each of the following is an R-payoff matrix, find (i) optimal strategy for R, (ii) optimal strategy for C, and (iii) value of the game.

   (a) $\begin{array}{c} I \\ S \end{array}\begin{array}{cc} I & S \\ \begin{bmatrix} 5 & -2 \\ -2 & -1 \end{bmatrix} \end{array}$ (b) $\begin{array}{c} I \\ S \end{array}\begin{array}{cc} I & S \\ \begin{bmatrix} 3 & -1 \\ -2 & 0 \end{bmatrix} \end{array}$ (c) $\begin{array}{c} I \\ S \end{array}\begin{array}{cc} I & S \\ \begin{bmatrix} 4 & -1 \\ -2 & -1 \end{bmatrix} \end{array}$

3. Player R chooses a number from the set $\{1, 2\}$ and player C chooses a number from the set $\{1, 3\}$. If the sum of the two chosen numbers is odd, R wins; if the sum is even, C wins; and the amount won is the sum of the chosen numbers.
   (a) Write the R-payoff matrix.
   (b) Find the optimal strategies for both R and C.
   (c) Find the value of the game.

4. True–False
   If matrix A (given in this section) is an R-payoff matrix, then
   (a) Its optimal strategies are unique.

$^{\circ}$(b) $\max_{\substack{(all\ i)}} \left[\min_{\substack{(all\ j)}} a_{ij} \right] \leq \min_{\substack{(all\ j)}} \left[\max_{\substack{(all\ i)}} a_{ij} \right].$

$^{\circ}$(c) If $(1, 0, \ldots, 0)$ is an optimal mixed strategy for R and $(0, 1, \ldots, 0)$ is an optimal mixed strategy for C, then $v = a_{12}$.

$^{\circ}$**5.** Prove the Minimax Theorem for any 2×2 matrix game.

9.5 An Application of Linear Programming to Game Theory

When finding the solution to a matrix game without a saddle point, we became involved with maximum and minimum problems involving linear equations. Therefore one may suspect that game theory is related to linear programming—and it is!

The relationship between linear programming and game theory was first established by von Neumann. In this section we shall show how the Matching Pennies game can be solved as a problem in linear programming. In order to do this, we proceed by means of the following eight steps.

(1) Write down the R-payoff matrix:

$$A = \begin{bmatrix} 1 & -1 \\ -1 & 1 \end{bmatrix}.$$

(2) Add the same number (e.g., 2) to each element of A so that each new element is positive. The new matrix is

$$B = \begin{bmatrix} 3 & 1 \\ 1 & 3 \end{bmatrix}$$

and determines the matrix game between players R' and C' (read "R-prime" and "C-prime") in which B serves as the R'-payoff matrix. [It should be intuitively clear that the optimal mixed strategies for both R' and R are the same, and that the value of the B-matrix game is 2 more than the value of the A-matrix game. (See Problem 3.)]

(3) Let $p_i \geq 0$, $p_1 + p_2 = 1$, and (p_1, p_2) be a mixed strategy for both R and R'.

(4) Use matrix B to compute the expectation for R' after assuming (i) C' selects pure strategies 1 and 2, respectively, and (ii) w is the "worst" expected value for R'. We then have the following expected values for R'

(*) $\begin{cases} E_1' = p_1(3) + p_2(1) \geq w \\ E_2' = p_1(1) + p_2(3) \geq w. \end{cases}$

(5) Note that $w > 0$. Then divide each member of (*) by w to obtain

$$(**) \qquad \begin{cases} \dfrac{E_1'}{w} = 3\dfrac{p_1}{w} + 1\dfrac{p_2}{w} \geq 1 \\[2mm] \dfrac{E_2'}{w} = 1\dfrac{p_1}{w} + 3\dfrac{p_2}{w} \geq 1. \end{cases}$$

(6) Let $x_1 = p_1/w$ and $x_2 = p_2/w$, so that $(**)$ becomes

$$3x_1 + x_2 \geq 1$$
$$x_1 + 3x_2 \geq 1,$$

where $x_i \geq 0$ and $x_1 + x_2 = 1/w$.

(7) Since we want the "best" of the "worst" for R', our next step is to find the maximum value of w. But since $1/w = x_1 + x_2$, w will have its maximum value when $x_1 + x_2$ has its minimum value. Therefore, we will now search for x_1 and x_2 such that

$$3x_1 + x_2 \geq 1$$
$$x_1 + 3x_2 \geq 1$$
$$x_1 \geq 0$$
$$x_2 \geq 0$$

$$x_1 + x_2 = \frac{1}{w} \text{ is a minimum.}$$

This is clearly a problem in linear programming, which when it is solved graphically (letting $x = x_1$ and $y = x_2$) as below

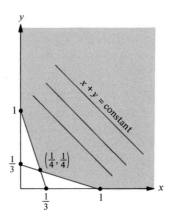

yields $x_1 = x_2 = \frac{1}{4}$; and thus

$$x_1 + x_2 = \frac{1}{w} = \frac{1}{2}$$

is the minimum value of $x_1 + x_2$. Hence $w = 2$ is the value of the new game.

(8) Since $x_1 = x_2 = \frac{1}{4}$ and $w = 2$, we find

$$p_1 = x_1 w = \frac{1}{4} \cdot 2 = \frac{1}{2}$$
$$p_2 = x_2 w = \frac{1}{4} \cdot 2 = \frac{1}{2},$$

and therefore the optimal mixed strategy for R is $(\frac{1}{2}, \frac{1}{2})$, and $v = 0$.

The optimal mixed strategy for C can be found in a similar way, and will be left as an exercise.

It turns out that every matrix game can be solved as a linear programming problem and also that every linear programming problem can be converted into a matrix game—and therefore matrix games and linear programming problems are equivalent.

Problem Set 9.5

1. Explain and justify the results of step (5).

2. In step (6) explain why $x_1 + x_2 = 1/w$.

3. If E_1 and E_2 represent the expectations for R when C selects pure strategies 1 and 2, respectively,
   (a) Write the formulas for E_1 and E_2.
   (b) Prove: $E_1' = 2 + E_1$ and $E_2' = 2 + E_2$.

4. (a) Solve the Matching Pennies game for R by use of linear programming, as above, *except* add 1 to each element of A in step (2).
   (b) Did you obtain the same final result? Why?

5. Use linear programming to find the optimal mixed strategy for R in each of the following R-payoff matrices.

   (a) $\begin{bmatrix} 5 & -2 \\ -2 & -1 \end{bmatrix}$.   (b) $\begin{bmatrix} 2 & 0 \\ 0 & 1 \end{bmatrix}$.

*6. Use linear programming to find C's optimal mixed strategy in the Matching Pennies game.

9.6 Nonzero-Sum Games

We will now return to the Gasoline-War game of Example 3A, which differs from the matrix games of Examples 1 and 2 because it is a *nonzero-sum game* (i.e., neither player gains what the other player loses). First, let us review this game by exhibiting the game rules as follows

A \ B	High	Low
High	(9, 9)	(5, 17)
Low	(17, 5)	(6, 6)

and invite the reader to return to Section 9.1 in case he has forgotten the meaning of the entries. When discussing this game earlier, we left the reader with two questions:

(1) If we assume that players *A* and *B* do not wish to cooperate or form a coalition (i.e., it is a *noncooperative* game), what are the "best" strategies for *A* and *B*?

(2) If we assume that players *A* and *B* want to cooperate (i.e., it is a *cooperative* game), what are the "best" strategies for *A* and *B*?

We will now investigate these questions separately.

CASE 1   NONCOOPERATIVE GAME

When both *A* and *B* charge the low price, the (6, 6) point is reached and therefore *A* and *B* will each receive 6 units. If either player now changes his strategy while his opponent maintains his, he will only succeed in cutting his own income. Therefore, (6, 6) is called an *equilibrium point*, and is also the *solution* to this game. The solution (6, 6) is also called *stable*, because neither player can, by himself, profitably change to another strategy.

The reader may feel that the equilibrium point solution does not make sense, because at the (9, 9) point each player is better off than at the equilibrium point. But the (9, 9) point is not stable, because either player can, by switching to the low price, improve his income from 9 to 17 (assuming that his opponent does not change).

CASE 2   COOPERATIVE GAME

If the players join together and cooperate to maximize their total intake, it should be clear that their "best" strategy is that one should charge High and the other Low—so that each player could obtain an income of 11 per day. This could be done in a variety of ways. For example, *A* and *B* could alternate the days on which they charged High and Low—or one could charge High every day and the other Low every day (saving them the trouble of changing signs), and then the "Low Man" could pay the "High Man" his share of the surplus.

The following nonzero-sum game illustrates a different type of application.

EXAMPLE 3B   The Student's Dilemma

While grading a test an instructor becomes suspicious when he finds identical answers for students *A* and *B*, who were sitting near each other. Since the instructor is determined to learn the truth, he isolates these two students and tells each one separately: "I believe that there has been cooperation between the two of you and I want you both to confess. However, if neither of you confesses there can be no penalty; if you both confess, then you will both lose 10 points; if one confesses, he will lose 5 points, whereas the other will lose 50 points. Therefore you had better confess before he does."

If we now organize the preceding information into a "game" by letting the pure strategies be designated by Y and N (for "Yes I confess' and "No I don't confess," respectively), then we have

A \ B	Y	N
Y	$(-10, -10)$	$(-5, -50)$
N	$(-50, -5)$	$(-0, -0)$

where the ordered pair $(-a, -b)$ means A loses a points and B loses b points. For example, if A confesses and B does not then the corresponding entry $(-5, -50)$ reflects that A loses 5 points and B loses 50 points.

Since $(-10, -10)$ is an equilibrium point (i.e., if one changes his strategy while the other maintains his, the changer's situation becomes worse), the best strategy is that both players should confess. But if both confess, they both do worse than if neither confesses. As in the Gasoline-War game, we conclude that it may be better for both to behave in an "unintelligent" way!

The preceding two examples illustrate the use of equilibrium point in obtaining a meaning for the solution to a noncooperative, nonzero-sum game. One may now ask whether every noncooperative, nonzero-sum game has an equilibrium point of pure strategies. The answer is no—but it turns out that there will always be an equilibrium point of mixed strategies.

Applications of the theory of games to areas such as economics, sociology, and political science often lead to nonzero-sum games.

9.7 Voting Games

We will now return to Example 4B, in which we revealed "Corporation II is owned by its three stockholders A, B, and C, who hold 100, 200, and 300 shares, respectively," and in which we raised the following two questions:

(1) Are $\frac{1}{6}$, $\frac{1}{3}$, and $\frac{1}{2}$ reasonable measures for the relative voting power of A, B, and C, respectively?

(2) If not, what are the reasonable measures?

Our next goal is to find reasonable answers to these questions.

We first note that there is a total of 600 votes and assume that a majority, or 301 votes, is a *winning coalition* (i.e., one that can elect candidates, pass resolutions, etc.). Now we will write down all possible orders (i.e., permutations) in which A, B, and C can enter the committee room.

$$AB\underline{C} \qquad BA\underline{C} \qquad C\underline{A}B$$
$$A\underline{C}B \qquad B\underline{C}A \qquad C\underline{B}A$$

A man is called *pivotal* (indicated by underline) if his entry into the room converts the set from a nonwinning coalition into a winning coalition. At this point it seems reasonable to say that the *relative voting power* or *power-index* of a player is directly related to the number of times he serves as a pivot, or, more formally, the probability that he is a pivot (when all arrangements of the players are regarded as equally likely). Hence the power-indices of A, B, and C are $\frac{1}{6}$, $\frac{1}{6}$, and $\frac{2}{3}$, respectively, since A and B serve as pivots once and C serves as a pivot four times. Thus, although C has $\frac{1}{2}$ of the votes, he has $\frac{2}{3}$ of the power; and although B has $\frac{1}{3}$ of the votes, he has only $\frac{1}{6}$ of the power.

We also observe that there cannot be a winning coalition without C, and therefore $\{C\}$ has a veto, or is a *blocking coalition*. It is customary to say that a set of players S is a *blocking coalition* iff neither S nor the players not in S form a winning coalition. Using this definition, we find that $\{A, B\}$ is another blocking coalition. Finally, the players not in a given winning coalition are said to form a *losing coalition*. Thus $\{B\}$ and $\{A\}$ are losing coalitions for Corporation II.

We will now consider an example of a voting game that has significance for all nations of the world.

EXAMPLE 4C   United Nations Security Council
The Security Council of the United Nations consists of 15 members, 5 of which are permanent and have veto powers. A winning coalition consists of 9 members, and must include all 5 of the permanent members. (In this example we are disregarding the possibility of abstention by a permanent member.)
Because the solution to this game is based on some formulas which are beyond the level of this book, we shall merely state the results. It turns out that the 5 permanent members have about 95 per cent of the voting power—or about 19 per cent each—and each nonpermanent member has about $\frac{1}{2}$ of 1 per cent of the voting power. Thus the veto gives the permanent members almost complete control over the Security Council. (For details see pages 320–327 of Owen's *Finite Mathematics*.)

Problem Set 9.7

1. If a corporation is owned by shareholders A, B, C, and a majority of votes (or shares) designates a winning coalition, find
   (i) the winning coalitions

    (ii) the losing coalitions
    (iii) the blocking coalitions
    (iv) the power-index for A, B, and C
        when the number of shares held by A, B, C are, respectively,

      (a) 500, 480, 20.   (e) 6, 4, 2.
      (b) 600, 500, 100.   (f) 4, 2, 1.
      (c) 5, 3, 1.   (g) 1, 1, 1.
      (d) 500, 300, 100.   (h) 100, 100, 100.

2. A corporation is owned by the four stockholders A, B, C, and D, who hold 1, 2, 3, and 4 shares of stock, respectively. If each share designates one vote and a majority of votes yields a winning coalition, find (a) the winning coalitions, (b) the losing coalitions, (c) the blocking coalitions, and (d) the power-index for A, B, C, and D.

3. A committee consists of the four members A, B, C, D with D as the chairman. If each member has 1 vote and there is majority rule, find the power-index of A, B, C, and D when the chairman has (a) ordinary voting privileges, °(b) voting privilege and power to break ties, °(c) voting privilege and veto power.

4. If a club has 5 members, each with one vote, and a certain two members agree to join forces and vote together at all times (i.e., form a coalition), then the voting game can be interpreted as having 4 players in which 1 "player" has 2 votes and the remaining players have 1 vote each. If there is majority rule,
   (a) What was the power-index of each player before the coalition?
   (b) What is the power-index of the coalition?
   (c) What is the power-index of each of the 3 players not in the coalition?

5. A university senate consists of the following 20 members: The president, 3 administrators, 12 faculty, and 4 students. If all 3 administrators and 9 of the faculty find that their "best" strategy is to always agree with the president and there is majority rule, what is the power-index of (a) the remaining 7 noncoalition members, (b) the president, (c) the president, if he has veto power.

6. True–False
   In a voting game,
   (a) The sum of the power-indices of all the players is always 1.
   (b) A set which is not a winning coalition must be a losing coalition.
   (c) The complement of a losing coalition is a winning coalition.

CHAPTER 10

Calculus

10.1 Introduction

Calculus has been called "the greatest invention of the human mind," "one of the cornerstones of modern mathematics," and "an indispensable tool of both the pure and applied sciences." Hence one may conclude that a person cannot be truly educated unless he has had some exposure to the calculus.

At some time in the past you may have asked questions about the calculus such as:

(1) *What* is it?
(2) *Why* was it invented?
(3) *Who* is responsible for it?
(4) *When* was it invented?
(5) *Where* was it invented?
(6) *How* does it work?

We shall now give answers to these questions in order to satisfy the curiosity of those who want to know.

WHAT?

Calculus can be described as the branch of mathematics that deals with *limiting processes*. It is divided into two parts called *differential calculus* and *integral calculus,* and they will now be discussed in a preliminary way.

Differential Calculus. The differential calculus deals with finding the (instantaneous) rate of change (roc) of one quantity with respect to (wrt) a second quantity. Some examples should help illustrate the meaning of this.

> NOTE: For the sake of simplicity we shall often omit all units of distance, time, and area. But this should not create any difficulty, since these units will be "implicitly present."

EXAMPLE 1
Suppose we know that a car has traveled 80 miles in 2 hours and we want to investigate its velocity during those 2 hours. One conclusion we can draw is that its average velocity was 40 miles per hour. (It should be noted that *average velocity*, which is the distance divided by the time, can be translated "average roc of distance wrt time".) If we also know that the car was traveling at a constant velocity, we can conclude that the car's speedometer (assuming it is accurate) always read 40 miles per hour—or that the "instantaneous roc of the distance wrt time" was 40 miles per hour at each instant.

EXAMPLE 2
Let P be a particle, with a built-in gauge, which is programmed to move s feet in t seconds according to the law $s = 2t$ (i.e., at the end of 1 second, $s = 2$; at the end of 2 seconds, $s = 4$, etc.). If we draw the graph of $s = 2t$ when $t \geq 0$, as below,

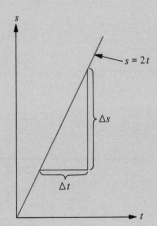

we note that it is a straight line. Therefore the ratio $\Delta s/\Delta t$, which is its slope, is a constant. This $\Delta s/\Delta t$ ratio represents the average roc of s wrt t and the average velocity of P in the time interval Δt—as well as the slope, and because it is a constant (i.e., 2) it has the same value no matter how small Δt is. Hence, P's speedometer shows 2 at each instant. Using the terminology of both mathematics and physics, the last statement can be translated into the following:

At each instant, the instantaneous velocity of P
$\qquad$ = the instantaneous roc of s wrt t

$\qquad$ = the limiting value of $\dfrac{\Delta s}{\Delta t}$ as Δt "approaches" zero

$\qquad$ = 2 feet per second.

Using the symbols of calculus, we write $ds/dt = 2$, where ds/dt (read "*ds dt*") is called the "derivative of s wrt t" or the "instantaneous roc of s wrt t" and represents the limiting value of $\Delta s/\Delta t$ as Δt "approaches" zero. Sometimes the symbol s' (read "s prime") is used in place of ds/dt.

We should note that it was very easy to find ds/dt in this example because P was traveling at a constant velocity.

EXAMPLE 3

Suppose L is a vertical line 2 units long which is moving along horizontally at the rate of 1 unit per second. Then L generates a rectangle of area A equal to $2x$ square units at the end of x seconds, as indicated in the figure below. If x is increased by Δx so that we have a corresponding increase in A, designated by ΔA (as in the figure), it should be clear that

$$\Delta A = 2\,\Delta x \qquad \text{or} \qquad \frac{\Delta A}{\Delta x} = 2,$$

where $\Delta A/\Delta x$ represents the average roc of A wrt x in the time interval Δx. Since $\Delta A/\Delta x = 2$ square units per second no matter how small Δx is, it follows that the limiting value of $\Delta A/\Delta x$ as Δx "approaches" zero is also equal to 2 square units per second. Using the symbols of the calculus, we write $dA/dx = 2$, where dA/dx represents the limiting value of $\Delta A/\Delta x$ as Δx "approaches" zero—or the instantaneous roc of A wrt x.

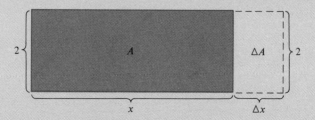

The statement

$$\frac{dA}{dx} = 2$$

might tempt one to write

$$dA = 2\,dx,$$

where intuitively dA means "a little change in A" or "a little bit of A" and dx means "a little change in x" or "a little bit of x." Later on we shall see that these interpretations for dA and dx are both valid and useful, when they are translated properly.

We should note that this example is a very simple one because the instantaneous roc is equal to the average roc. This resulted from the fact that the average roc was a constant, which in turn resulted from the fact that L was of constant length.

Integral Calculus. The fundamental problem of the integral calculus is:
Given:
   (1) The instantaneous roc of one quantity wrt a second quantity, and
   (2) the value of the first quantity for *some* given value of the second quantity.
Find:
The value of the first quantity for *any* given value of the second quantity.

We observe that this problem is essentially the reverse of the differential calculus problem, and we shall now exhibit some examples to confirm this.

EXAMPLE 4
Suppose particle P has a built-in speedometer and travels a distance of s feet in t seconds according to some law. If we are told that
   (1) The instantaneous roc of s wrt t is always 2 feet per second (i.e., P's speedometer always reads 2, which means that P always has an instantaneous velocity of 2 feet per second), and
   (2) P starts out at the initial point of reference (so that $s = 0$ when $t = 0$), then it should be clear that $s = 2t$ is the distance P has traveled at the end of t seconds (since $s = 2$ when $t = 1$, $s = 4$ when $t = 2$, etc.). Hence $s = 2t$ is the law we are seeking.
Using the symbols of the calculus, this integral calculus problem and solution can be stated as follows:
Given:

   (1) $\dfrac{ds}{dt} = 2$ (or $ds = 2\ dt$),

   (2) $s = 0$ when $t = 0$.

Find: s at any time t.

Solution:

$$s = \int_0^t 2\ dt = 2t,$$

where the expression in the middle is read "the integral of $2\ dt$ from 0 to t." (One may suspect that the integral sign $\int$, which looks like an elongated S, may have something to do with the word sum. Later on we shall see that indeed it does.)

If we draw the graphs of both

$$s' = \frac{ds}{dt} = 2 \qquad \text{and} \qquad s = 2t$$

when $t \geq 0$, we find

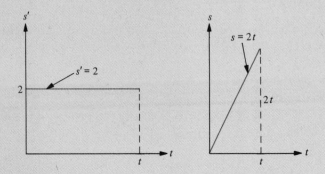

and observe that
  (1) $s = 2t$ is the area of the rectangle in the first figure,
  (2) $s' = 2$ is the slope of the line in the second figure,
thus providing us with a close relationship between slope and area.
The reader should now compare this example with Example 2.

EXAMPLE 5
If we modify Example 4 by assuming that the instantaneous roc of s wrt
t is still 2 feet per second, but that P starts out at a distance of 7 feet
from the initial point of reference (so that $s = 7$ when $t = 0$), then it should
be clear that $s = 2t + 7$ is P's distance from the initial point at the end of
t seconds.

EXAMPLE 6
Suppose L is a vertical line 2 units long which is moving along horizontally
at the rate of 1 unit per second, and L generates a region of area A such
that $dA = 2\,dx$ (as indicated in the following figure). If we assume that
there was no area when L started out (i.e., $A = 0$ when $x = 0$), then it
should be clear that $A = 2x$ at the end of x seconds.

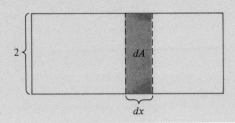

Using the symbols of calculus, this problem and solution can be stated:
Given:

(1) $dA = 2\,dx$ or $\dfrac{dA}{dx} = 2,$

(2) $A = 0$ when $x = 0.$
Find: A for any value of $x.$

Solution:

$$A = \int_0^x 2\,dx = 2x.$$

At this point we believe some readers may object to our procedure by saying, "Why bother with the dA and dx—for it is obvious that the region is a rectangle and therefore its area is length times width or $2x$?" Although we admit that this is a valid objection, we can defend our approach by replying, "It is this very dA and dx type of approach that is useful in solving problems that cannot be solved by previous methods—as we shall see."

We should now admit that all of the preceding examples are trivial and somewhat uninteresting because each instantaneous roc was a constant (i.e., 40 in Example 1 and 2 in each of the other examples). However, each of the examples contained a basic idea of the calculus—and it turns out that interesting and important results emerge when these basic ideas are applied to problems involving variable roc. In fact, the calculus is of fundamental importance because of its effectiveness in dealing with situations in which the roc is variable.

WHY?

Three problems gave rise to calculus. They are
(1) The problem of tangents.
(2) The problem of maxima and minima.
(3) The problem of areas.
The Problem of Tangents. This problem involves finding the slope of the tangent line to a curve at a point. For example, if the "nice" curve C is given and a tangent T_1 is drawn to the curve at P_1, as shown in the following figure,

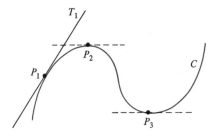

then the problem is to find the slope of T_1. It should be clear that the slope of the tangent line varies from point to point, since C is not a straight line. As we shall see, this problem leads us directly to an instantaneous roc, and therefore to the differential calculus.

The Problem of Maxima and Minima. In the preceding figure we observe that "nice" curve C has a maximum at P_2 and a minimum at P_3 and that the slopes of the tangent lines at both P_2 and P_3 are zero. Hence the problem of finding maximum and minimum points of "nice" curves is directly related to the problem of tangents, which means that this problem also leads us to the differential calculus.

The Problem of Areas. If we are given a "reasonably nice" curve C and want to find the area A bounded by C, the x-axis, and the vertical lines $x = a$ and $x = b$ (as shown below), we are intuitively led to the equation

$$dA = y \, dx \qquad \text{or} \qquad \frac{dA}{dx} = y,$$

which (after we have developed sufficient machinery) leads us to

$$A = \int_a^b y \, dx.$$

Hence, this problem leads us to the integral calculus.

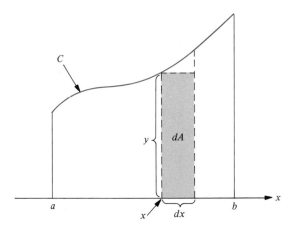

In this chapter we shall find solutions to the preceding three problems. In addition to serving as a tool for solving these problems, the calculus can be used to solve a wide range of "practical" problems—some of which were mentioned in previous chapters and others of which will be considered in this chapter. The reader who is interested in learning about more applications is invited to consult books such as Fobes and Smyth's *Calculus and Analytic Geometry* or Ceder and Outcalt's *A Short Course in Calculus*, 2nd ed.

WHO?

It is generally conceded that the real inventors of the calculus were Sir Isaac Newton (1642–1727) and Baron Gottfried Wilhelm von Leibniz (1646–1716). From their names one might guess that Newton was English and Leibniz was German. As the story goes, Newton invented his calculus about ten years before Leibniz invented his, but Leibniz published his calculus first—and this led to a heated 100-year controversy between England and Germany concerning who was the "true" inventor of the calculus. Because of nationalistic pride, it turned out that the continental mathematicians (including the Bernoullis and Euler) made far better progress during this time because they used the notation of Leibniz, while the English mathematicians clung to the awkward symbolism of Newton. It is interesting to note that today the notation of Leibniz is commonly used by all mathematicians throughout the world.

WHEN?

It is thought that Newton invented his calculus about 1665 and Leibniz invented his calculus about 1675. Although the first publication on the calculus was in 1684 (by Leibniz), the year 1680 is often given as the birth-year of the calculus.

WHERE?

From the preceding discussion one may conclude that the calculus was invented in both England and Germany.

HOW?

Probably the best way to find out how calculus works is to take a course or read a book that gives a real introduction to the subject. (Three of the best books, all with the title *Calculus*, are by Apostol, Bers, and Spivak.) In this chapter we shall give an intuitive approach to some of the basic concepts and techniques of the calculus.

10.2 Velocities and Slopes

In the simple-minded situation in Example 2 of the previous section we observed:
(1) The slope was constant.
(2) The (instantaneous) velocity was constant.
(3) The velocity was numerically equal to the slope.
We shall now consider more complicated situations.

EXAMPLE 1

Suppose a speedometer is attached to a particle P which is programmed to travel a distance of s feet in t seconds according to the law

$$s = t^2,$$

and we want to predict the reading on P's speedometer when $t = 1$ [i.e., we want to know $v(1)$—which will be our symbol for representing the (instantaneous) velocity of P when $t = 1$]. We will develop two methods for solving this problem.

Method I

One way of proceeding is to construct a table such as the following:

t	1	2	3	4
s	1	4	9	16

We observe that when t goes from 1 to 4, s goes from 1 to 16; and therefore P's average velocity in this time interval is

$$\bar{v}(1, 4) = \frac{\Delta s}{\Delta t} = \frac{16 - 1}{4 - 1} = \frac{15}{3} = 5.$$

Similarly we find

$$\bar{v}(1, 3) = \frac{\Delta s}{\Delta t} = \frac{9 - 1}{3 - 1} = \frac{8}{2} = 4$$

and

$$\bar{v}(1, 2) = \frac{\Delta s}{\Delta t} = \frac{4 - 1}{2 - 1} = \frac{3}{1} = 3.$$

From these calculations one may guess that $v(1)$ is less than 3, and that the correct value for $v(1)$ can be found by considering the following sequence:

$$\bar{v}(1, 1.5), \ \bar{v}(1, 1.1), \ \bar{v}(1, 1.01), \ \bar{v}(1, 1.001), \ \ldots.$$

However, this would eventually involve some complicated calculations, which makes it an unpleasant approach to the problem unless a computer is used. Even then, we would just be getting closer and closer to $v(1)$ without ever arriving there—for we are seeking the limiting value of a sequence with infinitely many different terms, and hence would not expect to reach an exact answer in a finite period of time.

Since this method appears to be leading us up a blind alley, we shall try another approach. We shall first write an algebraic expression for $\bar{v}(1, j)$ and assume that $j > 1$. Then, since $\bar{v}(1, j)$ represents the average velocity of P when t goes from 1 to j, $v(1)$ can be found by letting j "approach" 1.

In taking the first of these steps, we find

(1) $$\bar{v}(1, j) = \frac{\Delta s}{\Delta t} = \frac{j^2 - 1}{j - 1}.$$

If we now let j "approach" 1, we find ourselves in a very unpleasant situation—for the right-hand member of Equation (1) becomes converted to 0/0, which is meaningless (e.g., see Section A.2). We can avoid this unpleasantness by letting

(2) $$j = 1 + \Delta t.$$

For then $\Delta t > 0$ and Equation (1) becomes

(3) $$\bar{v}(1, 1 + \Delta t) = \frac{\Delta s}{\Delta t} = \frac{(1 + \Delta t)^2 - 1}{(1 + \Delta t) - 1} = \frac{2\,\Delta t + \overline{\Delta t}^2}{\Delta t} = 2 + \Delta t$$

by use of the distributive law, etc. Then, since j "approaches" 1 iff Δt "approaches" 0, $v(1)$ can be found from Equation (3) by letting Δt "approach" 0. We thus obtain

(4) $$v(1) = 2,$$

and the problem is solved.

Method II

Another method of attacking this problem is by means of a graph. Our first step will be to draw the graph of $s = t^2$ when $t \geq 0$, as indicated in the following figure.

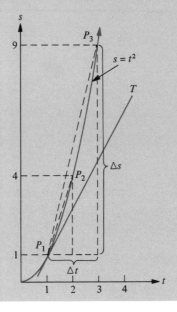

We then observe that $\bar{v}(1, 3)$ is the slope of $\overline{P_1P_3}$, $\bar{v}(1, 2)$ is the slope of $\overline{P_1P_2}$—and since the tangent line $\overline{P_1T}$ is the limiting position of $\overline{P_1P_j}$ as j "approaches" 1 (e.g., j takes on the values 1.5, 1.1, 1.01, 1.001, etc.), we would expect $v(1)$ to be the slope of $\overline{P_1T}$.

Now that we have observed the close connection between velocity and slope, we need to answer the question, "Since $v(1)$ is the slope of the tangent line to the curve at P_1, how can we find this slope?"

We could answer this question if we could find an algebraic expression for the slope of the tangent line. Since the tangent line $\overline{P_1T}$ is the limiting position of the lines $\overline{P_1P_3}$, $\overline{P_1P_2}$, $\overline{P_1P_{1.5}}$, . . . , and the slope of each of these lines is $\Delta s/\Delta t$, we can conclude that the slope of $\overline{P_1T}$ can be found by obtaining $\Delta s/\Delta t$ and then letting Δt "approach" zero (without ever reaching zero; e.g., let Δt take on the values 2, 1, .5, .1, .01, .001, . . .). We will now proceed with this task.

Since the coordinates of every point on the curve must satisfy the equation $s = t^2$ and the point $(1 + \Delta t, 1 + \Delta s)$ lies on the curve, it follows that

(5) $$1 + \Delta s = (1 + \Delta t)^2.$$

On expanding we obtain

(6) $$1 + \Delta s = 1 + 2\,\Delta t + \overline{\Delta t}^2,$$

and therefore

(7) $$\Delta s = 2\,\Delta t + \overline{\Delta t}^2.$$

If we now divide each member of Equation (7) by Δt (which we know is different from zero), we obtain

(8) $$\frac{\Delta s}{\Delta t} = 2 + \Delta t.$$

Therefore the limiting value of $\Delta s/\Delta t$ as Δt approaches 0 $\Big($symbolized by $\lim\limits_{\Delta t \to 0} \dfrac{\Delta s}{\Delta t}\Big)$ is 2. We have thus found that $v(1) = 2$, and our problem is again solved.

EXAMPLE 2

We shall again assume that particle P has a speedometer attached to it and is programmed to travel a distance of s feet in t seconds according to the law $s = t^2$. But now we want to be able to predict the reading on P's speedometer at *any* time t [i.e., we want to find $v(t)$—which will be our symbol for representing the (instantaneous) velocity of P at time t].

We shall first draw a *magnified graph* of $s = t^2$ for $t \geq 0$ and then consider two points on this graph, called Q and R, as indicated in the following figure.

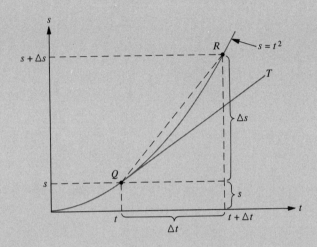

As before, we can find $v(t)$ by first obtaining the average velocity $\Delta s / \Delta t$ from time t to time $t + \Delta t$, and then letting Δt "approach" 0. It will probably come as no surprise that $v(t)$ is numerically equal to the slope of the tangent line $\overline{QT}$. Therefore we have

$$(9) \qquad\qquad v(t) = \text{slope of } \overline{QT} = \lim_{\Delta t \to 0} \frac{\Delta s}{\Delta t}.$$

In order to find this limiting value we proceed as before by observing that if a point lies on a curve, its coordinates must satisfy the equation of that curve. Then since Q and R lie on the curve, we have

$$(10) \qquad\qquad s = t^2$$

and

$$(11) \qquad\qquad s + \Delta s = (t + \Delta t)^2,$$

respectively. This latter equation can be written as

$$(12) \qquad\qquad s + \Delta s = t^2 + 2t\,\Delta t + \overline{\Delta t}^2$$

after the right-hand member is expanded. If we now subtract Equation (10) from Equation (12) we obtain

$$(13) \qquad\qquad \Delta s = 2t\,\Delta t + \overline{\Delta t}^2,$$

and dividing each member of (13) by Δt (which we know is different from zero), we obtain

(14)
$$\frac{\Delta s}{\Delta t} = 2t + \Delta t.$$

Therefore Equation (9) yields

(15)
$$v(t) = \lim_{\Delta t \to 0} \frac{\Delta s}{\Delta t} = 2t,$$

and our problem is solved.

Since the value of $2t$ varies with the value of t, it should be clear that $v(t)$ is not a constant in this example. We now want to emphasize that although the instantaneous velocity at time t and the slope of the tangent line to the curve at point (t, s) are not constants (as in Example 2 of Section 10.1), the instantaneous velocity at time t is still numerically equal to the slope of the tangent line at point (t, s) [as indicated in Equation (9)], and one may suspect that this is true in general.

This relationship between instantaneous velocity and slope of tangent line is significant, and the investigation of either of these entities leads to the study of the differential calculus—when dealing with nontrivial situations.

Problem Set 10.2

1. If particle P travels a distance of s feet in t seconds according to some law and the graph is drawn, does it necessarily follow that its instantaneous velocity at time t is numerically equal to the slope of the tangent line at point (t, s)? Explain.

2. If particle P travels a distance of s feet in t seconds according to the law $s = t^2 + t$, find
   (a) The instantaneous velocity of P when $t = 2$.
   (b) The slope of the tangent line to the curve $s = t^2 + t$ at the point $(2, 6)$.
   (c) The instantaneous velocity of P at any time t.
   (d) The slope of the tangent line to the curve $s = t^2 + t$ at the point (t, s).

10.3 Functions

In the previous section we were concerned with the particle P which is programmed to move a distance of s feet in t seconds according to the law $s = t^2$. In this situation the value of s "depends on" the value of t—or using mathematical terminology we say s "is a function of" t. Since mathematicians are often lazy people, they like to use symbols, and often replace "a function of" with the symbol f. Hence they may replace "s is a function of t" with "$s = f(t)$" [read "s equals f of t"].

We can now describe the motion of particle P as follows:

$$s = f(t) \qquad \text{where} \qquad f(t) = t^2,$$

and should note that the expression $s = f(t)$ merely means that s "depends on" t in some way.

There are many advantages in having the symbol $f(t)$. For example, when determining values for s when t takes on the values 1, 2, 3, we observe that $s = 1$ when $t = 1$, $s = 4$ when $t = 2$, $s = 9$ when $t = 3$; and the $f(t)$ notation permits us to write these three statements more compactly as $f(1) = 1$, $f(2) = 4$, $f(3) = 9$, respectively.

Another observation, which may seem trivial, is that $s = f(t)$ means "when the value of t is given, the value of s is determined." Therefore in the expression $s = f(t)$, t is called the *independent variable* and s, which "depends on" t, is called the *dependent variable*.

Since the most common independent variable is x and the most common dependent variable is y, we shall now summarize the preceding discussion by describing $y = f(x)$. Four useful descriptions or translations of $y = f(x)$ are:

(1) y is a function of x.

(2) y depends on x.

(3) If x is given, y is (uniquely) determined.

(4) f is a "rule" which assigns to each x in some set X a (unique) value $f(x)$ (called y) in some set Y.

The reader should observe that (3) and (4) reveal the meaning of $y = f(x)$, whereas (1) and (2) are merely translations.

EXAMPLE
If $f(x) = 2x + 1$, then $f(0) = 2 \cdot 0 + 1 = 1$, $f(1) = 2 \cdot 1 + 1 = 3$, $f(2) = 2 \cdot 2 + 1 = 5$, $f(-1) = 2(-1) + 1 = -1$, $f(a) = 2a + 1$, $f(w) = 2w + 1$, $f(x + h) = 2(x + h) + 1$, etc. In order to obtain the graph of this function we let $y = f(x)$ and draw the graph of $y = 2x + 1$. Since this graph is a straight line, $2x + 1$ is called a *linear function*.

In the previous section we introduced the symbol $v(t)$ to represent the instantaneous velocity of particle P at time t. This $v(t)$ symbol was a convenient one because it designated the value of the velocity when the time t was given. Since $v(t)$ "depends on" t for its value in the sense that the value of $v(t)$ is determined when the value of t is given, we can now conclude that $v(t)$ is a function of t, and that the symbol v designates the function or rule.

Any symbol can be used to designate a function—and although f is most common, the symbols F, g, h are frequently used. It should be emphasized that each such symbol merely represents a rule.

When we started out in Example 2 of the previous section, we could not be sure that $v(t)$ would be equal to a single expression in t—but nevertheless $v(t)$ represented a function of t. The statement "y is equal to an expression in x" can always be translated $y = f(x)$. However, it sometimes turns out that $y = f(x)$ even though y is not equal to any expression in x. For example, the cost y of sending a parcel post package depends on its weight x, and therefore we can write $y = f(x)$—but $f(x)$ cannot be replaced by a single expression in x. Other examples are (1) the temperature y at a given place on a certain day depends on the time x, so that $y = F(x)$; and (2) the height y of Queen Elizabeth II is a function of her age x and therefore we can write $y = g(x)$. Thus the concept of function reaches beyond the world of formulas.

Problem Set 10.3

1. If $f(x) = 1/x$, find: (a) $f(2)$, (b) $f(1)$, (c) $f(0)$, (d) $f(-1)$, (e) $f(-2)$, (f) $f(p)$, (g) $f(p) + f(q)$, (h) $f(p + q)$.

2. If $g(x) = x^3$, find: (a) $g(1)$, (b) $g(-1)$, (c) $g(2)$, (d) $g(-2)$, (e) $g(0)$, (f) $g(w)$, (g) $g(-w)$, (h) $g(x + h)$.

3. If $h(t) = (t - 3)/(t + 1)$, find: (a) $h(2)$, (b) $h(3)$, (c) $h(0)$, (d) $h(-1)$, (e) $h(q)$, (f) $h(-3)$.

4. Let the absolute value of x be designated by the symbol $|x|$. If $|x| = x$ when $x \geq 0$ and $|x| = -x$ when $x < 0$ [e.g., $|3| = 3$ and $|-3| = -(-3) = 3$],
   (a) Draw the graph of $y = |x|$.
   (b) Is $|x|$ a function of x?

5. Draw the graph of each of the following, and indicate which of them determine y as a function of x.
   (a) $y = 3$.
   (b) $y^2 = x$.
   (c) $y = 1$ when $x \geq 0$ and $y = 2$ when $x \leq 0$.
   (d) $y = 1$ when $x \geq 0$ and $y = 2$ when $x < 0$.
   (e) $x = 3$.

6. If $f(x)$ is a function of x,
   (a) Does $[f(p) = f(q)]$ imply that $[p = q]$?
   (b) Does $[p = q]$ imply that $[f(p) = f(q)]$?

7. Find a function $f(x)$ such that
   (a) $f(ax) = af(x)$.
   (b) $f(x + y) = f(x) + f(y)$.
   (c) Both (a) and (b) hold.

*8. Make up an example of a function $f(x)$ that cannot be written as a single expression in x.

9. Is the statement, "The capitol city y of a country depends on the country x," an example of $y = f(x)$? Explain.

10.4 The Derivative and Geometry

In Section 10.2 we were interested in finding the instantaneous velocity of a particle that moved a distance of s feet in t seconds according to some law, and our investigation led us to the expression

$$\lim_{\Delta t \to 0} \frac{\Delta s}{\Delta t}.$$

Since this expression is of theoretical and practical importance even when s does not represent distance and t does not represent time, we shall now generalize it by replacing t, s by x, y, respectively (with the understanding that x and y may be interpreted in various ways), and shall give it a name.

DEF 10.4.1
If y is a function of x, then

$$\frac{dy}{dx} \equiv \lim_{\Delta x \to 0} \frac{\Delta y}{\Delta x},$$

where Δx (which is *always* different from zero) designates a change in x, Δy designates a change in y (as indicated in Fig. 10.1), and the symbol on the right should be interpreted to mean: first find $\Delta y/\Delta x$ and then let Δx "approach" zero. The symbol dy/dx is read "dy dx" and is called the *derivative of y with respect to x at the point* (x, y). If $y = f(x)$, symbols commonly used in place of dy/dx include y' and $f'(x)$ (read "y prime" and "f prime of x," respectively).

The reader may now ask, "Does every function have a derivative at every point?" It turns out that only a "nice" function has a derivative at every point, and that a "nice" function has a "nice" graph. The fact that some functions do not have derivatives at certain points will not hinder us, since we will only be dealing with "nice" functions.

We observe that dy/dx represents an instantaneous velocity when $x = t$ and $y = s$ (where, as usual, t represents time and s represents distance), and hence we have a physical interpretation for dy/dx. In order to find a geometric interpretation for dy/dx we will first draw the nice graph of a nice function $y = f(x)$, as indicated in Fig. 10.1.

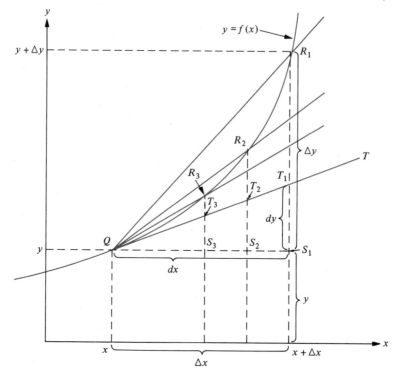

FIGURE 10.1.

The reader should now observe:

(1) $\dfrac{\Delta y}{\Delta x}$ is the slope of $\overline{QR_1}$.

(2) $\overline{QT}$ is the tangent line to the graph of $y = f(x)$ at $Q(x, y)$.

(3) As $\Delta x \to 0$: (a) R_1 slides down the curve toward Q (making brief stops at R_2, R_3, etc. so that $\overline{QR_2}$, $\overline{QR_3}$, etc., can be drawn),

(b) $\overline{QR_1} \to \overline{QT}$, and

(c) slope of $\overline{QR_1} \to$ slope of $\overline{QT}$.

(4) By virtue of steps (3) and (1):

$$\lim_{\Delta x \to 0} \frac{\Delta y}{\Delta x} = \text{slope of } \overline{QT}.$$

(5) Hence Def. 10.4.1 and step (2) yield

$$\frac{dy}{dx} = \left\{\begin{array}{l}\text{slope of the tangent line to the graph} \\ \text{of } y = f(x) \text{ at the point } (x, y).\end{array}\right\}$$

This geometric interpretation of dy/dx is one of the basic properties of the calculus, and we shall now give it a formal listing.

THEOREM 10.4.1 *If $f(x)$ is a nice function, then dy/dx is the slope of the tangent line to the graph of $y = f(x)$ at the point (x, y).*

After finding a geometric interpretation for dy/dx one may wonder whether there are geometric interpretations for dy and dx. Therefore we shall return to Fig. 10.1. Now since dy/dx represents the slope of $\overline{QT}$, we are naturally tempted to try to represent dy as a "rise" and dx as a "run" so that

$$\frac{dy}{dx} = \frac{\text{rise}}{\text{run}} = \text{slope of } \overline{QT}.$$

It should be clear that the dy and dx shown in Fig. 10.1 can properly serve in these roles of rise and run. However, $\overline{S_2T_2}$ and $\overline{QS_2}$ as well as $\overline{S_3T_3}$ and $\overline{QS_3}$ could also serve as dy and dx (where it should be understood that we are now using the symbol for a line segment to represent its length).

We note that when Δx is smaller, dy is a better approximation to Δy. For example, when $\Delta x = \overline{QS_3}$, dy is closer to Δy (where $dy = \overline{S_3T_3}$ and $\Delta y = \overline{S_3R_3}$) than when $\Delta x = \overline{QS_1}$ (for then $dy = \overline{S_1T_1}$ and $\Delta y = \overline{S_1R_1}$). Thus dy can serve as a good approximation to Δy when Δx is "small," and is therefore called an approximate change in y. This property of dy can be very useful because it is often easier to calculate dy than Δy, as we shall see.

The preceding geometric interpretations for dy and dx make it possible for us to consider dy/dx as a fraction, and this in turn makes it legitimate for us to write

$$dy = f'(x)\, dx$$

whenever $y = f(x)$ is a nice function and $dy/dx = f'(x)$.

Our geometric interpretations for dy and dx can now be used to motivate the following definition.

DEF 10.4.2
If $y = f(x)$ is a nice function, then $dx \equiv \Delta x$ and $dy \equiv f'(x)\, dx$. The symbols dx and dy are called *differentials*, dx is called the *differential of x*, and dy is called the *differential of y*.

From the preceding definition, we observe that $dx = \Delta x$ can be selected at will, but dy is completely determined by $f'(x)$ and dx.

Now that we have succeeded in finding significant geometric interpretations for dy/dx, dy, and dx, we shall consider some examples.

EXAMPLE 1
Problem:
Find the slope of the tangent line to the graph of $y = x^2$ at the point $(3, 9)$.

Solution:

If we let $f(x) = x^2$, then Theorem 10.4.1 reveals that the slope of the tangent line to the graph of $y = f(x)$ at $(3, 9)$ is the value of dy/dx at $x = 3$, which can be symbolized by $f'(3)$. In order to find $f'(3)$, we will first need to find dy/dx. We will now proceed to find dy/dx by means of the following steps.

(I) Write the equation:

$$(1) \qquad y = x^2.$$

(II) Replace x by $x + \Delta x$ so that y becomes $y + \Delta y$ and $(x + \Delta x, y + \Delta y)$ is a point on the graph of Equation (1). Therefore,

$$(2) \qquad y + \Delta y = (x + \Delta x)^2 = x^2 + 2x \Delta x + \overline{\Delta x}^2,$$

since the coordinates of every point on a graph satisfy the equation of the graph.

(III) Subtract Equation (1) from Equation (2):

$$(3) \qquad \Delta y = 2x \Delta x + \overline{\Delta x}^2.$$

(IV) Divide each member by $\Delta x \neq 0$:

$$(4) \qquad \frac{\Delta y}{\Delta x} = 2x + \Delta x.$$

(V) Take the limit of each member as $\Delta x \to 0$:

$$(5) \qquad \lim_{\Delta x \to 0} \frac{\Delta y}{\Delta x} = 2x.$$

(VI) Apply Def 10.4.1:

$$(6) \qquad \frac{dy}{dx} = f'(x) = 2x.$$

The answer to the problem is now found to be $f'(3) = 6$, which indicates that the tangent line at the point $(3, 9)$ is rising and is very steep.

Besides providing us with the answer to the problem, Formula (6) can be used to reveal some properties of the graph of $y = x^2$. For example, it shows that the slope of the tangent line varies from point to point and in particular:

(1) If $x > 0$, then $\dfrac{dy}{dx} > 0$ and hence the graph is rising.

(2) If $x < 0$, then $\dfrac{dy}{dx} < 0$ and hence the graph is falling.

(3) If $x = 0$, then $\dfrac{dy}{dx} = 0$ and hence $(0, 0)$ is a *stationary point*.

These features can now be used to assist us in drawing the graph of $y = x^2$, as indicated in the following figure.

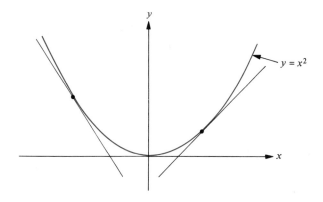

EXAMPLE 2

Let S be an expanding square whose sides are increasing at the rate of 1 unit per second, so that each side is x units long at the end of x seconds. Then at the end of x seconds the area of S is

(7) $$A = x^2,$$

and at the end of $x + \Delta x$ seconds the area of S is

(8) $$A + \Delta A = (x + \Delta x)^2,$$

as indicated in the following figure.

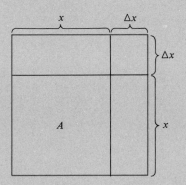

Since Equations (7) and (8) are essentially the same as Equations (1) and (2) of Example 1 when A is replaced by y, we can use the results of that example to obtain

(9) $$\Delta A = 2x\,\Delta x + \overline{\Delta x}^2$$

and

(10)
$$\frac{dA}{dx} = 2x.$$

If we now apply Def 10.4.2, then Equation (10) can be written as

(11)
$$dA = 2x\, dx = 2x\, \Delta x.$$

The preceding diagram reveals that ΔA is indeed the exact change in A when x is increased by Δx, and that

$$dA = \Delta A - \overline{\Delta x}^2;$$

so that dA is a "good" approximation to ΔA when Δx is "small." For example, if we want to find the change in area, ΔA, when the length of a side of S increases from 5 to 5.04, we can use Equation (9) to obtain

$$\Delta A = 2(5)(.04) + (.04)^2 = .4016.$$

However, the approximate change in area, dA, which can be found by means of Equation (11), turns out to be

$$dA = 2(5)(.04) = .4$$

which is "very close" to ΔA—and is therefore probably a good approximation to ΔA.

Problem Set 10.4

°**1.** Find an example of a function which is not "nice."

2. Find the slope of the tangent line to the graph of $y = x^2$ at each of the following points: (a) (2, 4), (b) (0, 0), (c) (−2, 4).

3. Let C be an expanding circle whose radius is increasing at the rate of 1 unit per second, so that its radius is x units at the end of x seconds. If A represents the area of C at the end of x seconds, find (a) ΔA, (b) dA.

4. If the area of a circular ring is considered to be an increment of area of a circle, find the approximate area of a ring whose inner and outer radii are 3 feet and 3.02 feet respectively.

5. If particle P moves a distance of s feet in t seconds according to the law $s = t^2$, find the approximate change in the *velocity* when t changes from 4 to 4.03.

°6. If the volume of a spherical shell is considered to be an increment of volume of a sphere, find the approximate volume of a spherical shell whose outer diameter is 8 inches and whose thickness is .02 inches.

7. True–False
  (a) If $f(x)$ is a nice function, then $d[f(x)] = f'(x)\,dx$.
  °(b) If $f(x)$ is a nice function of x and $f'(x) = 0$ when $x = 2$, then the graph of $y = f(x)$ has a maximum or minimum at the point where $x = 2$ and $y = f(2)$.

10.5 The Delta Process

Now that we have seen some interesting interpretations for the derivative, we shall develop a procedure for finding derivatives.

In Example 1 of the previous section we found dy/dx by means of the following steps:

(I)   Write

(1) $$y = f(x).$$

(II)   Replace x by $x + \Delta x$ so that y becomes $y + \Delta y$ and $(x + \Delta x, y + \Delta y)$ is a point on the graph of Equation (1). Therefore:

(2) $$y + \Delta y = f(x + \Delta x),$$

since the coordinates of every point on a graph satisfy the equation of the graph.

(III) Subtract Equation (1) from Equation (2):

(3) $$\Delta y = f(x + \Delta x) - f(x)$$

(IV) Divide each member by $\Delta x \neq 0$:

(4) $$\frac{\Delta y}{\Delta x} = \frac{f(x + \Delta x) - f(x)}{\Delta x}$$

(V)   Take the limit of each member as $\Delta x \to 0$:

(5) $$\lim_{\Delta x \to 0} \frac{\Delta y}{\Delta x} = \lim_{\Delta x \to 0} \frac{f(x + \Delta x) - f(x)}{\Delta x}$$

(VI) Hence:

(6) $$\frac{dy}{dx} = \lim_{\Delta x \to 0} \frac{f(x + \Delta x) - f(x)}{\Delta x}.$$

This procedure is called the *Delta Process*, and the reader should now return to Example 1 of the previous section to see how this process was used there. We shall now apply the Delta Process to some other nice and simple functions.

EXAMPLE 1 $y = 3$
 (I) $y = 3$.
 (II) $y + \Delta y = 3$.
 (III) $\Delta y = 0$.

 (IV) $\dfrac{\Delta y}{\Delta x} = 0$.

 (V) $\lim\limits_{\Delta x \to 0} \dfrac{\Delta y}{\Delta x} = 0$.

 (VI) $\dfrac{dy}{dx} = 0$.

This result should come as no surprise, since the graph of $y = 3$ is a horizontal line and the slope of a horizontal line is zero. Also, if particle P moves a distance of y feet in x seconds according to the law $y = 3$, then clearly P is stationary and therefore its instantaneous velocity $dy/dx = 0$ at all times.

It should be clear that if the number 3 were replaced by any other real number, we would obtain the same result—and therefore we have the following theorem.

THEOREM 10.5.1 *If $y = c$, then $dy/dx = 0$.*

We note that the result in the preceding theorem could also be stated as: (1) $dc/dx = 0$, (2) $c' = 0$, or (3) the derivative of a constant is zero.

EXAMPLE 2 $y = x$
 (I) $y = x$.
 (II) $y + \Delta y = x + \Delta x$.
 (III) $\Delta y = \Delta x$.

 (IV) $\dfrac{\Delta y}{\Delta x} = 1$.

 (V) $\lim\limits_{\Delta x \to 0} \dfrac{\Delta y}{\Delta x} = 1$.

 (VI) $\dfrac{dy}{dx} = 1$.

This result should have been predicted since $y = x$ represents a straight line whose slope is 1.

EXAMPLE 3 $y = mx + q$
 (I) $y = mx + q$.
 (II) $y + \Delta y = m(x + \Delta x) + q = mx + m \Delta x + q$.

(III) $\Delta y = m \, \Delta x.$

(IV) $\dfrac{\Delta y}{\Delta x} = m.$

(V) $\lim\limits_{\Delta x \to 0} \dfrac{\Delta y}{\Delta x} = m.$

(VI) $\dfrac{dy}{dx} = m.$

Again the result was predictable since $y = mx + q$ represents a straight line with slope m.

EXAMPLE 4 $y = ax^2$

(I) $y = ax^2.$

(II) $y + \Delta y = a(x + \Delta x)^2 = ax^2 + 2ax \, \Delta x + a \, \overline{\Delta x}^2.$

(III) $\Delta y = 2ax \, \Delta x + a \, \overline{\Delta x}^2$

(IV) $\dfrac{\Delta y}{\Delta x} = 2ax + a \, \Delta x$

(V) $\lim\limits_{\Delta x \to 0} \dfrac{\Delta y}{\Delta x} = 2ax.$

(VI) $\dfrac{dy}{dx} = 2ax.$

In this situation we observe that the slope of the tangent line varies from point to point if $a \neq 0$. The reader should try to draw other conclusions from this result.

EXAMPLE 5 $y = ax^2 + bx + c$

(I) $y = ax^2 + bx + c.$

(II) $y + \Delta y = a(x + \Delta x)^2 + b(x + \Delta x) + c$

$\qquad\qquad = ax^2 + 2ax \, \Delta x + a \, \overline{\Delta x}^2 + bx + b \, \Delta x + c.$

(III) $\Delta y = 2ax \, \Delta x + a \, \overline{\Delta x}^2 + b \, \Delta x.$

(IV) $\dfrac{\Delta y}{\Delta x} = 2ax + a \, \Delta x + b.$

(V) $\lim\limits_{\Delta x \to 0} \dfrac{\Delta y}{\Delta x} = 2ax + b.$

(VI) $\dfrac{dy}{dx} = 2ax + b.$

We now ask the reader, "Could you have predicted this result?"

While using the Delta Process or the Six-Step Method, the reader may feel like a machine. In particular, he may feel like a programmed robot, but he should assure himself that he is really performing a noble task!

Problem Set 10.5

1. Use the result of Example 4 as an aid in graphing $y = -x^2$.

2. Use the Delta Process to find dy/dx when:
  (a) $y = 7x$.
  (b) $y = 3x^2 - x + 4$.
  °(c) $y = x^3$.
  °(d) $y = 2x^3$.
  °(e) $y = ax^3 + bx^2 + cx + e$.
  °(f) $y = x^4$.
  °(g) $y = 7x^4$.

  °(h) $y = \dfrac{1}{x}$.

  °(i) $y = \sqrt{x}$ [where $(\sqrt{x})^2 = x$].
  °(j) $y = \sqrt[3]{x}$ [where $(\sqrt[3]{x})^3 = x$].

10.6 Some Shortcuts

If we are given

$$y = 4x^2 + 5x + 2,$$

the reader may guess that dy/dx can be found by taking the derivative of each term separately to obtain

$$\frac{dy}{dx} = 8x + 5;$$

and the Delta Process can be used to show that this answer is correct. But although the statement "the derivative of the sum is equal to the sum of the derivatives" sounds legitimate and works in the preceding example, can we be sure that it will always work? We shall now proceed to answer this question, and others, by listing some shortcuts for finding the derivative. These shortcuts will permit us to avoid the Delta Process, except on rare occasions.

THEOREM 10.6.1 *If U and V are nice functions of x, c is any constant, and*

$$y' = \frac{dy}{dx}, \quad U' = \frac{dU}{dx}, \quad V' = \frac{dV}{dx}, \quad then:$$

(a) *If $y = U + V$, then $y' = U' + V'$ (i.e., the derivative of a sum is the sum of the derivatives).*

(b) *If $y = cU$, then $y' = cU'$ (i.e., the derivative of a constant times a function is the constant times the derivative of the function).*

(c) *If $y = U - V$, then $y' = U' - V'$ (i.e., the derivative of a difference is the difference of the derivatives).*

(d) *If $y = UV$, then $y' = U'V + UV'$ (i.e., the derivative of a product is the derivative of the first times the second, plus the first times the derivative of the second).*

Before proving the various parts of this theorem, we shall give some examples.

EXAMPLE OF (b)
If $y = 7x^2$, then $y' = 7(2x) = 14x$.

EXAMPLE OF (c)
If $y = 9x - x^2$, then $y' = 9 - 2x$.

EXAMPLE OF (d)
If $y = (x^2 + 2)(5x + 3)$, then
$$y' = 2x(5x + 3) + (x^2 + 2)(5) = 15x^2 + 6x + 10$$

We will now use either the Delta Process or previous results to prove parts (a), (b), and (c) of Theorem 10.6.1. (Since the proof of part (d) is more interesting than the others, we shall leave it as an exercise for the reader.) However, we should admit that we will be assuming basic rules for limits, which are probably intuitively evident.

Proof of (a):
By use of the Delta Process we have

(I) $y = U + V.$

(II) $y + \Delta y = U + \Delta U + V + \Delta V.$

(III) $\Delta y = \Delta U + \Delta V.$

(IV) $\dfrac{\Delta y}{\Delta x} = \dfrac{\Delta U}{\Delta x} + \dfrac{\Delta V}{\Delta x}.$

(V) $\lim\limits_{\Delta x \to 0} \dfrac{\Delta y}{\Delta x} = \lim\limits_{\Delta x \to 0} \dfrac{\Delta U}{\Delta x} + \lim\limits_{\Delta x \to 0} \dfrac{\Delta V}{\Delta x}.$

(VI) $\dfrac{dy}{dx} = \dfrac{dU}{dx} + \dfrac{dV}{dx}.$

Proof of (b):

By use of the Delta Process we have

(I) $y = cU.$

(II) $y + \Delta y = c(U + \Delta U) = cU + c\,\Delta U$

(III) $\Delta y = c\,\Delta U.$

(IV) $\dfrac{\Delta y}{\Delta x} = c\,\dfrac{\Delta U}{\Delta x}.$

(V) $\lim\limits_{\Delta x \to 0} \dfrac{\Delta y}{\Delta x} = c\,\lim\limits_{\Delta x \to 0} \dfrac{\Delta U}{\Delta x}.$

(VI) $\dfrac{dy}{dx} = c\,\dfrac{dU}{dx}.$

Proof of (c):

Since $-V = (-1)V$, it follows that

$$y = U - V = U + (-1)V.$$

Therefore parts (a) and (b) can be used to obtain

$$\frac{dy}{dx} = \frac{dU}{dx} + (-1)\frac{dV}{dx} = \frac{dU}{dx} - \frac{dV}{dx}.$$

We could now use the rules for finding derivatives of sums, differences, and products of functions, if we knew the derivatives of some functions. Since a most basic function is x^n, we shall now try to find a shortcut for obtaining the derivative of this function.

In order to find a formula for y' when $y = x^n$ and n is a positive integer, we shall first see what happens when $n = 1, 2, 3, 4$.

By virtue of Example 2 of the previous section,

$$(y = x) \quad \text{yields} \quad (y' = 1).$$

If we now apply the *product rule* [i.e., Theorem 10.6.1(d)], we find that

$$(y = x^2 = x \cdot x) \quad \text{yields} \quad (y' = 1 \cdot x + x \cdot 1 = 2x)$$
$$(y = x^3 = x^2 \cdot x) \quad \text{yields} \quad (y' = 2x \cdot x + x^2 \cdot 1 = 3x^2)$$
$$(y = x^4 = x^3 \cdot x) \quad \text{yields} \quad (y' = 3x^2 \cdot x + x^3 \cdot 1 = 4x^3),$$

and therefore we are led to suspect that

(1)
$$\boxed{\text{If } y = x^n, \text{ then } y' = nx^{n-1}}$$

We observe that Formula (1) holds when $n = 1$ if we assume

(2)
$$x^0 = 1,$$

and this we shall do. It turns out that Formula (1) is true when n is *any* positive integer, and this can be proved by means of *mathematical induction*. Thus, Formula (1) serves as the desired shortcut.

Problem Set 10.6

1. True–False
   (a) The derivative of a product is the product of the derivatives.
   *(b) If V is a nice function of x and $\Delta x \to 0$, then $\Delta V \to 0$.

2. Find y' when
   (a) $y = \dfrac{x^2}{10}$

   (b) $y = 6x^2 + x - 5$
   (c) $y = (2 - 7x)(1 - x^3)$.

*3. Prove part (d) of Theorem 10.6.1

4. Use part (d) of Theorem 10.6.1 to prove part (b).

5. If $y = x^5 = x^4 \cdot x$, use the product rule to find y'.

6. Use Formula (1) to find y' when $y = x^{100}$.

7. If U is a nice function of x, find y' when (a) $y = U^2$, (b) $y = U^3$,
   (c) $y = U^4$, (d) $y = U^5$, *(e) $y = U^n$.

*8. If $y = (x^2 + 1)^5$, find y' by use of part (d) of the preceding problem.

*9. If $y^2 = x$, find y'.

*10. If U, V, and W are nice functions of x, and b is any constant different
   from zero, find y' if (a) $y = U/b$, (b) $y = UVW$, (c) $y = 1/V$,
   (d) $y = U/V$.

*11. Prove that Formula (1) holds when n is a negative integer. (**HINT:**
   Let m be a positive integer, $n = -m$; and assume $x^{-m} = 1/x^m$.)

10.7 Maxima and Minima

If C is a nice curve with both maximum and minimum points, such as the
one appearing on page 212, then it should be clear that it has a horizontal
tangent at both its maximum and minimum points, and hence that the slope
of the tangent line is zero at both its maximum and minimum points. Therefore, if y is some nice function of x, we can find its maximum and minimum
points by setting $y' = 0$. We shall now illustrate this procedure by means of
examples in both the geometric and "practical" worlds.

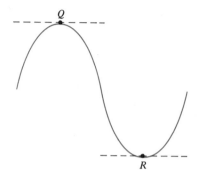

EXAMPLE 1
Problem:
Find all maximum and minimum points for the graph of

$$y = 3x^2 - 6x + 5.$$

Solution:
Using the results of the previous section we obtain

$$y' = 6x - 6,$$

and since $y' = 0$ yields $x = 1$, we know that any maximum or minimum point must have its x coordinate equal to 1. In order to determine whether $x = 1$ yields a maximum or minimum (or possibly neither), we could:
(a) test the values of y on either side of $x = 1$, or
(b) test the values of y' on either side of $x = 1$.
On examining the preceding figure we observe that when going from left to right: y' goes from $+$ to $-$ when passing the maximum point Q, and y' goes from $-$ to $+$ when passing the minimum point R. Since this change in the sign of y' can be used to characterize maximum and minimum points, and

$$y' < 0 \text{ when } x < 1 \quad \text{and} \quad y' > 0 \text{ when } x > 1,$$

we can conclude that y' goes from $-$ to $+$ and hence $x = 1$ yields a minimum. Since $y = 2$ when $x = 1$, the answer to our problem is that the graph has a minimum at $(1, 2)$ and no maximum point.

EXAMPLE 2
Problem:
Find all maximum and minimum points for the graph of $y = x^3$.

Solution:
Since $y' = 3x^2$, $y' = 0$ yields $x = 0$. It should be clear that $y' > 0$ on either side of $x = 0$, and therefore the graph has neither a maximum nor minimum. This property is illustrated in the following figure.

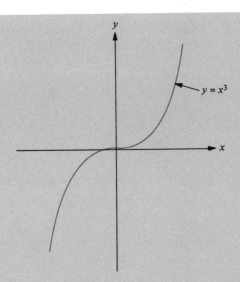

$y = x^3$

EXAMPLE 3

Problem:

A rectangular garden is to be formed and enclosed by 100 yards of fencing. Find the dimensions of the rectangle that will provide a maximum area for the garden.

Solution:

Let the length and width of the rectangle be designated by x and y, respectively. Then the perimeter is

$$(1) \qquad\qquad 2x + 2y = 100,$$

and the area which is to be maximized is

$$(2) \qquad\qquad A = xy.$$

In order to maximumize A we first need to write A as a function of x, and this is easily accomplished by use of Equation (1). For that equation yields $x + y = 50$, and hence

$$(3) \qquad\qquad y = 50 - x;$$

and substituting this value for y into Equation (2) provides us with

$$(4) \qquad\qquad A = x(50 - x) = 50x - x^2.$$

Now that A is written as a function of x, we can proceed to maximize A by finding A' and setting it equal to zero. Since $A' = 50 - 2x$, $A' = 0$ yields $x = 25$; and hence $y = 25$ by virtue of Equation (3). We can now conclude that the area is a maximum when both dimensions are 25 yards.

The reader may now ask, "How do you know that $A' = 0$ yields a maximum? Why couldn't it yield a minimum?" The answer is given in the Doctrine: "If E is a 'natural entity' to be maximized or minimized, then the equation $E' = 0$ yields the optimal solution for E"—and those readers who are nonbelievers are hereby invited to test each result for themselves.

EXAMPLE 4

Problem:

A ball B is thrown upward so that it reaches a height of s feet in t seconds according to the law

$$(5) \qquad\qquad s = 96t - 16t^2$$

What is the maximum height reached by B?

Solution:

Since $s' = 96 - 32t$, $s' = 0$ yields $t = 3$. Hence (by the Doctrine enunciated in Example 3) B reaches its maximum height at the end of 3 seconds, and this maximum height can be obtained by substituting $t = 3$ into (5). In this way we find that the maximum height reached by B is 144 feet.

In this problem s' represents the instantaneous velocity of B at the end of t seconds, and when we are solving $s' = 0$ for t we are finding the instant at which B is stationary (i.e., not traveling upward or downward). Thus we see an advantage in interpreting slope as a velocity.

EXAMPLE 5

Problem:

The Moonlite Airlines is offering a special flight to the moon. The fare is 790 if only one person makes the trip, and a reduction of 10 is given to each person for each additional passenger. That is, if there are two passengers, each pays 780; and if there are three, the price for each ticket is 770. If the airline wants to obtain a maximum income, how many passengers should they have on their special flight to the moon?

Solution:

Let x represent the number of passengers and y represent the income. Then

$$y = (800 - 10x)x = 800x - 10x^2$$

is to be maximized. Since $y' = 800 - 20x$, $y' = 0$ yields $x = 40$. Therefore we know (by virtue of the Doctrine enunciated in Example 3) that the airline needs 40 passengers in order to obtain a maximum income.

Problem Set 10.7

1. Use the result of Example 1 as an aid in drawing the graph of $y = 3x^2 - 6x + 5$.

2. Find all maximum and minimum points for each of the following graphs:
   (a) $y = x^2 - 4x + 3$.
   (b) $y = x^3 - 3x$.
   (c) $y = x^3 + 3x$.
   (d) $y = 3x + 2$.
   (e) $y = x^2 - 1$.
   (f) $y = x^5 + 2$.

3. Leone and Walt are making plans for an enclosed rectangular garden and have 80 yards of fencing with which to enclose it.
   (a) Find the dimensions of the rectangle that will yield the maximum area.
   (b) What is the maximum area?

4. Ball B is thrown straight up with an initial velocity of 64 feet per second from a height of 5 feet, and reaches a height of s feet in t seconds according to the law

$$s = 5 + 64t - 16t^2$$

   (a) At what time does B reach its maximum height?
   (b) What is B's maximum height?

°5. An open box is to be made from a square piece of cardboard 6 inches on each side by cutting out equal squares from the corners and folding up the sides.
   (a) If the box is to have a maximum volume, how long should the edge of each cut-out square be?
   (b) What is the maximum volume?

6. Kathy is in the business of making superduper ties. The first tie costs her $20 to make and each succeeding tie will cost her $2. She estimates that she can sell 200 of these ties and that if she sells x ties the selling price per tie will be $(8 - x/10)$ dollars (since it is assumed that when ties become less rare, they also become less expensive).
   (a) How many ties should Kathy make in order to maximize her profit?
   (b) What is the maximum profit?

10.8 The Antiderivative and the Intuitive Integral

In this section we shall investigate the motion of two special particles named *P* and *Q*.

EXAMPLE 1   Particle *P*

Let us suppose that particle *P* has a built-in speedometer and that it travels a distance of *s* feet in *t* seconds according to some unknown law. If the speedometer reveals that *P*'s velocity at the end of *t* seconds is $2t$ (for each value of *t*), then we can write

(1) $$\frac{ds}{dt} = 2t.$$

If we want to know how far *P* has traveled in *t* seconds (for each value of *t*), we need to solve Equation (1) for *s*; i.e., we need to work backward from ds/dt to *s*. We shall now consider two methods for doing this.

Method I   Antiderivative

From our earlier discussion (e.g., see Example 5 of Section 10.5) it should be clear that Equation (1) yields

(2) $$s = t^2 + c$$

where *c* can represent any constant. However, since we are implicitly assuming that $s = 0$ when $t = 0$ (for we want to find the distance from the starting point—wherever that may be), it follows that

$$c = 0,$$

and therefore the solution is

(3) $$s = t^2.$$

We can now say that *s* is an *antiderivative* of ds/dt, since it was obtained by reversing the differentiation process.

Method II   Intuitive Integral

Since $ds/dt = 2t$, we can write

(4) $$ds = 2t \, dt,$$

where, intuitively, *ds* means "a little bit of *s*" and *dt* means "a little bit of *t*." We shall now pursue this intuitive approach by observing that *s* can be found by "summing up" all the *ds* (i.e., all the "little bits of *s*"). If we use the symbol $\int$, which is called an *integral*, to perform this summing-up process, we can write

(5) $$\int ds = s.$$

Now, since the same legal operation can be performed on each side of an equation, Equation (4) can be converted to

(6)
$$s = \int ds = \int 2t \, dt$$

(where time goes from 0 to t).

Before attempting to find the value of

(7)
$$\int 2t \, dt$$

(where time goes from 0 to t), we will dress it up with a shoe and a hat in order to convert it to the *definite integral*

(8)
$$\int_0^t 2t \, dt.$$

The advantage of this symbol [called "the (definite) integral of $2t \, dt$ from 0 to t"] over that of (7) is that it includes the starting and stopping times at its extremities (called *lower* and *upper limits*, respectively), thus providing us with a device for omitting the parenthetical statement following (7).

We may now interpret (8) to be the sum of terms of the form $2t \, dt$—from 0 to t—or, more precisely, the limit of the sum of terms of the form $2t_j \, \Delta t$, when t_j takes on values between 0 and t, and Δt "approaches" zero. In order to determine what this may mean, we will now draw the graph of $s' = 2t$ from 0 to t, as indicated in the following figure.

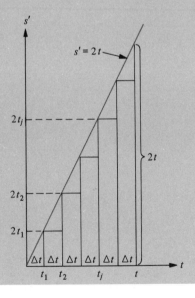

We now observe that the "sum of terms of the form $2t_j \Delta t$" can be translated into

(9) $$2t_1 \Delta t + 2t_2 \Delta t + \cdots + 2t_j \Delta t + \cdots + 2t_n \Delta t,$$

and that each term designates the area of a rectangle in the preceding figure. Therefore the sum is a good approximation to the area under the line $s' = 2t$ from 0 to t if Δt is "small"—and as Δt "approaches" zero, it should be intuitively evident that (9) closes in on this area. Since the figure in question is a right triangle, its area is easily found to be

$$\tfrac{1}{2}(t)(2t) = t^2;$$

and hence, with the aid of the preceding figure, we are intuitively led to conclude that

(10) $$\int_0^t 2t \, dt = t^2,$$

which together with (6), (7), and (8) yields $s = t^2$ as before.

If we now want to know how far P has traveled from the end of the ath second to the end of the bth second (i.e., from $t = a$ to $t = b$), we should observe that P has traveled a distance of b^2 in b seconds and a distance of a^2 in a seconds (since $s = t^2$), and hence that P travels a distance of $b^2 - a^2$ in this time interval. If we now let the definite integral

(11) $$\int_a^b 2t \, dt = t^2 \Big|_a^b = b^2 - a^2,$$

we note that it represents the distance traveled by P from $t = a$ to $t = b$.

Some Observations

If we let

(12) $$f(t) = 2t$$

and

(13) $$F(t) = t^2,$$

we can make the following observations concerning the preceding results.

(I) $$F'(t) = f(t) = s'.$$

(II) $$s = \int_0^t s' \, dt = \int_0^t f(t) \, dt = \int_0^t F'(t) dt = F(t),$$

which illustrates that the integral can serve as an antidifferentiator as well as a sum.

(III) $F(t)$ represents the area under the graph of $s' = f(t)$ from 0 to t, as well as the distance traveled by P from 0 to t.

(IV) The formula

$$(14) \qquad \int_a^b f(t)\, dt = F(t) \Big|_a^b = F(b) - F(a).$$

(V) The formula

$$(15) \qquad \int_a^b F'(t)\, dt = F(t) \Big|_a^b = F(b) - F(a).$$

(VI) $\int_a^b f(t)\, dt$ represents the area under $s' = f(t)$ from $t = a$ to $t = b$, as well as the distance traveled by P from $t = a$ to $t = b$.

The reader may now wonder whether other functions of t have the same interesting properties as $f(t) = 2t$. The following example helps to provide an answer to this question.

EXAMPLE 2   Particle Q

We shall now consider particle Q, which also has a built-in speedometer, but since it is out of order, it only reveals that Q's (instantaneous) velocity at the end of t seconds is *some* function of t called $f(t)$. [It should be emphasized that $f(t)$ is not necessarily equal to $2t$.] Then if s represents the distance which Q has traveled in t seconds, we can write

$$s' = \frac{ds}{dt} = f(t)$$

or

$$ds = f(t)\, dt.$$

Using an argument similar to that used in Method II of Example 1, we obtain

$$(16) \qquad s = \int_0^t f(t)\, dt = F(t)$$

where $F(t)$ is some function of t. Since $s = F(t)$ and $s' = f(t)$, we can conclude that

$$(17) \qquad F'(t) = s' = f(t),$$

as in Example 1.

We can now use the definite integral to represent the distance traveled from $t = a$ to $t = b$ as follows:

$$(18) \qquad \int_a^b f(t)\, dt = F(t) \Big|_a^b = F(b) - F(a),$$

where $F'(t) = f(t)$. Since Equations (17) and (18) can be combined into
the single equation

(19)
$$\int_a^b F'(t)\, dt = F(b) - F(a),$$

we find that Equations (14) and (15) hold in the more general case.

The reader should now try to determine which of the observations for
particle P also hold for particle Q.

The interrelationship between the antiderivative and the integral, as given
in (19), when stated in precise terms, is called the *Fundamental Theorem of
the Integral Calculus*. However, it should be emphasized that since our
development of the integral is intuitive at this time, our development of
Equation (19) must also be regarded as intuitive.

In the next section we shall see how the concept of area leads to a modified
form of the Fundamental Theorem of the Integral Calculus—and shall consider
some applications.

Problem Set 10.8

1. Suppose particle P moves a distance of s feet in t seconds according
   to some law. If we know that P's instantaneous velocity at the end
   of t seconds is t^2 (for each t), find s at the end of t seconds.

2. Let $v = ds/dt$. Then if the instantaneous roc of v wrt t is 32; and if
   $v = 80$ and $s = 60$ when $t = 0$, find
   (a) v at any time t.
   (b) s at any time t.

3. Determine which of the observations for particle P in Example 1 hold
   for particle Q in Example 2.

4. Evaluate the following definite integrals by use of Formula (18).

   (a) $\displaystyle\int_2^6 t\, dt.$ (d) $\displaystyle\int_3^7 5\, dt.$

   (b) $\displaystyle\int_1^2 3t^2\, dt.$ (e) $\displaystyle\int_a^b dt.$

   (c) $\displaystyle\int_0^4 t^2\, dt.$ °(f) $\displaystyle\int_a^b t^n\, dt.$

5. True–False

(a) $\displaystyle\int_a^b [f(t) + g(t)]\, dt = \int_a^b f(t)\, dt + \int_a^b g(t)\, dt.$

(b) $\displaystyle\int_a^b cf(t)\, dt = c \int_a^b f(t)\, dt.$

(c) $\displaystyle\int_a^b tf(t)\, dt = t \int_a^b f(t)\, dt.$

10.9 Areas and Integrals

In Section 10.1 we examined the region which was generated by a vertical line of constant length moving horizontally at the rate of 1 unit per second, and found that it was a rectangle whose area at the end of x seconds was x times the length of the line. We shall now see what happens when a vertical line of variable length y moves horizontally at the rate of 1 unit per second. (For example, if the vertical "line" is a "thin" metal rod which is being expanded or contracted in some special way by means of a heating or cooling process, then its length can vary as it moves along.)

Let us suppose that vertical line L is moving to the right at the rate of 1 unit per second and that its length y at the end of x seconds is given by

$$y = f(x),$$

which has a graph like that in the following figure.

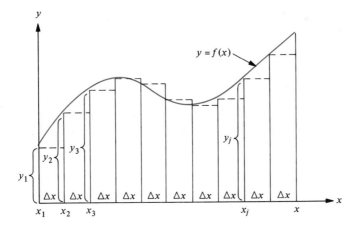

Before we can find the area generated by L, we need to develop a technique for finding the area of such a region. One way of attacking this problem is as follows:

(I) Consider the sum

(1) $$y_1 \Delta x + y_2 \Delta x + \cdots + y_j \Delta x + \cdots + y_n \Delta x,$$

which serves as an approximation to the desired area, since each term represents the area of an approximating rectangle (as indicated in the preceding figure).

(II) Note that (1) is a better approximation to the area when Δx is smaller.

(III) Evaluate the sums in (1) as Δx "approaches" zero—or, take the "limit of the sum in (1) as Δx approaches zero."

(IV) Note that the procedure described in (III) does indeed lead us to the desired area.

On the basis of these four steps, we shall now define the area of a region such as that in the preceding figure to be

(2) $$A \equiv \lim_{\Delta x \to 0} (y_1 \Delta x + y_2 \Delta x + \cdots + y_n \Delta x).$$

Since the symbol in the right-hand member of (2) looks complicated and does not visibly reveal that L has moved from 0 to x, we shall now introduce the symbol $\int_0^x y \, dx$ [called "the (definite) integral of $y \, dx$ from 0 to x"] to represent it. Hence the area from 0 to x is

(3) $$A \equiv \int_0^x y \, dx \equiv \lim_{\Delta x \to 0} (y_1 \Delta x + y_2 \Delta x + \cdots + y_n \Delta x).$$

Since $y = f(x)$, we can replace y_1 by $f(x_1)$, y_2 by $f(x_2)$, etc., and hence (3) can be converted to

(4) $$A \equiv \int_0^x f(x) \, dx \equiv \lim_{\Delta x \to 0} [f(x_1) \Delta x + f(x_2) \Delta x + \cdots + f(x_n) \Delta x].$$

Now that we have a definition for the area and a convenient symbol (i.e., the definite integral) to represent it, we could find the area by using the indicated procedure directly. However, this procedure can be quite complicated (and is beyond the scope of this book), and therefore we will now develop a different method for finding this area—one which works easily in many cases.

Method for Finding Area

In order to find the desired area, we shall first draw the figure again as indicated on page 223. This figure illustrates that line L has now moved on from x to $x + \Delta x$, thus generating the shaded area represented by ΔA. On examining the figure we observe that

(5) $$y \Delta x \leq \Delta A \leq (y + \Delta y) \Delta x,$$

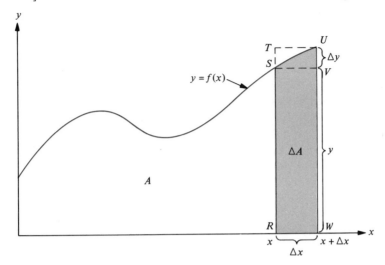

since ΔA is the area of the shaded region $RSUW$ and hence it must lie between the areas of rectangle $RSVW$ and rectangle $RTUW$. Since $\Delta x > 0$, (5) yields

(6)
$$y \leq \frac{\Delta A}{\Delta x} \leq y + \Delta y.$$

If we now let $\Delta x \to 0$, then $\Delta y \to 0$ and $\dfrac{\Delta A}{\Delta x} \to \dfrac{dA}{dx}$; and therefore we obtain

(7)
$$y \leq \frac{dA}{dx} \leq y.$$

It should now be clear that $\dfrac{dA}{dx}$ can satisfy (7) only when

(8)
$$\frac{dA}{dx} = y = f(x);$$

and hence A is an antiderivative.

Since A depends on both x and $f(x)$, it is reasonable to let

(9)
$$A = F(x).$$

We now observe that

(10)
$$F'(x) = f(x)$$

by virtue of (8), and that

(11)
$$F(0) = 0$$

because $A = 0$ when $x = 0$. Hence we have "found" the desired area; for if we combine (4), (9), (10) and (11), we obtain the area from 0 to x:

(12) $\qquad A = \int_0^x f(x)\, dx = F(x)$, where $F'(x) = f(x)$ and $F(0) = 0$.

In order to find the area generated when L moves from $x = a$ to $x = b$ (where $a < b$), we observe that the area from 0 to b is $F(b)$ and the area from 0 to a is $F(a)$—and hence the desired area is $F(b) - F(a)$. We now introduce the definite integral

$$\int_a^b f(x)\, dx$$

to represent this area bounded by $y = f(x)$, the x-axis, and the vertical lines $x = a, x = b$. The preceding discussion now yields the following modified form of the Fundamental Theorem of the Integral Calculus.

THEOREM 10.9.1 *If $f(x)$ is given as above, $a < b$, and $F'(x) = f(x)$, then*

(13) $$\int_a^b f(x)\, dx = F(x) \Big|_a^b = F(b) - F(a)$$

is the area bounded by $y = f(x)$, the x-axis, and the vertical lines $x = a$, $x = b$.

The preceding theorem is called a modified form of the Fundamental Theorem because the function $f(x)$ was restricted in the way in which it was formed [e.g., $f(x)$ cannot be negative for any value of x].

The reader may now ask, "If $f(x)$ is any given function of x, is it always possible to find a function $F(x)$ such that $F'(x) = f(x)$?" The answer is yes if and only if $f(x)$ is "reasonably nice"—but this will not cause us any difficulty since we will not be considering any functions that are not "reasonably nice."

NOTE: Henceforth we shall assume that Formula (13) holds whenever there exists an $F(x)$ such that $F'(x) = f(x)$.

EXAMPLE
Problem:
Find the area bounded by $y = x^2$, the x-axis, and the vertical lines $x = 1$, $x = 2$.

Solution:
First, let the required area be designated by A and let $f(x) = x^2$. Then Theorem 10.9.1 yields

$$A = \int_1^2 x^2\, dx.$$

Before we can evaluate A we need to find a function $F(x)$ such that $F'(x) = f(x) = x^2$. It should be clear that

$$F(x) = \frac{x^3}{3}$$

works, and hence (13) reveals that

$$A = \int_1^2 x^2 \, dx = \frac{x^3}{3} \bigg|_1^2 = \frac{2^3}{3} - \frac{1^3}{3} = \frac{7}{3}.$$

The reader should note that we were able to find a somewhat complicated area by use of an integral in the preceding example—whereas in Method II of Example 1 in the previous section, we obtained the value of the integral after we had found the area.

In addition to its use in finding areas such as those considered above, integrals can be used to find surface areas and volumes of solids, and lengths of curves, as well as to solve a variety of problems in physics (e.g., in the computation of forces, work, and energy). Integrals are also useful in defining new functions. For example, the function

(14) $$l(x) \equiv \int_1^x \frac{dt}{t} \quad \text{when} \quad x > 0$$

has many interesting and useful properties and is called *the logarithm of x*. Some of these properties will be investigated in the following Problem Set.

It may also be of interest to note that

(15) $$\frac{\pi}{4} = \int_0^1 \frac{dx}{1 + x^2}.$$

Problem Set 10.9

1. Evaluate the following and indicate the geometric interpretation of each answer.

   (a) $\int_2^6 x \, dx.$ (b) $\int_1^2 3t^2 \, dt.$ (c) $\int_0^4 x^2 \, dx.$

   (d) $\int_3^7 5 \, dx.$ (e) $\int_a^b dx.$ °(f) $\int_a^b x^n \, dx.$

2. Find the area bounded by $y = x^3$, the x-axis, and the vertical lines $x = 1, x = 2$.

°3. (a) Evaluate $\int_{-1}^1 x \, dx.$

   (b) What is the geometric significance of your answer to part (a)?

4. True–False

(a) $\int_a^b c\,dx = c(b-a)$.

(b) $\int_a^a f(x)\,dx = 0$.

(c) $\int_a^b f(x)\,dx = \int_a^c f(x)\,dx + \int_c^b f(x)\,dx$.

(d) $\int_b^a f(x)\,dx = -\int_a^b f(x)\,dx$.

(e) $\int_a^b [f(x)+g(x)]\,dx = \int_a^b f(x)\,dx + \int_a^b g(x)\,dx$.

(f) $\int_a^b cf(x)\,dx = c\int_a^b f(x)\,dx$.

(g) $\int_a^b xf(x)\,dx = x\int_a^b f(x)\,dx$.

(h) If $a < b$ and $f(x) \le g(x)$ for all x, then $\int_a^b f(x)\,dx \le \int_a^b g(x)\,dx$.

(i) $\int_a^b f(x)\,dx = \int_a^b f(t)\,dt = \int_a^b f(u)\,du$.

°**5.** Do you agree with the following statement: "Slope is related to area as derivative is related to integral"? Why?

6. Let $x > 0$, $x_1 > 0$, and $x_2 > 0$. If $l(x) = \int_1^x \dfrac{dt}{t}$, prove:

(a) $l(1) = 0$.

(b) $0 < l(2) < 1$.

(c) $l(\tfrac{1}{2}) < 0$.

(d) $l(x_1) > l(x_2)$ when $x_1 > x_2$.

(e) If $l(x_1) = l(x_2)$, then $x_1 = x_2$.

(f) $l'(x) = \dfrac{1}{x}$.

°(g) $l(x_1 x_2) = l(x_1) + l(x_2)$.

(h) $l(x^2) = 2l(x)$.

(i) $l(x^3) = 3l(x)$.

(j) $l\!\left(\dfrac{1}{x}\right) = -l(x)$.

°(k) $l\!\left(\dfrac{x_1}{x_2}\right) = l(x_1) - l(x_2)$.

7. If $l(x)$ is defined as in Problem 6 and $l(x) = 1$, what can you say about the value of x?

°**8.** If $l(x)$ is defined as in Problem 6, draw the graph of $y = l(x)$. [The graph of $y = l(x)$ reveals that if y is given any real value, then the value of x is uniquely determined, and hence x is a function of y!

This function, called the *inverse logarthimic function* of y or the *exponential function* of y, is of fundamental importance and will be symbolized by $e(y)$. Thus $x = e(y)$ is equivalent to $y = l(x)$. We note that $e(1) = 2.71828 \ldots$ is the fundamentally important number which is traditionally symbolized by e and which has some significant relationships with the number π. The reader may be interested to learn that:

(a) $l(x)$ is often written as $\log x$ or $\ln x$.

(b) $e(x)$ is often written as $\exp x$ or e^x.

(c) $x = e[l(x)] = l[e(x)]$ when $x > 0$.

(d) $e(x_1 + x_2) = e(x_1)e(x_2)$.

(e) If $y = e(x)$, then $y' = e'(x) = e(x) = y$.

(f) $l(1 + x) = x - \dfrac{x^2}{2} + \dfrac{x^3}{3} - \dfrac{x^4}{4} + \cdots$ if $-1 < x \leq 1$.

(g) $e(x) = \lim\limits_{h \to 0} (1 + hx)^{1/h}$.

(h) $e(x) = 1 + x + \dfrac{x^2}{2!} + \dfrac{x^3}{3!} + \cdots$ for all x.

(i) If $i^2 = -1$, then $e^{i\pi} = -1$.

(j) If $x > 0$, then $x^a = e^{a \ln x}$].

*9. Use the symbolism developed in the discussion following Problem 8 to draw the graph of $y = e(x)$ and prove:

(a) $x = e[l(x)]$ when $x > 0$. 　　　(e) $e'(x) = e(x)$.

(b) $y = l[e(y)]$. 　　　　　　　　　(f) $x = e^{\ln x}$ when $x > 0$.

(c) $e(x_1 + x_2) = e(x_1)e(x_2)$. 　　(g) $x^2 = e^{2 \ln x}$ when $x > 0$.

(d) $e(2x) = [e(x)]^2$. 　　　　　　 (h) $x^3 = e^{3 \ln x}$ when $x > 0$.

*10. If $x > 0$ and a represents any real number, give a reasonable definition for x^a. Explain.

11.　(a) Evaluate $\displaystyle\int_0^a 2\pi r \, dr$.

　　　*(b) What is the geometric interpretation of your answer to part (a)? Explain.

*12. Find an example of a function which is not "reasonably nice."

CHAPTER 11

Computers

11.1 Introduction

An ordinary human being can be considered a high-level computer with the ability to follow instructions, make decisions, and retain certain facts by means of a memory. We think of a computer as something that is *programmed*, since if certain things are "fed" to a computer in special ways, it will (if it is "healthy") necessarily respond in certain predictable ways. A similar statement can be made concerning ordinary humans.

For example, in the case of the computer, if $1 + 2$ is fed into it, it will respond with 3—or if a complicated equation is fed into it (together with "instructions"), it will respond by either (1) producing a solution, or (2) producing an approximate solution, or (3) indicating that there is no solution.

In the case of the ordinary human being, if $\frac{17}{3}$ is fed to him, he will probably respond with $5\frac{2}{3}$, because he has been programmed by his teachers to do this. When asked, "How are you?" many people are programmed to say, "Fine." A more complicated situation exists when the sound of an alarm-clock buzzer is fed to a nondeaf human. For if the alarm was set for some special purpose (e.g., wake up, feed the baby, take a pill, turn off the oven, go to class), he will undoubtedly be programmed to do the following: (1) turn off the alarm, and (2) make a decision as to whether he should follow the dictates of the alarm. This decision will be based on certain facts, some of which may be stored in his memory (e.g., Must he go to work? Is the baby crying? Does he have any pills? Is the oven on? Is there a test scheduled?).

We will now use a *flow chart* to illustrate how a college student who hears the alarm buzzer may have been programmed. Observe that the rectangular boxes in the flow chart represent actions to be taken, the diamond-shaped boxes are decisions, and the circles are at the start and stop.

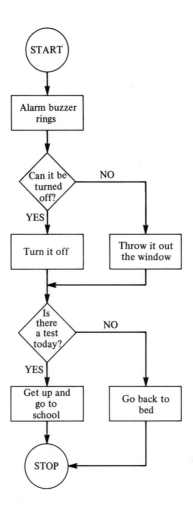

The preceding program may contain a subprogram, resulting from the problem on the next page.

PROBLEM
How to be sure that socks and shoes (with laces) are on properly.

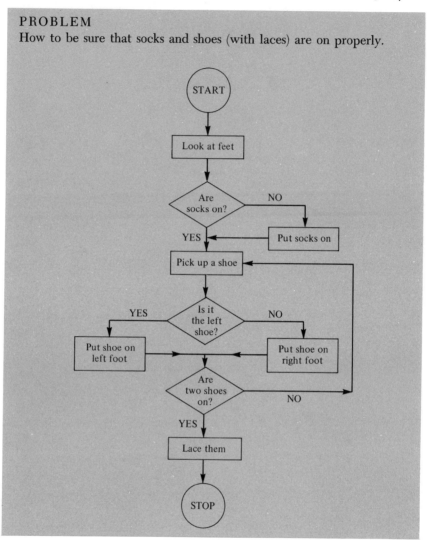

Flow charts similar to these two are actually used by computer programmers in the first stages of preparing material for a computer. In the next section we will use flow charts to illustrate how computers can be programmed.

Problem Set 11.1

1. Construct a flow chart for
   (a) Searching through a bunch of keys for the right one.
   (b) Cooking or baking or constructing something.

(c) Writing a translation of a passage written in a foreign language—with the aid of a dictionary.

(d) A problem of your own.

11.2 A Computer Language: FORTRAN

We are all familiar with methods for programming human beings, and are aware that languages of some sort are needed for communication purposes. Therefore in order to program a computer, we will need to have a language. One of the most popular languages that the computer can understand is called FORTRAN (which is a contraction of *Formula Translation*). In the FORTRAN language one can write formulas in algebra in much the same way as in high school algebra. The computer assumes the responsibility for translating your formulas into its own machine language.

In writing FORTRAN formulas, we need to remember that statements must be given to the computer line by line, and therefore all formulas must be written out line by line. For instance, the fraction

$$\frac{X}{Y + Z}$$

written in FORTRAN will have to appear all on one line. This can be done as follows:

$$\frac{X}{Y + Z} = X/(Y + Z).$$

We will now list some typical algebraic expressions and terms together with their FORTRAN equivalents.

Algebra	FORTRAN
$X + Y$	$X + Y$
$X - Y$	$X - Y$
XY	$X*Y$
$\dfrac{X}{Y}$	X/Y
X^Y	$X**Y$
is replaced by	$=$
$(X + Y)^2$	$(X + Y)**2$

We should emphasize that the symbol $=$ in FORTRAN does *not* mean the same thing as $=$ in algebra. For example, if X is a variable (i.e., a quantity whose value may change), we may want to alter the value of X by successively adding one to it (e.g., X may be the variable that keeps track of the number of steps that have been performed). Then the program will include the statement

$$X = X + 1,$$

which merely means that the "old X" or the "X-position" is replaced by the "old X" + 1. Since the statement $X = X + 1$ is virtually meaningless in ordinary algebra (since, for example, it would yield $3 = 4$ when $X = 3$), we must be careful not to let our algebraic prejudices lead us into a state of disbelief or shock.

We shall now illustrate the role of FORTRAN by means of a flow chart.

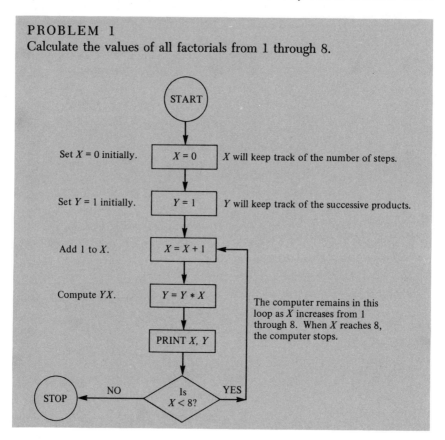

PROBLEM 1
Calculate the values of all factorials from 1 through 8.

START

Set $X = 0$ initially. $X = 0$ X will keep track of the number of steps.

Set $Y = 1$ initially. $Y = 1$ Y will keep track of the successive products.

Add 1 to X. $X = X + 1$

Compute YX. $Y = Y * X$ The computer remains in this loop as X increases from 1 through 8. When X reaches 8, the computer stops.

                               PRINT X, Y

STOP ◄—— NO —— Is $X < 8$? —— YES

Following along the flow chart, at the first stage we have

$$X = 0, \ Y = 1$$

then

$$X = 1, \ Y = 1 \cdot 1$$

then

PRINT 1, 1

then

$X = 2, Y = 1 \cdot 2$

then

PRINT 2, 2

then

$X = 3, Y = 2 \cdot 3$

then

PRINT 3, 6

then

$X = 4, Y = 6 \cdot 4$

then

PRINT 4, 24

$\vdots$

then, finally

PRINT 8, 40320

From the successive print-outs we can conclude: $1! = 1$, $2! = 2$, $3! = 6$, $4! = 24$, . . . , and $8! = 40{,}320$. We note that the preceding program can be easily modified to find the values of all factorials from 1 through 1,000, by replacing 8 in the diamond-shaped box with 1,000.

We will next indicate how a computer can be programmed to perform the operation of division. First, let us analyze some simple examples. One way of obtaining the answer to the problem $6 \div 2$ (or $\frac{6}{2}$) is to perform the following steps in order:

(1) $6 - 2 = 4$.
(2) $4 - 2 = 2$.
(3) $2 - 2 = 0$.

We can then conclude that $\frac{6}{2} = 3$, since division can be interpreted as successive subtraction, and it required 3 steps of successively subtracting 2 to reach 0 (i.e., $6 - 3 \cdot 2 = 0$).

If we now want to find the answer to the problem $\frac{33}{7}$, we can proceed in a similar way by performing the following steps in order.

(1) $33 - 7 = 26$.
(2) $26 - 7 = 19$.
(3) $19 - 7 = 12$.
(4) $12 - 7 = 5$.

From these steps we can conclude that the *quotient* is 4 (since 4 steps were required to obtain a difference of less than 7) and the *remainder* is 5 (i.e., $33 - 4 \cdot 7 = 5$). Hence,

$$\frac{33}{7} = 4 + \frac{5}{7}.$$

We will now use a flow chart to indicate how to obtain a general program for division by using repeated subtraction.

PROBLEM 2

If A and B are counting numbers or zero, and A is greater than B, find $A \div B$ by using repeated subtraction.

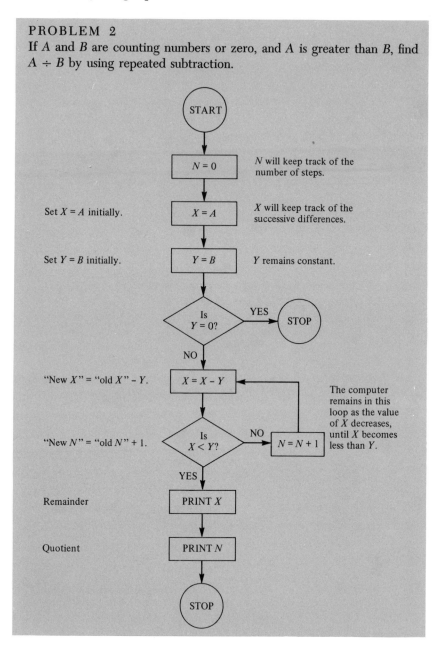

The reader should now follow along the preceding flow chart to verify that the problem is actually solved. For example, let $A = 33$, and $B = 7$.

A computer can perform the following four basic types of operations:
(1) Numerical computations such as addition, subtraction, multiplication, and division.
(2) Logical procedures such as deciding which statement to proceed to next or comparing two numbers.
(3) Intake of data for its memory.
(4) Output of data from its memory.

Theoretically there is nothing that a computer does that cannot be done on a desk calculator, given enough paper for all the data, enough logical organization, enough clerical assistance, and enough time and patience. In practice, however, it would take years to accomplish what some modern high-speed computers are able to do in minutes, since these computers perform more than a million computations a second!

Problem Set 11.2

1. Draw a flow chart for finding the sum of
   (a) The first 100 counting numbers.
   *(b) The first 100 even counting numbers.
   *(c) The first 100 odd counting numbers.

*2. Construct a flow chart for finding the product of two counting numbers by means of repeated addition.

3. Read and write a report on one of the following:
   (a) David Bergamini, *Mathematics*. New York: Life Science Library, Time, Incorporated, 1963, pp. 18–37.
   (b) Lord Bowden, "The Language of Computers," *American Scientist*, Vol. 58, No. 1 (January–February, 1970), pp. 43–53.
   (c) Irwin D. J. Bross et al., "Feasibility of Automated Information Systems in the Users' Natural Language," *American Scientist*, Vol. 57, No. 2 (1969), pp. 193–205.
   (d) M. Goldstein, "Computer Languages," *The American Mathematical Monthly*, Vol. 72 (1965), pp. 141–146.
   (e) The article on Computers in a recent edition of *Encyclopaedia Britannica*.
   (f) An article from an issue of *Computing Surveys*.

11.3 Applications of Computers

Since the end of World War II, computers have become a vital part of virtually all phases of human endeavor. This argument is reinforced by the fact that computers increased from one in 1944 to more than 60,000 in 1972, and the end to this growth is nowhere in sight!

A computer is used for essentially three reasons:
(1) To provide economy.
(2) To perform operations not otherwise feasible.
(3) To give insights into operations and processes.

We shall now consider the following five general categories of applications for computers (listed alphabetically): business, education, mathematics, science, and society.

Business

(1) Keeps record of payrolls, customer accounts, inventory and production schedules.
(2) Makes possible the rapid availability of information on airline reservations, bank balances, and stock transactions.
(3) Solves linear programming problems.
(4) Performs data processing (sorting, alphabetizing, and tabulating) by using punched cards or magnetic recording media.
(5) Simulates the flow of customers through a proposed supermarket.
(6) Prints books by means of computerized type setting.

Education

(1) Serves as teacher in programmed learning.
(2) Helps schedule classes.
(3) Simulates learning behavior.
(4) Performs data processing (see Business).
(5) Assists in translating languages.
(6) Grades tests and analyzes test results (e.g., types of errors made).

Mathematics

(1) Compiles mathematical tables.
(2) Proves conjectures false. (Since computers have facilitated computation, conjectures dealing with number relations—such as in number theory or combinatorial analysis—can be tested more quickly and for many more cases than was possible before.)
(3) Inspires new conjectures. (When in the process of testing an old conjecture, patterns inspiring new conjectures may arise.)
(4) Proves theorems. (While in the process of producing a proof of a theorem, some computers have even inspired new theorems for which no one had been looking!)
(5) Stimulates the study of many research problems in pure mathematics. (The design of computers, the formulation of programs, the questions of solvability of a problem, and problems of accuracy have all led to fundamental mathematical questions.)

Science

(1) Performs lengthy computations needed for space flights.
(2) Controls space capsule orbiting the moon.
(3) Keeps track of orbits of satellites.

(4) Predicts weather.

(5) Helps to locate brain tumors.

(6) Performs data retrieval.

Society

(1) Simulates some events that cannot be carried out in the "real world" (e.g., changes in environment caused by the building of a dam).

(2) Predicts elections.

(3) Keeps track of library books.

(4) Computes TV ratings.

Thus in addition to doing what are now considered to be routine jobs, computers have served to inspire a whole new way of life. It might be interesting to speculate what the world would be like without computers, but it would probably take a computer to come up with a valid answer!

Problem Set 11.3

1. Read and write a report on one of the following:

   (a) R. F. Churchouse and J. C. Herz, Editors, *Computers in Mathematical Research*. Amsterdam: North-Holland, 1968.

   (b) Anthony G. Oettinger, "The Uses of Computers in Science," *Scientific American*, Vol. 215 (September, 1966), pp. 160–172.

   (c) Patrick Suppes, "The Uses of Computers in Education," *Scientific American*, Vol. 215 (September, 1966), pp. 206–220.

11.4 History of Computers

One of the earliest devices used in computing was the abacus. It was used by the Greeks before the time of Christ, and is still used by many people throughout the world. The principle of the abacus, with its beads which slide on wires, is the same principle employed in all calculating machines— including computers. Therefore the abacus can be regarded as an ancestor of our present-day computers.

In the seventeenth century, the principle of the abacus was incorporated into mechanical calculating devices. One such device was the adding machine constructed in 1642 by the French mathematician Blaise Pascal (1623–1662) at the age of 19, and the other was an arithmetic calculating machine constructed in 1674 by the German mathematician, philosopher, and diplomat Baron Gottfried Wilhelm von Leibniz (1646–1716). Leibniz's machine was the forerunner of our present-day electromechanical desk calculators. [Leibniz is also an inventor of the calculus and can be considered a father to AMS (Logic).]

A significant difference between the desk calculator and the computer is that the former requires a human operator to perform each successive arithmetic operation, whereas a computer is capable of performing a whole string of arithmetic operations, making decisions every step of the way concerning whether it should continue to calculate and what operation should be performed next.

The first person to envision a calculator performing such a sequence of operations automatically was the English mathematician Charles Babbage (1792–1871). After constructing a rather sophisticated calculator in 1822, Babbage designed an "analytical engine" in 1833, which had the basic properties of a modern computer. However, Babbage's idea could not be realized until the invention of suitable electric circuitry more than a century later.

The first electrically operated computer was the Mark I, installed at Harvard University in 1944. Next came the ENIAC (Electronic Numerical Integrator And Calculator), installed at the University of Pennsylvania in 1946. Since that time there has been a development of more sophisticated electronic equipment, and the conceptual developments of mathematicians such as the Hungarian-born American John von Neumann (1903–1957) and the American Norbert Wiener (1894–1964) have emerged. Von Neumann introduced the idea of storing operating instructions as well as data inside the computer memory and Wiener, referred to as the father of automation, introduced *cybernetics*, in which information-handling machines are compared with the human nervous system.

Along with the rapid development of computers (or *hardware*) there has been a rapid development of programming techniques (or *software*). The greatest of all programming strides was the development of FORTRAN in 1957. Since then ALGOL (Algorithmic Language), developed in 1960, and PL/I (Programming Language I), developed in 1968, have been introduced and are generally admitted to be superior to the more popular FORTRAN. ALGOL has now been designated the official international scientific programming language and PL/I is a universal language suited for both scientific and business purposes. However, the most widely used language is probably COBOL (Common Business Oriented Language).

Besides these high-level languages, there are some languages that are almost conversational. BASIC (Beginner's All-purpose Symbolic Instruction Code) is the best known of these. Some disadvantages of this language are

(1) There are many computer systems on which it cannot be used.

(2) Some types of problems do not easily lend themselves to this language. Recently a more convenient and more powerful conversational language called APL (A Programming Language) has become very popular.

Problem Set 11.4

1. Read and write a report on one of the following:
   (a) Jeremy Bernstein, *The Analytical Engine: Computers—Past, Present, and Future*. New York: Random House, Inc., 1964.

(b) Philip Morrison, and Emily Morrison, "The Strange Life of Charles Babbage," *Scientific American,* Vol. 186 (April, 1952), pp. 66–73.

(c) R. D. Richtmyer, "The Post-War Computer Development," *The American Mathematical Monthly,* Vol. 72 (1965), pp. 8–14.

(d) Jerry M. Rosenberg, *The Computer Prophets.* Toronto: Collier-Macmillan, 1969.

(e) John von Neumann, "The General and Logical Theory of Automata," in *The World of Mathematics,* Vol. 4, (J. R. Newman, Editor). New York: Simon & Schuster, Inc., 1956, pp. 2070–2098.

11.5 Computers vs. Humans

The subject of possible future computers often stimulates a discussion on the similarities and differences between a computer and the human brain. Computers already have "memories" and their storage capabilities will undoubtedly exceed that of the human brain at some time in the future. Also, computers have the following advantages: (1) they do not forget, (2) they do not get tired, and (3) they do not require emotional motivation to do any task. However, although computers equipped with optical scanners can "see," their ability to recognize patterns is very crude compared to the ability of humans. Also, although computers have been programmed to "learn" (e.g., the checker-playing skills of computers have increased after the computers have "studied" games already played), they have not been able to discover similarities or learn general principles—thus far!

There have been some exciting and imaginative plans developed for possible future computers. For example, A. M. Turing has shown that a universal machine can be built that will imitate any other existing machine, and von Neumann has shown that it is possible to build a machine that can "reproduce" itself! Even if these machines of the future are never built, the study of their possibility has lead to a greater understanding of the human information-processing system—for example, it has given rise to Wiener's cybernetics.

In comparing computers with humans, we might conclude that although computers have certain advantages over humans (and as time goes on, they will undoubtedly acquire more and more advantages), they will never be able to think—and therefore they will never be able to outsmart us. But how can this be proved?

Problem Set 11.5

1. Read and write a report on one of the following:
   (a) John G. Kemeny, "Man Viewed as a Machine," *Scientific American,* Vol. 192 (April, 1955), pp. 58–67.

(b) A. M. Turing, "Can a Machine Think?" in J. R. Newman, Editor, *The World of Mathematics*, Vol. 4. New York: Simon & Schuster, Inc., 1956, pp. 2099–2123.

(c) John von Neumann, *The Computer and the Brain*. New Haven: Yale University Press, 1958.

APPENDIX

The Real Number System

A.1 The Real Numbers

Since a formal development of the real number system requires techniques that are beyond the level of this text, we shall merely describe the real numbers in an intuitive way and then develop some of their fundamental operations and properties. The reader who is interested in a formal development of the real number system should consult either Landau's *Foundations of Analysis* or Thurston's *The Number System*.

We shall give an intuitive meaning to *real number* by identifying every point on the *x*-axis (e.g., see Section 5.5) with a real number. If we draw the *x*-axis (or *real number line*) as below, then we can represent the real numbers $-3, -\frac{5}{2}, -2, -1, 0, \frac{1}{2}, 1, \sqrt{2}, 2, 3, \pi, 4, 4.2$, as indicated.

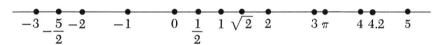

The set of real numbers to the right of 0 are called *positive* and those to the left of 0 are called *negative*.

The collection of numbers that can be reached by taking unit jumps from 0 are called *integers*.

DEF A.1.1

$J \equiv \{\ldots, -3, -2, -1, 0, 1, 2, 3, \ldots\}$ is called the *set of integers*.

The reader should note that a counting number is a positive integer.

Another special class of real numbers is obtained when integers are divided by integers—provided, of course, that we do not divide by zero.

DEF A.1.2

$Q \equiv \{a/b \mid a \in J, b \in J, b \neq 0\}$ is called the *set of rational numbers*.

[241

Thus a *rational number* is any number which can be written in the form a/b where a and b are integers but $b \neq 0$. Since $a/1 = a$ for every integer a, it follows that every integer is also a rational number.

One may now ask whether every number on the real number line is a rational number. It turns out that numbers such as $\sqrt{2}$ [where $(\sqrt{2})^2 = 2$] and π are real numbers that are not rational. At this point one may tend to believe that there are more rational numbers than there are nonrational real (or *irrational*) numbers. However, it can be proved that there are far more irrational numbers than rational numbers, but we shall not establish this here. For a discussion of this question the reader is invited to consult Allendoerfer's *Principles of Arithmetic and Geometry*, pages 523–524, and Abian's *The Theory of Sets and Transfinite Arithmetic*, pages 277–278.

Problem Set A.1

1. True–False
   (a) 0 is rational and an integer.
   (b) -7 is a negative integer.
   (c) 3 is a positive integer.
   (d) $-\frac{3}{2}$ is rational.
   (e) J is a subset of Q.
   (f) Every real number is either rational or irrational.
   °(g) $n(Q) = \aleph_0$.

*2. Prove $\sqrt{2}$ is not rational. (*Hint:* Assume $\sqrt{2}$ is a rational number and try to reach a contradiction.)

*3. Prove $\sqrt{3}$ is not rational.

A.2 Arithmetic Operations for Signed Numbers

Since all real numbers to the right of zero can be preceded by a plus sign, all those to the left of zero can be preceded by a minus sign, and zero itself can be preceded by either a plus or a minus sign, the real numbers are often called *signed numbers*. When a signed number has its sign removed, it will be called an *absolute value*. For example, the absolute value of both $(+3)$ and (-3) is 3. In this section we shall develop operations for the signed numbers, and special attention will have to be given to the signs. We shall start with some examples of addition, seek reasonable answers, and then establish a rule for adding two signed numbers.

Suppose we want answers to the following addition problems.
   (1) $(+2) + (+5)$.
   (2) $(+2) + (-5)$.
   (3) $(-2) + (+5)$.

(4) $(-2) + (-5)$.
(5) $(-4) + 0$.
(6) $(+4) + (-4)$.

If we interpret $(+2)$ to mean "a gain of 2 pounds," (-2) to mean "a loss of 2 pounds," and the addition sign between numbers to mean "and then," the answers to the preceding problems will be $+7$, -3, $+3$, -7, -4 and 0, respectively [since, for example in problem (2), a gain of 2 pounds and then a loss of 5 pounds produces a net loss of 3 pounds]. The preceding interpretation now leads us to the following rule.

RULE +

To add two signed numbers with like signs, add the absolute values (as in elementary arithmetic) and use the common sign. To add two signed numbers with unlike signs, subtract the absolute values (as in elementary arithmetic) and use the sign of the number with the larger absolute value. Also, $x + 0 = x$ and $x + (-x) = 0$.

The reader should note that $2x = x + x$, $3x = x + x + x$, and in general nx represents the sum of n x's (when n is a positive integer). It should also be noted that $+x = x$.

If a and b are real numbers and we want to find an x such that $a + x = b$, then we ordinarily write $x = b - a$.

DEF A.2.1

$b - a = x$ means $a + x = b$.

If we want to find answers to the following four subtraction problems:
(7) $(+2) - (+5)$,
(8) $(+2) - (-5)$,
(9) $(-2) - (+5)$,
(10) $(-2) - (-5)$,
we merely apply Def. A.2.1 and find that the answers are -3, $+7$, -7, and $+3$, respectively. Since using Def. A.2.1 is a rather indirect method, the reader may prefer the following simpler rule for finding the answers to the preceding problems.

RULE −

To subtract two signed numbers, change the sign of the number to be subtracted and add. Thus

$$a - b = a - (+b) = a + (-b) \text{ and } a - (-b) = a + (+b) = a + b$$

The reader should verify that Rule − works in the preceding four examples, and also that problems (7), (8), and (9) can be written as $2 - 5$, $2 - (-5)$, and $-2 - 5$, respectively.

We next consider multiplication of signed numbers. If we want to find the following products:

(11) $(+2) \cdot (+3)$,

(12) $(+2) \cdot (-3)$,

(13) $(-2) \cdot (+3)$,

(14) $(-2) \cdot (-3)$,

(15) $(-2) \cdot 0$,

we can give them the following football interpretations. Let $(+3)$ mean "a gain of 3 yards on every down," (-3) mean "a loss of 3 yards on every down," $(+2)$ mean "2 downs from now," (-2) mean "2 downs ago," and the product mean "change in position." With these interpretations, the answers to the preceding problems are $+6$, -6, -6, $+6$, and 0, respectively. A study of these results now leads us to the following rule.

RULE •

To multiply two signed numbers, multiply their absolute values (as in elementary arithmetic), and then if the signs are alike the answer will be $+$, and if the signs are unlike the answer will be $-$. Also, $x \cdot 0 = 0$ for every x.

By virtue of the preceding rule we can conclude that $x^2 = x \cdot x$ can never be a negative number. The reader should note that $x^3 = x \cdot x \cdot x$, $x^4 = x \cdot x \cdot x \cdot x$, and in general x^n represents the product of n x's (when n is a positive integer). It should also be noted that

$$a \cdot b = a \times b = ab = (a)(b) = (a)b = a(b).$$

If a and b are real numbers and we want to find an x such that $a \cdot x = b$, then we ordinarily write $x = b/a$. However, if $a = 0$ this procedure leads to complications. For if

$(*)$ $$0 \cdot x = b$$

and $b \neq 0$, clearly no real value of x will satisfy this equation. On the other hand, if $b = 0$, then every real value of x will satisfy $(*)$.

DEF A.2.2

Let $a \neq 0$. Then $b/a = x$ means $a \cdot x = b$. (Also, $b \div a \equiv b/a$).

If we now want to find answers to the following problems:

(16) $\dfrac{+6}{+2}$,

(17) $\dfrac{+6}{-2}$,

(18) $\dfrac{-6}{+2}$,

(19) $\dfrac{-6}{-2}$,

(20) $\dfrac{0}{+4}$,

we can apply Def. A.2.2 to find that the answers are $+3$, -3, -3, $+3$, and 0, respectively. In working the preceding problems the reader may have observed the following simple rule for dividing two signed numbers.

RULE ÷
To divide two signed numbers (except "Thou shalt not divide by zero"), divide their absolute values as in elementary arithmetic, and then if the signs are alike the answer will be $+$, and if the signs are unlike the answer will be $-$. If $x \neq 0$, then $0/x = 0$ and $1/x = x^{-1}$.

Problem Set A.2

1. Perform the indicated operations.

(a) $(+3) + (+7)$.   (j) $-3 + 7$.
(b) $(+3) - (+7)$.   (k) $-3 - 7$.
(c) $(+3) - (-7)$.   (l) $3 - (-7)$.
(d) $(-3) - (-7)$.   (m) $0 - (-7)$.
(e) $(+3) + (-7)$.   (n) $3 + (-7)$.
(f) $(+3)(-5)$.   (o) $3(-5)$.
(g) $(-3)(-5)$.   (p) $(-3) \cdot 0$.

(h) $\dfrac{+8}{-2}$.   (q) $\dfrac{8}{-2}$.

(i) $\dfrac{-8}{-2}$.   (r) $\dfrac{0}{-2}$.

2. If x is a real number, explain why x^2 cannot be negative.

3. True–False

(a) $\dfrac{1}{0} = 0$.   (b) $\dfrac{0}{-3} = 0$.   (c) $(-1)^2 = 1$.   (d) $(-5) \cdot 0 = 0$.

(e) If $x^2 = -1$, then x cannot be real.
(f) $(-1)^{17} = -1$.

4. True–False
If x, y, and z are any real numbers, then
(a) $xy = (-x)(-y)$.   (d) $x + y = y + x$.
(b) $x(-y) = -xy$.   (e) $xy = yx$.
(c) $(-1)x = -x$.   (f) $x + (-x) = 0$.

(g) $x(yz) = (xy)z$.
(h) $x(y + z) = xy + xz$.
(i) $x^2 \cdot x^3 = x^6$.

(j) If $xy = 0$, then $(x = 0)$ or $(y = 0)$.
(k) $1x = x$.
(l) $x^1 = x$.

*5. Prove that Rule $-$ is equivalent to Def. A.2.1.

A.3 The Real Number Field

In this section we will state the fundamental properties of the real numbers which form the foundation of both elementary arithmetic and elementary algebra.

Fundamental Properties of the Real Numbers. If a, b, c represent any real numbers, then

(R_1) $a + b$ is a unique real number   (Closure $+$).
(R_2) $a + (b + c) = (a + b) + c$ (Associative $+$).
(R_3) $a + 0 = 0 + a = a$ (Identity $+$).
(R_4) $a + (-a) = (-a) + a = 0$ (Inverse $+$).
(R_5) $a + b = b + a$ (Commutative $+$).
(R_6) ab is a unique real number   (Closure $\times$).
(R_7) $a(bc) = (ab)c$ (Associative $\times$).
(R_8) $a1 = 1a = a$ (Identity $\times$).
(R_9) $aa^{-1} = a^{-1}a = 1$ when $a \neq 0$ (Inverse $\times$).
(R_{10}) $ab = ba$ (Commutative $\times$).
(R_{11}) $a(b + c) = ab + ac$ (Distributive).

The reader should give special values to a, b, c (e.g., $a = -3$, $b = 2$, $c = -7$) and use the operations developed in the previous section to verify each of the preceding properties.

Any set of numbers that satisfies the Fundamental Properties of the Real Numbers is called a *field*, and therefore we often use the term *real number field* when referring to the real number system. It should be noted that when we say, "S is a field," it is understood that all symbols in the list of Properties (R_1) through (R_{11}) represent elements in S, and that Properties (R_1) and (R_6) are modified by replacing "real number" with "element of S."

Problem Set A.3

*1. True–False
  (a) The integers form a field.
  (b) The rational numbers form a field.
  (c) The irrational numbers form a field.
  (d) The set $\{1, 0, -1\}$ forms a field.

*2. Define AMS (Field).

*3. Try to find an example of a field which has exactly (a) Two elements.
(b) Three elements. (c) Four elements. (*Hint:* See Problem 6 in Problem Set 2.2.)

4. If x, y, z, w represent any real numbers, use the Fundamental Properties of the Real Numbers to prove each of the following.
   (a) $xy + xz = x(y + z)$.
   (b) $yx + zx = (y + z)x$.
   (c) $(x + y)z = xz + yz$.
   (d) $(x + y)(z + w) = xz + xw + yz + yw$.
   (e) $(x + y)^2 = x^2 + 2xy + y^2$.
   °(f) $x(y - z) = xy - xz$.
   °(g) $(x - y)(x + y) = x^2 - y^2$.
   *(h) If $xy = 0$, then $(x = 0)$ or $(y = 0)$.

5. True–False
   If x and y are real numbers, then
   (a) $(2x)(3x) = 6x^2$.
   (b) $(xy)^2 = x^2y^2$.
   (c) $(x + y)^2 = x^2 + y^2$.
   (d) $(x^2)^3 = x^6$.
   (e) $-(-x) = x$.

A.4 Fractions

In this section we shall assume that a, b, c, d, x, and y represent real numbers, and shall base all our results on:
(1) The Fundamental Properties of the Real Numbers.
(2) The assumption that we can add or multiply each member of an equation by the same real number.
(3) The following two definitions.

DEF A.4.1
$a - b \equiv a + (-b)$.

DEF A.4.2
If $b \neq 0$, then $a \div b \equiv a/b \equiv a \cdot b^{-1}$; and a/b is called a *fraction* with *numerator* a and *denominator* b.

We can now establish the following two theorems, which should look familiar.

THEOREM A.4.1 *If $a - b = x$, then $a = x + b$.*

Proof:

Let $a - b = x$. Then by Def. A.4.1 we have

(*) $a + (-b) = x.$

If we now add b to each member of (*) and apply Properties (R_2), (R_4), and (R_3) from Section A.3, in that order, we obtain

$$[a + (-b)] + b = x + b$$
$$a + [(-b) + b] = x + b$$
$$a + 0 = x + b$$
$$a = x + b,$$

and hence the theorem is proved.

THEOREM A.4.2 *If $b \neq 0$ and $a/b = x$, then $a = xb$.*

Proof:

Let $a/b = x$. Then by Def. A.4.2 we have

(**) $ab^{-1} = x.$

If we now multiply each member of (**) by b and apply Properties (R_7), (R_9), and (R_8), in that order, we obtain

$$(ab^{-1})b = xb$$
$$a(b^{-1}b) = xb$$
$$a1 = xb$$
$$a = xb,$$

and hence the theorem is proved.

The following list of basic rules for fractions should be useful—but the reader will probably not want to accept them until he has proved them all!

Basic Rules for Fractions. If $bdx \neq 0$, then

(F_1) $\left(\dfrac{a}{b} = \dfrac{c}{d} \right)$ iff $(ad = bc)$.

(F_2) $\dfrac{ax}{bx} = \dfrac{a}{b}.$

(F_3) $\dfrac{a}{b} \cdot \dfrac{c}{d} = \dfrac{ac}{bd}.$

(F_4) $\dfrac{a}{b} \div \dfrac{c}{d} = \dfrac{a}{b} \cdot \dfrac{d}{c}.$

(F_5) $\dfrac{a}{b} + \dfrac{c}{b} = \dfrac{a + c}{b}.$

(F$_6$) $\dfrac{a}{b} - \dfrac{c}{b} = \dfrac{a - c}{b}$.

(F$_7$) $\dfrac{a}{1} = a$.

Problem Set A.4

1. Use words to describe each of the Basic Rules for Fractions.

°2. Prove each of the Basic Rules for Fractions.

3. Perform the indicated operations and simplify.

(a) $\dfrac{-2}{3} + \dfrac{5}{7}$.

(f) $\dfrac{-4}{5} + \dfrac{8}{10}$.

(b) $\dfrac{-2}{3} - \dfrac{5}{7}$.

(g) $-5 \cdot \dfrac{3}{4}$.

(c) $\dfrac{-2}{3} \cdot \dfrac{5}{-7}$.

(h) $\dfrac{-3}{4} \div 5$.

(d) $\dfrac{-2}{3} \div \dfrac{5}{7}$.

(i) $\dfrac{3}{7} + \dfrac{2}{7}$.

(e) $\dfrac{-3}{4} + \dfrac{5}{6}$.

(j) $\dfrac{5}{7} - \dfrac{2}{7}$.

4. True–False (Assume all denominators and divisors are different from zero.)

(a) $\dfrac{x}{1} = x$.

(i) $\dfrac{2x + 2y}{2} = x + y$.

(b) $\dfrac{2x}{2y} = \dfrac{x}{y}$.

(j) $\dfrac{2x + 2y}{4xy} = 1$.

(c) $1 \div \dfrac{1}{x} = x$.

(k) $\dfrac{x}{3} = \dfrac{1}{3}x$.

(d) $\dfrac{3}{x} + \dfrac{2}{x} = \dfrac{5}{x}$.

(l) $\dfrac{x}{y} = x \cdot \dfrac{1}{y}$.

(e) $\dfrac{12}{16} = \dfrac{3}{4}$.

(m) $\dfrac{a}{b} \div x = \dfrac{a}{x} \div b = \dfrac{a}{bx}$.

(f) $\dfrac{3}{x} - \dfrac{2}{x} = \dfrac{1}{x}$.

(n) $\dfrac{-x}{-y} = \dfrac{x}{y}$.

(g) $\dfrac{a}{b} + \dfrac{c}{d} = \dfrac{ad + bc}{bd}$.

(o) $\dfrac{-x}{y} = \dfrac{x}{-y}$.

(h) $\dfrac{a}{b} - \dfrac{c}{d} = \dfrac{ad - bc}{bd}$.

(p) $x = \dfrac{x}{y} \cdot y$.

(q) If $x + b = a$, then $x = a - b$.

(r) If $b \neq 0$ and $bx = a$, then $x = \dfrac{a}{b}$.

*5. Is Def. A.4.2 equivalent to Def. A.2.2? Explain.

A.5 Inequalities

Since all the real numbers can be placed on the x-axis (or real number line), they can be ordered in a very natural way. That is, if a is to the right of b, then we can write $a > b$, where this relation has the following properties when x, y, and z represent real numbers.

(I$_1$) Law of Trichotomy. If x and y are any two real numbers, then one and only one of the following three statements is true:

$$x > y. \qquad x = y. \qquad y > x.$$

(I$_2$) Transitive Law. If $x > y$ and $y > z$, then $x > z$.

(I$_3$) Addition Law. If $x > y$, then $x + z > y + z$.

(I$_4$) Multiplication Law. If $x > y$ and $z > 0$, then $xz > yz$.

Because the field of real numbers satisfies the preceding four laws, it is called an *ordered field*. We will now give a more formal definition to *greater than* in order to establish these four laws and others.

DEF A.5.1

If x and y are real numbers, then
$x > 0$ iff x is to the right of 0.
$x > y$ iff $x - y > 0$.
$x \geq y$ iff $x > y$ or $x = y$.
$y < x$ iff $x > y$.
$y \leq x$ iff $x \geq y$.

From our earlier discussion,
$x > 0$ means "x is positive."
$x < 0$ means "x is negative."
$x > y$ is read "x is greater than y."
$x < y$ is read "x is less than y."
$x \geq y$ is read "x is greater than or equal to y."
$x \leq y$ is read "x is less than or equal to y."

Problem Set A.5

If x, y, z, and w are real numbers, use Def. A.5.1 to determine which of the following conjectures are true and which are false. Prove your answers. (**HINT**: First check each conjecture by letting x, y, z, w be negative or zero as well as positive.)

*1. If $x \neq y$, then $x > y$ or $x < y$.

*2. If $x > y$ and $y > z$, then $x > z$.

3. If $x < y$ and $y < z$, then $x < z$.

4. If $x > y$, then $x + z > y + z$.

5. If $x < y$, then $x + z < y + z$.

6. If $x > y$, then $x - z > y - z$.

7. If $x > y$ and $z > w$, then $x + z > y + w$.

8. If $x > 0$ and $y > 0$, then $x + y > 0$.

9. If $x < 0$ and $y < 0$, then $x + y < 0$.

10. If $x > y$, then $xz > yz$.

11. If $x > y$, then $x^2 > y^2$.

*12. If $x > y$ and $z > 0$, then $xz > yz$.

13. If $x < y$ and $z > 0$, then $xz < yz$.

*14. If $x > y$ and $z > 0$, then $\dfrac{x}{z} > \dfrac{y}{z}$.

15. If $x < y$ and $z > 0$, then $\dfrac{x}{z} < \dfrac{y}{z}$.

16. If $x > 0$ and $y > 0$, then $xy > 0$.

*17. If $x < 0$ and $y < 0$, then $xy > 0$.

18. If $x < 0$ and $y > 0$, then $xy < 0$.

19. If $x > 0$ and $y < 0$, then $xy < 0$.

20. If $x < 0$, then $-x > 0$.

21. If $x > 0$, then $-x < 0$.

22. If $x > y$, then $-x < -y$.

23. If $x > y$ and $z < 0$, then $xz < yz$.

24. If $x < y$ and $z < 0$, then $xz > yz$.

25. If $x > y > 0$, then $\dfrac{1}{x} < \dfrac{1}{y}$.

26. If $x < y < 0$, then $\dfrac{1}{x} > \dfrac{1}{y}$.

*27. If $x < y$, then $x < \dfrac{x + y}{2} < y$.

28. If $x^2 > y^2$, then $x > y$.

29. If $x^2 < y^2$, then $x < y$.

30. $x^2 \geq 0$.

Suggestions for Further Reading

ABBOTT, E. A. *Flatland*, 5th ed. New York: Barnes & Noble, Inc., 1963.

BALL, W. W. R., and H. S. M. COXETER. *Mathematical Recreations and Essays*, rev. ed. New York: The Macmillan Company, 1962.

BELL, E. T. *Men of Mathematics*. New York: Simon & Schuster, Inc., 1961.

COURANT, R., and H. ROBBINS. *What Is Mathematics?* New York: Oxford University Press, 1941.

EVES, HOWARD. *An Introduction to the History of Mathematics*, 3rd ed. New York: Holt, Rinehart & Winston, Inc., 1969.

GELBAUM, B. R., and J. G. MARCH. *Mathematics for the Social and Behavioral Sciences*, Vol. 1. Philadelphia: W. B. Saunders Company, 1969.

HARDY, G. H. *A Mathematician's Apology*, rev. ed. New York: Cambridge University Press, 1967.

HUFF, D. *How to Lie with Statistics*. New York: W. W. Norton and Company, Inc., 1954.

KASNER, E., and J. NEWMAN. *Mathematics and the Imagination*. New York: Simon & Schuster, Inc., 1940.

KRAITCHIK, M. *Mathematical Recreations*, 2nd ed. New York: Dover Publications, Inc., 1953.

KRAMER, E. E. *The Nature and Growth of Modern Mathematics*. New York: Hawthorn Books, 1970.

MESCHKOWSKI, H. *Evolution of Mathematical Thought*. San Francisco: Holden-Day, Inc., 1965.

NEWMAN, J. R. *The World of Mathematics*, 4 Vols. New York: Simon & Schuster, Inc., 1962.

NORTHROP, E. P. *Riddles in Mathematics*. New York: Van Nostrand Reinhold Company, 1944.

RADEMACHER, H., and O. TOEPLITZ. *The Enjoyment of Mathematics*. Princeton, N.J.: Princeton University Press, 1965.

RENYI, A. *Dialogues on Mathematics*. San Francisco: Holden-Day, Inc., 1967.

RICHARDSON, M. *Fundamentals of Mathematics*, 3rd ed. New York: The Macmillan Company, 1966.

SAWYER, W. W. *The Search for Pattern*. Baltimore, Md.: Penguin Books, Inc., 1970.

SCIENTIFIC AMERICAN EDITORS. *Mathematics in the Modern World*. San Francisco: W. H. Freeman and Co., Publishers, 1968.

STEINHAUS, H. *Mathematical Snapshots*, 2nd ed. New York: Oxford University Press, 1969.

VILENKIN, N. YA. *Stories About Sets*. New York: Academic Press, Inc., 1968.

Hints and Answers to Selected Problems

Section 1.1

2. (a) 12.
   (b) Only one, if it is long enough.
   (c) Only halfway—for then you start walking out.
   (d) There is no dirt in a hole.
   (e) Brother and sister.

5. At the end of 27 days the cat is 3 feet from the top. Hence, she can be out of the well on the twenty-eighth day.

6. **HINT:** Form a triangular pyramid.

12. (a) $7 = 8 - 1 = 2^3 - 1$.
    (b) $15 = 16 - 1 = 2^4 - 1$.
    (c) $31 = 32 - 1 = 2^5 - 1$.

Section 1.2

4. (a) $40 \times 81 = 3{,}240$.
   (c) $12 \times 50 + 25 = 625 = 25^2$.

6. (b) 15, 21.
   (c) 120, 720.
   (f) 7, 11.

8. (a) 3.
   (b) 6.

9. (a) $\dfrac{3}{4} = 1 - \dfrac{1}{4} = 1 - \dfrac{1}{2^2}.$

   (b) $\dfrac{7}{8} = 1 - \dfrac{1}{8} = 1 - \dfrac{1}{2^3}.$

   (c) $\dfrac{15}{16} = 1 - \dfrac{1}{16} = 1 - \dfrac{1}{2^4}.$

Section 2.2

1. Parts (a), (b), (e), (f), (g), and (h) are theorems.

3. (c) $a \otimes (a \oplus b) = a.$

Section 3.1

Arguments in 3, 4, 6, 7, 9b are valid.
Arguments in 5, 8, 9a are not valid.

Section 3.2

1. Both (b) and (c).

3. (d).

4. (b).

5. (d).

8. (b) False.
   (c) True.
   (d) True.
   (g) False.
   (i) True.

9. Parts (m) and (x) are not theorems.

10. (i) No.
    (ii) No.
    (iii) Yes.

Section 3.4

2. (a) (i) If it goes down, then it goes up.
       (ii) If it does not go down, then it does not go up.

(e) (i) If you can think, then you are a monkey.

     (ii) If you cannot think, then you are not a monkey.

(m) (i) If Ed cannot find it, then it does not exist.

     (ii) If Ed can find it, then it does exist.

(t) (i) All who are strong are football players (*or* If he is strong, then he is a football player).

     (ii) All who are not strong are not football players (*or* If he is not strong, then he is not a football player).

Section 3.5

Arguments in 2, 3, 9 are valid.
Arguments in 4, 10 are not valid.

16. You do not drink milk.
18. If you like to exercise, then you are a mathematician.
20. He either knows or he does not know.
23. He is not riding a bicycle.
25. He says nothing.

Section 4.3

1. (a) True.
   (b) False.
   (c) True.

2. (a) $101 \leftrightarrow 1,\ 102 \leftrightarrow 2, \ldots, (100 + n) \leftrightarrow n, \ldots$

3. 6.

Section 4.4

1. (a) $\{1, 2, 3, 5, 7\}$, $\{1, 3\}$.
   (b) $\{1, 2, 3, \ldots\}$, $\varnothing$.
   (c) B, A.
   (d) $\{1, 2, 3, \ldots\}$, B.

2. (a) (i) $\{3, 4, 5\}$.
       (ii) $\{2, 4\}$.
       (iii) $\{2, 3, 4, 5\}$.
       (iv) $\{4\}$.
       (v) $\{4\}$.
       (vi) $\{2, 3, 4, 5\}$.

3. (a) A.
   (b) B.
   (c) Ø.
   (d) U.
   (e) B'.

9. Parts (a), (d), (e), (f), (g), and (h) are theorems.

Section 4.5

1. (a) Ø.
   (b) A.
   (d) A'.

Section 4.6

2. $(a + b) + c$.

Section 5.2

1. (b) (i) 20 inches.
        (ii) 25 square inches.

2. (b) 30 square feet.

3. (a) 6π inches.
   (b) 9π square inches.

4. (a) False.
   (b) True.
   (c) True.
   (d) True.
   (e) True.

Section 5.3

3. (a) $100^2 - 99^2 = (100 + 99)(100 - 99) = 199 \cdot 1 = 199$.
   (h) $53 \times 47 = (50 + 3)(50 - 3) = 50^2 - 3^2 = 2{,}500 - 9 = 2{,}491$.

Section 5.4

1. (b) 24 square miles, 8 cubic miles.
   (c) 36π square feet, 36π cubic feet.

2. (a) 48π square feet.
   (b) 80π square feet.
   (c) 96π cubic feet.

4. $(a + b)^3 = a^3 + 3a^2b + 3ab^2 + b^3$.

Section 5.5

3. Parts (a), (b), (c), (g).

Section 5.6

2. (a) $\dfrac{6 - 1}{5 - 2} = \dfrac{5}{3}$.

   (b) $\dfrac{2 - 7}{5 - 4} = \dfrac{-5}{1} = -5$.

3. (a) 3.
   (b) 0.
   (c) -1.
   (d) 3.
   (e) No slope.

5. (a) $y - 1 = \dfrac{5}{3}(x - 2)$ or $5x - 3y - 7 = 0$.

6. (a) 32.
   (b) 212.
   (d) 14.
   (e) -4.

7. Yes.

Section 6.2

1. $4 \cdot 3 = 12$.

2. (a) $5 \cdot 4 = 20$.
   (b) $5 \cdot 5 = 25$.

7. $12 \cdot 11 \cdot 10 = 1{,}320$.

9. $9 \cdot 4 = 36$.

10. $26 \cdot 9 \cdot 9 \cdot 8$ for second part of problem.

12. (a) $2 \cdot 2 = 2^2$.
   (b) $2 \cdot 2 \cdot 2 = 2^3$.
   (c) $2 \cdot 2 \cdot 2 \cdot 2 = 2^4$.

15. $m_1 \times m_2 \times \cdots \times m_n$.

Section 6.3

1. (b) 56.
   (e) $7 \cdot 6 \cdot 5 = 210$.

2. (a) $_5P_2 = 5 \cdot 4 = 20$.
   (b) $_5P_5 = 5 \cdot 4 \cdot 3 \cdot 2 \cdot 1 = 120$.

6. $9!$.

7. $n!$.

8. 1.

Section 6.4

1. Combination. $_{20}C_2 = \dfrac{20 \cdot 19}{2 \cdot 1} = 190$.

3. Permutation. $_7P_7 = 7!$.

4. Combination. $_{10}C_2 = \dfrac{10 \cdot 9}{2 \cdot 1} = 45$.

10. (a) 15.
   (d) $\dfrac{7 \cdot 6 \cdot 5 \cdot 4}{4 \cdot 3 \cdot 2 \cdot 1} = 35$.

14. (b) True.
   (d) True.

15. $_nC_0 = {_nC_n} = 1$.

19. $_5C_0 + {_5C_1} + {_5C_2} + {_5C_3} + {_5C_4} + {_5C_5} = 2^5 = 32$.

23. $_7C_3 = \dfrac{7 \cdot 6 \cdot 5}{3 \cdot 2 \cdot 1} = 35.$

25. $[_5C_3][_{10}C_7] = 10 \cdot 120 = 1{,}200.$

Section 6.5

1. (a) $\dfrac{13}{52} = \dfrac{1}{4}.$

   (b) $1 - \dfrac{13}{52} = 1 - \dfrac{1}{4} = \dfrac{3}{4}.$

   (c) $\dfrac{4}{52} = \dfrac{1}{13}.$

2. (a) $\dfrac{3}{6} = \dfrac{1}{2}.$

   (e) $\dfrac{5}{6}.$

   (f) $\dfrac{0}{6} = 0.$

3. $1 - \dfrac{1}{8} = \dfrac{7}{8}.$

5. (a) $\dfrac{2 \cdot 1}{5 \cdot 4} = \dfrac{1}{10}.$

   (c) $\dfrac{2}{5}.$

   (d) $\dfrac{2 \cdot 3}{5 \cdot 4} = \dfrac{3}{10}.$

6. (a) $\dfrac{1 \cdot 1 \cdot 1}{2 \cdot 2 \cdot 2} = \dfrac{1}{8}.$

   (b) $\dfrac{3}{8} + \dfrac{1}{8} = \dfrac{4}{8} = \dfrac{1}{2}.$

   (c) Same as Part (b).

8. (a) $\dfrac{1}{6}.$

   (b) $\dfrac{1}{36}.$

   (c) $\dfrac{6}{36} = \dfrac{1}{6}.$

10. $\dfrac{3+2}{10} = \dfrac{5}{10} = \dfrac{1}{2}.$

12. $\dfrac{5 \cdot 3}{8 \cdot 7} = \dfrac{15}{56}.$

14. (a) $\dfrac{8}{52} = \dfrac{2}{13}.$

    (c) $\dfrac{16}{52} = \dfrac{4}{13}.$

18. (d) True.

Section 6.6

1. (a) $\dfrac{1}{7}.$

    (b) $\dfrac{3}{5}.$

    (e) 0.

2. (a) $\dfrac{7}{1}.$

    (b) $\dfrac{5}{3}.$

    (e) Does not exist.

6. $\left(\dfrac{1}{4} \cdot 0\right) + \left(\dfrac{2}{4} \cdot 1\right) + \left(\dfrac{1}{4} \cdot 2\right) = 0 + \dfrac{1}{2} + \dfrac{1}{2} = 1.$

8. (a) $\dfrac{1}{500}(1{,}000) = 2.$

    (b) 20.

9. (a) 0.

14. $\dfrac{4}{10}(1) + \dfrac{3}{10}(5) + \dfrac{2}{10}(10) + \dfrac{1}{10}(25) = \dfrac{64}{10} = 6.4.$

Section 7.2

1. (g) Mean = 4, median = 4.
    (h) Mean = 4.5, median = 4.5.

7. This provision will not help a student if all his grades are the same or within the same grade range.

12. (b) False.
    (f) False.
    (h) True.
    (i) True.

Section 7.3

4. (a) True.
   (b) True.
   (d) True.

Section 7.4

1. (a) $\dfrac{1}{64}$.   (c) $\dfrac{15}{64}$.

   (b) $\dfrac{6}{64}$.   (d) $\dfrac{20}{64}$.

2. (a) 100.   (c) 1,500.
   (b) 600.   (d) 2,000.

5. (a) 2.3 per cent.
   (b) 0.1 per cent.
   (c) 97.6 per cent.

8. $\dfrac{1}{\sqrt{2\pi}} \doteq .4$.

10. (e) False.

Section 8.1

2. (a) Identity.
   (b) Conditional; $x = 4$.
   (f) Conditional; $x = 3, x = -3$.
   (k) Pathological.
   (n) Conditional; $x = 0$.
   (o) Pathological.

Section 8.2

2. (a) By virtue of Laws 3 and 4, ($bx = a$ and $dy = c$) iff ($x = a/b$ and $y = c/d$). Hence (using Laws 3 and 4), if ($a/b = c/d$), then ($x = y$) and ($ad = bdx = bdy = bc$); and if ($ad = bc$), then $bdx = bdy$, which yields ($x = y$) and ($a/b = c/d$).

2. (b) **HINT:** Use part (a).

4. (a) If ($bx = a$) and ($dy = c$), then $bdxy = ac$ by Law 4. Hence $xy = ac/bd$ by Law 3.

  (b) If ($bx = a$) and ($dy = c$), then $bcx = ady$ by Law 4. Hence $x/y = ad/bc$ by Law 3.

  (c) If ($bx = a$) and ($dy = c$), then ($bdx = ad$) and ($bdy = bc$) by Law 4, and $bdx + bdy = bd(x + y) = ad + bc$ by virtue of the distributive law and Law 2. Hence $x + y = (ad + bc)/bd$ by Law 3.

5. (a) $\dfrac{a}{b} \cdot \dfrac{c}{d} = \dfrac{ac}{bd}$.

  (b) $\dfrac{a}{b} \div \dfrac{c}{d} = \dfrac{ad}{bc} = \dfrac{a}{b} \cdot \dfrac{d}{c}$.

  (c) $\dfrac{a}{b} + \dfrac{c}{d} = \dfrac{ad + bc}{bd}$.

  (d) $\dfrac{a}{b} - \dfrac{c}{d} = \dfrac{ad - bc}{bd}$.

6. (a) $\dfrac{10}{21}$.   (d) $-\dfrac{1}{21}$.

  (b) $\dfrac{14}{15}$.   (h) $\dfrac{16}{3}$.

  (c) $\dfrac{29}{21}$.   (i) $\dfrac{4}{7}$.

7. (b) $y = -\dfrac{3}{4}x - \dfrac{5}{4}$.   (d) $y = \dfrac{5}{9}x - \dfrac{160}{9}$.

Section 8.3

2. $\begin{bmatrix} 2 & 3 \\ 7 & 5 \end{bmatrix} \begin{bmatrix} x_1 \\ x_2 \end{bmatrix} = \begin{bmatrix} 1 \\ 9 \end{bmatrix}$.

5. (a) $x_1 = \dfrac{\begin{vmatrix} 5 & 3 \\ 6 & 4 \end{vmatrix}}{\begin{vmatrix} 2 & 3 \\ 7 & 4 \end{vmatrix}} = \dfrac{20 - 18}{8 - 21} = \dfrac{2}{-13} = -\dfrac{2}{13}$.

Section 8.4

2. $A - B \equiv A + (-B)$.

5. Yes.

8. All are true.

Section 8.5

2. If $BA = C$, then

$$c_{ij} = b_{i1}a_{1j} + b_{i2}a_{2j} + b_{i3}a_{3j} + \cdots + b_{in}a_{nj},$$

where $i = 1,2, \cdots, m$ and $j = 1,2, \cdots, p$.

13. (a) False.   (e) False.
    (b) False.   (f) False.
    (c) False.   (g) True.
    (d) True.

Section 8.7

3. 35 cents.

5. 3 of each.

Section 9.2

1. (b) A matrix game with a saddle point is fair iff its saddle value is zero.

3. (e) Row 2; column 3; 2.

6. (a) $0 : 2$.
   (b) 0.

8. (a) N.

9. (d) False.

Section 9.4

1. (b) $\left(\frac{3}{5}, \frac{2}{5}\right)$; $\left(\frac{2}{5}, \frac{3}{5}\right)$; $\frac{1}{5}$.

3. (c) 3.

4. (c) True.

Section 9.5

3. (a) $E_1 = p_1(1) + p_2(-1)$, $E_2 = p_1(-1) + p_2(1)$.
   (b) $E_1' = p_1(2 + 1) + p_2(-1 + 2) = p_1(2) + [p_1(1) + p_2(-1)] + p_2(2)$
   $= p_1(2) + E_1 + p_2(2) = E_1 + (p_1 + p_2)2 = E_1 + 2$.

Section 9.7

1. (a) (i) $\{AB\}$, $\{AC\}$, $\{ABC\}$.
       (ii) $\{C\}$, $\{B\}$, $\emptyset$.
       (iii) $\{A\}$, $\{BC\}$.

       (iv) $\dfrac{4}{6}, \dfrac{1}{6}, \dfrac{1}{6}$ for A, B, C, respectively.

   (c) (i) $\{A\}$, $\{AB\}$, $\{AC\}$, $\{ABC\}$.
       (ii) $\{BC\}$, $\{C\}$, $\{B\}$, $\emptyset$.
       (iii) No blocking coalitions.
       (iv) 1, 0, 0 for A, B, C, respectively.

4. (a) $\dfrac{1}{5}$.

   (b) $\dfrac{12}{24} = \dfrac{1}{2}$.

   (c) $\dfrac{1}{6}$.

6. (a) True.
   (b) False.
   (c) True.

Section 10.2

2. (a) 5 feet per second.
   (d) $2t + 1$.

Section 10.3

2. (b) -1.
   (d) -8.
   (h) $(x + h)^3 = x^3 + 3x^2h + 3xh^2 + h^3$.

3. (c) -3.
   (d) Does not exist.
   (f) 3.

5. Only parts (a) and (d) determine y as a function of x.

6. (a) No.
   (b) Yes.

Section 10.4

1. **HINT:** See Problem 4 of Problem Set 10.3.

3. (a) $2\pi x\, \Delta x + \pi\, \overline{\Delta x}^2$.
   (b) $2\pi x\, \Delta x$.

5. .06 ft./sec.

7. (a) True.
   (b) False.

Section 10.5

2. (c) $3x^2$.
   (d) $6x^2$.
   (f) $4x^3$.
   (h) $-\dfrac{1}{x^2}$.
   (i) $\dfrac{1}{2\sqrt{x}}$ [**HINT:** $(a - b)(a + b) = a^2 - b^2$.]
   (j) $\dfrac{1}{3(\sqrt[3]{x})^2}$ [**HINT:** $(a - b)(a^2 + ab + b^2) = a^3 - b^3$.]

Section 10.6

1. (b) True. [**HINT:** $\Delta V = \dfrac{\Delta V}{\Delta x} \cdot \Delta x$ when $\Delta x \neq 0$.]

7. (a) If $y = U^2 = UU$, then the product rule yields
$$y' = U'U + UU' = 2UU'.$$
   (b) If $y = U^3 = U^2U$, then the product rule yields
$$y' = (2UU')U + U^2U' = 3U^2U'.$$

9. $y' = \dfrac{1}{2y}$.

10. (a) If $y = \dfrac{U}{b} = \dfrac{1}{b}U$, then $y' = \dfrac{1}{b}U' = \dfrac{U'}{b}$.

   (b) **HINT:** $UVW = (UV)W$.

   (c) $y' = -\dfrac{V'}{V^2}$.

   (d) $y' = \dfrac{VU' - UV'}{V^2}$ $\left(\textbf{HINT:}\ \dfrac{U}{V} = U \cdot \dfrac{1}{V}\right)$.

Section 10.7

2. (b) Min at $(1, -2)$ and Max at $(-1, 2)$.

6. (a) 30 ties.

Section 10.8

2. (a) $v = 32t + 80$.
   (b) $s = 16t^2 + 80t + 60$.

4. (a) $\dfrac{6^2}{2} - \dfrac{2^2}{2} = 16$.

   (e) $b - a$.

   (f) $\dfrac{1}{n+1}(b^{n+1} - a^{n+1})$.

5. (a) True.
   (b) True.
   (c) False.

Section 10.9

1. (c) $\dfrac{4^3}{3} - \dfrac{0^3}{3} = \dfrac{64}{3}$.

   (d) $5 \cdot 7 - 5 \cdot 3 = 20$.

2. $\dfrac{15}{4}$.

4. All true except (g).

6. (g) **HINT:** $\displaystyle\int_1^{x_1 x_2} \dfrac{dt}{t} = \int_1^{x_1} \dfrac{dt}{t} + \int_{x_1}^{x_1 x_2} \dfrac{dt}{t}$.

(k) **HINT**: Observe $x_1 = \dfrac{x_1}{x_2} \cdot x_2$ and use part (g).

11. (a) πa^2.

12. $f(x) = \begin{cases} 0 \text{ if } x \text{ is rational} \\ 1 \text{ if } x \text{ is irrational} \end{cases}$.

Section A.1

1. All are true.

Section A.2

1. (b) -4.
   (c) $+10 = 10$.
   (d) $+4 = 4$.
   (e) -4.
   (f) -15.
   (g) $+15 = 15$.
   (h) -4.
   (i) $+4 = 4$.
   (k) -10.
   (l) 10.
   (m) 7.
   (n) -4.
   (o) -15.
   (p) 0.
   (q) -4.
   (r) 0.

3. (a) False.

Section A.3

1. (a) False.   (c) False.
   (b) True.   (d) False.

5. (a) True.   (c) False.
   (b) True.   (d) True.

Section A.4

3. (a) $\dfrac{1}{21}$.

  (g) $\dfrac{-15}{4}$.

  (b) $\dfrac{-29}{21}$.

  (h) $\dfrac{-3}{20}$.

  (c) $\dfrac{10}{21}$.

  (i) $\dfrac{5}{7}$.

  (d) $\dfrac{-14}{15}$.

  (j) $\dfrac{3}{7}$.

Index